TRANSISTOR
CIRCUIT
ENGINEERING

TRANSISTOR

CIRCUIT
ENGINEERING

Edited by
RICHARD F. SHEA

Knolls Atomic Power Laboratory
General Electric Company
Schenectady, New York

Authors

WOO FOUNG CHOW

SORAB K. GHANDHI

EDWARD KEONJIAN

VERNON P. MATHIS

DONALD A. PAYNTER

JOHN A. A. RAPER

ARTHUR P. STERN

JEROME J. SURAN

Electronics Laboratory
General Electric Company
Syracuse, New York

JOHN WILEY & SONS, INC., NEW YORK
CHAPMAN & HALL, LIMITED, LONDON

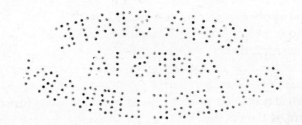

Preface

In 1953 I had the pleasure of collaborating with eight other members of the staff of the General Electric Company's Electronics Laboratory in writing "Principles of Transistor Circuits." In the intervening years this infant industry has made tremendous strides in the introduction of new devices and in the application of these new devices to an ever-widening field of utilization. It seems appropriate, therefore, to bring out at this time a new book detailing much of this additional new information. To this end a number of the original authors have joined forces with three new contributors to prepare this new work. We sincerely hope it will fill the needs of the would-be students and applicants of this new technology.

In this book our objective has been to combine a proper mixture of basic transistor theory with examples of its proper application in typical circuits. The mathematical treatment is frequently limited to the amount necessary for clarity. Similarly the material on solid state physics is restricted to that needed to give a basic understanding of the nature of the devices. Our major difficulty has been in holding the volume of material to a satisfactory minimum, without at the same time detracting from the completeness of the treatment. To do this adequately with respect to a device that has now worked its way into nearly every branch of electronic circuits is no mean task!

In order to make this book as self-sufficient as possible we have started with a presentation of basic transistor theory and of the application of network theory thereto. We have found that the modern forms of circuit analysis, including such tools as matrix representations, are ideal vehicles for transistor applications. The reader who masters these tools will find himself applying them in all other forms of circuits, even those incorporating those prosaic devices—tubes!

v

503920

Once we have established what a transistor is and how it works, the next step is to lay down some ground rules. One of the most important of these is that a transistor requires special attention to its bias circuits. Early in its life the transistor acquired an unjustified reputation as a temperature-sensitive device, and use over extensive temperature ranges was considered extremely risky. It was not appreciated that the transistor parameters, which dictated circuit performance, were only moderately temperature-sensitive. They were, however, extremely dependent on operating bias conditions, and the bias, unless properly stabilized, *was* very temperature-dependent. Even today we see many circuits published where the effect of temperature will be more severe than is necessary. For this reason we have devoted a full chapter to this very important subject.

In the next chapter will be found the basic essentials necessary to do an intelligent job of audio-amplifier designing. This chapter, in addition to its utility for those whose prime interest is the design of audio equipment, will serve admirably as an introduction to the application of transistors in other fields, where the problems become more severe because of such factors as the complex nature of the transistor parameters, large-signal operation, and transient effects.

The subject of d-c amplifiers is one of considerable interest to many industrial users, and in many military applications. Though these amplifiers may be considered to be a special form of audio amplifiers, they have many special problems of their own, one of the most plaguing being the problem of reducing zero drift. Consequently a considerable amount of this chapter is devoted to this subject. The application of d-c amplifiers in various types of operational, differentiating, and integrating amplifiers is treated in some detail.

With the extension of the use of transistors up into the VHF and UHF bands, and imminent entrance into the kilomegacycle region, the high-frequency characteristics of transistors assume great importance. The subject of high-frequency equivalent circuits has had considerable treatment in the literature during recent years. Although the subject is far from resolved, we have attempted to present the material in such a way as to facilitate application of available data to the utilization of transistors in high-frequency tuned circuits and video amplifiers. We appreciate that newer forms of high-frequency transistors will be continually coming from the many laboratories feverishly at work on these devices; however, we feel that the treatment we have given will permit application of the data on these new forms as issued.

The subject of oscillators incorporates a large portion of the basic circuit theory delineated in the first part of the book. This chapter covers all the common types of oscillators, both linear and nonlinear, in considerable detail, together with specific examples of design. While the subject of multivibrators is also covered in considerable detail in a subsequent chapter, the groundwork for this treatment is laid here.

The next subject receiving considerable treatment is modulation, mixing, and detection. Considering that one of the earliest forms of detectors, the galena crystal, was a forefather of the transistor, it may truly be said that these devices have a proprietary interest in this field; and the most successful mixer used in wartime radar equipment was a semiconductor.

The transistor has shown signs of taking over the computer field almost as completely as it did that of the hearing aid, although progress in this field is so rapid that there are already strong signs of competition from magnetic and superconductive devices! The importance of this application warrants the devotion of a chapter to the treatment of pulse and computer applications; in fact this application could easily be the subject of a book in itself.

In order to tie the various pieces together we have included a chapter on systems. Since so many circuits are dependent on each other for proper operation, the system must be considered as a whole before satisfactory performance can be insured. An excellent example is the ever-present television receiver, incorporating every type of circuit included in this book.

Finally, wherever an attempt is made to compartmentalize a wide field of applications, there will be exceptions that do not fit too well in any compartment, yet that are too important to omit. We here, therefore, finished our book with a number of special circuits, some of which ideally exemplify transistor potentialities, and some which are most suitable as examples of the application of the techniques described here.

We have included problems with which the reader can test his grasp of the related material. An extensive bibliography is supplied for those who wish to study specific subjects in greater detail, and, in addition, references to particularly pertinent articles are included with each chapter.

A work such as this always involves more than the original material of the authors. I wish, therefore, to extend my sincere appreciation to those whose unpublished material we have used, including Messrs. E. P. Cleary, R. S. Hill, F. A. Reibert, F. M. Schlecht and J. W.

Stanton, to C. D. Aiken, C. E. Forson, R. B. Goldner, T. L. Grettenberg, Dr. E. L. Steele, and members of the Advanced Circuits Subsection of the Electronics Laboratory for reviewing and criticizing this material; to Dr. S. K. Ghandhi for coordinating the material of his co-authors; to Mrs. Dorothy Fullmer for her invaluable assistance with the manuscript, and to Mr. I. J. Kaar, Dr. G. L. Haller, Dr. L. T. DeVore, Dr. H. M. Sullivan, Dr. J. B. Russell, and Mr. A. D. Arsem for their support. Some of the circuits described in the chapter on d-c amplifiers represent the result of work that was performed under Contract NObsr-57409, sponsored by the Navy Department, Bureau of Ships, Electronics Division.

R. F. SHEA

March 1957

Contents

Symbols

The symbols used in this book are based on the Institute of Radio Engineers Symbol Standard for Semiconductor Devices, 56 IRE28S1. In this standard capital and lower-case letters are used as symbols and subscripts with the following general connotations:

1. Instantaneous values of current, voltage, and power, which vary with time, are represented by the lower-case letter of the proper symbol.

2. Maximum, average (d-c), and root-mean-square values are represented by the upper-case letter of the proper symbol.

3. D-c values and instantaneous total values are indicated by upper-case subscripts.

4. Varying component values are indicated by lower-case subscripts.

5. If necessary to distinguish between maximum, average, or root-mean-square values, maximum or average values may be represented by the addition of a subscript m or av.

6. Supply voltages are indicated by repeating the electrode subscript. The reference electrode may be designated by a third subscript.

7. Transistor parameters, resistances, impedances, or admittances are indicated by lower-case symbols. External circuit elements are indicated by capital symbols.

The reader is referred to the above IRE Standard for more detailed explanation.

Symbol	Description	First used on page
A	Area of magnetic core	263
A	Multivibrator design parameter	252
A_c	Peak amplitude of carrier signal	272
A_i	Current-transfer ratio	61
A_m	Peak value of modulating signal	271
A_n	Short-circuit current-transfer ratio of a three-terminal network	415
A_t	Short-circuit current-transfer ratio of a transistor	415
a	Multiplication factor for the internal current generator	26
a_{ij}	Term in a matrix	22

Symbol	Description	First used on page
g_i'	Transformed conductive component of transistor input admittance	165
g_{ij}	Term in g matrix	22
g_{is}	Equivalent series input conductance	161
G_{l0}	Minimum value of load conductance for which real component of input impedance is always positive	188
g_o	Output conductance	161
H_c	Coercive force	263
h_{ij}	Term in h matrix	5
h_{ij}'	h parameter of the ideal transistor	30
h_{ijb}	h parameter in the common-base configuration	27
h_{ijc}	h parameter in the common-collector configuration	27
h_{ije}	h parameter in the common-emitter configuration	27
$(h_{ij})_0$	Low-frequency h parameter	29
h_m	The product $(h_{12}h_{21})$	187
I	Current	2
I_A	Current through diode A	146
I_B	Current through diode B	146
I_B	Magnetic core coercive current	263
I_{CBO}	Saturation current, collector-to-base diode	52
I_{CO}	Saturation current, collector-to-base diode	52
I_E	D-c emitter current	14
I_{EO}	Reverse emitter current for open collector	311
$(I_E)_0$	Quiescent bias point	270
I_i	Input current	162
i_{IN}	D-c input signal current	145
I_O	Output current	140
I_o	Short-circuit output current	161
I_S	Diode saturation current	154
I_s	Junction saturation current	249
I_0	Quiescent bias point	270
I_1, I_2	Current	2
$(I_1)_0, (I_2)_0$	Operating current	3
i_{in}	Input current	101
i_o	Internal current generator	86
i_D	Diode current	154
i_P	Peak current coordinate of negative resistance characteristic	247
i_Q	Valley current coordinate of negative resistance characteristic	247
i_1	Small-signal current variation	4
i_2	Small-signal current variation	4
J	Junction	13
j	$\sqrt{-1}$	30
K	A constant	47
K	Multivibrator design parameter	252
k	Boltzmann's constant	29

SYMBOLS

Greek Symbols

Symbol	Description	*First used on page*
α_{b0}	Common-base low-frequency short-circuit current-transfer ratio	29
α_{fb}	Normal alpha, common-base	310
α_i	Abscissa of the center of the circle of vanishing input resistive component in load-admittance plane	188
α_o	Abscissa of the center of the circle of vanishing output conductive component in the source-impedance plane	189
α_{rb}	Inverted alpha, common-base	310
β (beta)	Current feedback factor	225
β	Transport factor	29
β_i	Ordinate of the center of the circle of vanishing input resistive component in load-admittance plane	188
β_o	Ordinate of the center of the circle of vanishing output conductive component in the source-impedance plane	189
β_0	Low-frequency value of β	29
γ (gamma)	Emitter efficiency	29
γ_0	Low-frequency internal current-amplification factor	247
Δ (delta)	Determinant	74
Δ	Increment of	53
Δ^h	Determinant of the h matrix	74
ΔI	Magnitude of the error current	146
ΔV	Magnitude of the error voltage	146
∂	The partial-differential operator	4
η (eta)	Efficiency	108
η	Power-transfer efficiency	166
η	Rectification efficiency	269
η_{max}	Maximum power-transfer efficiency	167
θ (theta)	Shape factor of coupled tuned circuit response	177
μ_0 (mu)	Low-frequency reverse-voltage transfer ratio	29
ρ_i (rho)	Radius of the circle of vanishing input resistive component in the load-admittance plane	188
ρ_o	Radius of the circle of vanishing output conductive component in the source-impedance plane	189
τ (tau)	Average lifetime of holes in the base region	30
ϕ (phi)	Magnetic flux	257
ϕ_C	Collector junction voltage	309
ϕ_E	Emitter junction voltage	309
ϕ_m	Saturation valve of magnetic flux	257
ψ (psi)	Multivibrator design parameter	252

Chapter 1

Characteristics and Characteristic Curves

1.0 Introduction

The solution of an engineering problem results from the utilization of devices with known characteristics to effect a desired result. The engineering problem may comprise the design of a specific circuit, such as an oscillator or an amplifier stage, or it may comprise the design of an overall system of component circuits such as an audio amplifier or a complete television receiver. The utilization of semiconductor devices is most efficiently realized by the combination of the general technical knowledge of the engineer and the specific engineering data supplied by the manufacturer.

An important part of the information supplied by the manufacturer takes the form of sets of static characteristic curves. This chapter reviews and expands the theory and utilization of static characteristics as applied to the engineering use of semiconductor devices. In order to keep the material applicable to all semiconductor devices, the treatment is a general one. Specific semiconductor devices are considered, their curves presented, and their behavior explained on a physical basis.

1.1 Basic Considerations

1.1.1 Definition of a Characteristic Curve

A characteristic curve (or a set of such curves) is a graph showing the functional relationship between two or more quantities of interest. To the engineer interested in the utilization of semiconductor devices, the curves of interest are those that display the voltages and currents that may be applied simultaneously to the device independent of the external circuit. Such graphs are called static characteristics, and from them it is possible to predict some aspects of the behavior of the device in an operating circuit. The choice of functional relationship for the device will depend on its application, as well as on the number of its ports or terminal pairs.

1

1.1.2 One-Port Device

A one-port device has one pair of terminals; its electrical properties are defined by the relationship of the current entering the device to the voltage across it. The static characteristic thus takes the form of a single curve.

1.1.3 Two-Port Device

The simplest case of the two-port device occurs when one terminal is common to each port. This device has three terminals: one input, one

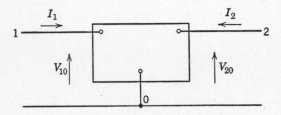

Fig. 1.1   Two-port device

output, and one common to both input and output. Such a device is illustrated in Fig. 1.1.

The general case is illustrated in Fig. 1.2. This device has four terminals, two of which are the input and two the output.

In either case the device behavior is characterized by the four electrical quantities, V_{10}, V_{20}, I_1, I_2. Since a graph can conveniently illus-

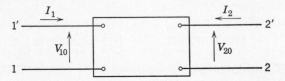

Fig. 1.2   Sign convention for four-terminal network

trate the relationship of only three quantities, two graphs are necessary to specify the behavior of such a device. Each of these graphs is a plot of two quantities with a third taken as the parameter.

1.1.4 Multiport Device

For the majority of circuits, the engineer is concerned with the transfer of a signal through a device. Thus a multiport device may be considered in signal applications as a two-port device with one terminal common to each port, and its properties defined by two sets of characteristic curves. Since the other terminals are usually set at appropriate bias levels, this information must also be given with the graphs.

1.2   Interpretation and Use of Static Characteristics

The static characteristics of a device as supplied by the manufacturer are subject to a variety of assumptions. For example, the effects of aging are not considered. Under present standards of reliability this is valid. A second point is that the curves usually represent the design center for the device and are often drawn as if with a wide brush so as to indicate the normal spread of behavior due to production tolerances. A third point is that transistors are temperature-sensitive, and that any one set of curves must be taken at one specific temperature and under isothermal conditions. Since the transistor does not require an initially high temperature for its operation, its properties are susceptible to the small temperature changes produced by the bias or by the signal level. The specific effects of temperature are discussed in Chapters 2 and 3.

With these assumptions in mind it is possible to use the static characteristics of a device: (a) to determine completely the d-c properties of the device as well as its low-frequency a-c properties, and (b) to determine graphically the effects of external elements such as generator and load impedances on the performance of the actual operating circuit.

1.2.1   Determination of D-C Properties

Static characteristics provide a complete specification of the range of operating points at which a device may be maintained. For the simplest case of a one-port device, completely specified by its V,I characteristic, a choice of either variable determines the other.

It has been shown that a two-port device is specified by two families of curves. For such a device the operating point may be set by a choice of any two electrical quantities, and, in so doing, the remaining two electrical quantities are specifically determined. Thus, for example, if the input current and the output voltage are each independently chosen, the operating point is set and the output current and input voltage are automatically determined. By way of example, Fig. 1.3 shows the output characteristics of a device with constant input current as the parameter. Choosing an input current $(I_1)_0$ and an output voltage $(V_2)_0$, the operating point P is located, and the output current $(I_2)_0$ is determined. The input voltage may now be read as $(V_1)_0$ from the input characteristics.

Once the operating point has been located, the d-c behavior of the device is known. Thus, in order to maintain the operating point P for the above device, a power of $(V_2)_0(I_2)_0$ must be dissipated on the output side, and a power of $(V_1)_0(I_1)_0$ on the input side. The rectangular hyperbola $I_2V_2 = (I_2)_0(V_2)_0$, drawn in dashed line on Fig. 1.3, is a curve of constant output power dissipation in the device; any operating point located on this curve results in an output dissipation of $(V_2)_0(I_2)_0$. Such curves are useful in indicating the output-power dissipation limits

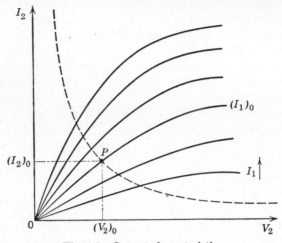

Fig. 1.3   Output characteristics

of the device. The slope of the line joining P to the origin is the d-c output conductance of the device.

1.2.2   Determination of the Small-Signal Low-Frequency Properties

Once the operating point has been determined, it is possible to study the effect of a perturbation about this point. A small signal applied to a suitably biased device causes just such a perturbation in its operating point; accordingly, these perturbations relate to the small-signal properties of the device.

Consider a set of static characteristics:

$$I_2 = f(I_1, V_2) \qquad (1.1)$$

The small-signal variation of I_2, namely i_2, is given in terms of the small-signal variations of V_2 and I_1, namely v_2 and i_1, by

$$dI_2 = \frac{\partial I_2}{\partial I_1}\bigg|_{V_2 = \text{const}} dI_1 + \frac{\partial I_2}{\partial V_2}\bigg|_{I_1 = \text{const}} dV_2 \qquad (1.2)$$

Therefore, $i_2 = (\partial I_2/\partial I_1)i_1 + (\partial I_2/\partial V_2)v_2$

and
$$i_2/i_1 = \partial I_2/\partial I_1 \quad \text{when} \quad v_2 = 0 \tag{1.3}$$

$$i_2/v_2 = \partial I_2/\partial V_2 \quad \text{when} \quad i_1 = 0 \tag{1.4}$$

These parameters * may be identified on the static characteristics of Fig. 1.4.

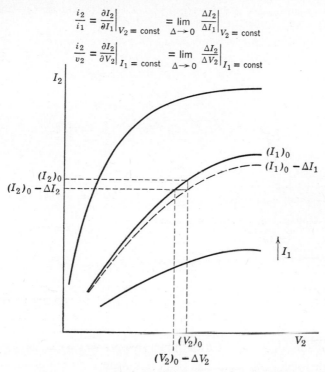

Fig. 1.4 Incremental representation of parameters

1.2.3 Determination of Large-Signal A-C Properties

By an extension of the techniques of Sec. 1.2.2, the "large-signal" properties of the device may be obtained. A word of caution must be added here; every set of static characteristics will exhibit some curvature if sufficiently extended. As a result of this curvature, a sinusoidal perturbation of any one electrical quantity illustrated in the characteristics results in nonsinusoidal perturbations in the other quantities. It is therefore essential that the magnitude of the nonsinusoidal perturbation, as well as the magnitude of the sinusoidal perturbation itself, be defined in an unambiguous manner.

---

* These two quantities will later be identified as h_{21} and h_{22}, respectively.

By way of example, the large signal value of i_2/i_1 may be defined as the ratio of the rms, positive-peak, negative peak, peak-to-peak, fundamental component, or average values of i_2 and i_1. In general, the method of defining the large-signal perturbations will be dictated by the manner in which the device is to be used.

1.3 Transformation of Characteristic Curves

The majority of devices used in semiconductor engineering are of the three-terminal variety, operated as two-port devices with one terminal common to both ports. Such devices may be operated in three configu-

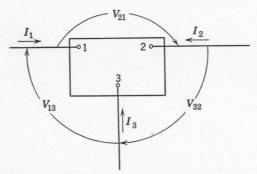

Fig. 1.5   Three-terminal device

rations corresponding to the use of one of the three terminals as common. It will now be shown that, if the static characteristics of such a device are known for any one configuration, curves for any other configuration may be readily obtained.

Consider the three-terminal device of Fig. 1.5.   For such a device

$$I_1 + I_2 + I_3 = 0 \tag{1.5}$$

and $$V_{21} + V_{13} + V_{32} = 0 \tag{1.6}$$

The static characteristics of such a device portray the relationships of two currents and two voltages, and any operating point located on these curves defines the simultaneous values of these four quantities. Using eqs. 1.5 and 1.6, the unknown voltage and current may be computed. By a point-to-point technique of this sort it is possible to construct any static characteristic set corresponding to any device configuration.

1.4 Methods of Obtaining Characteristic Curves

Usually, characteristic curves for the device are supplied by the manufacturer for the configuration of interest, together with complete specifications as to the conditions under which the curves were taken. If curves are not supplied with the device or if specific information for one particular device is needed, the user must plot the necessary characteristics himself.

No attempt will be made in this section to describe in detail the various equipments for curve plotting. Such information is available in the references at the end of the chapter. The choice of a measurement technique involves many factors, some of which are discussed in the following sections.

1.4.1   Point-by-Point Method

As the name implies, this method consists of a point-by-point plot of a number of successive operating points for the device. The method usually requires a minimum of instrumentation, but a maximum of time, patience, and care. The method becomes unsuitable in the range where self-heating is significant because isothermal conditions cannot be maintained.

1.4.2   Continuous Trace Methods

With a view to speeding up the process of taking curves, to help reduce the possibility of operator error, or to aid in maintaining near-isothermal conditions, techniques have been developed for obtaining a continuous trace of the desired characteristic. Continuous trace methods may be divided into two categories:

(a) *X,Y Recorder.* This equipment produces a plot of one electrical quantity as a function of another on a sheet of graph paper. A variation of the method utilizes a *Y, time* recorder and converts the independent *X* variable to a known function of time. Instruments of either type are highly accurate and calibration is quite simple.

(b) *Oscilloscope.* This method is extremely rapid and is well suited to applications where high accuracy or permanent records are not required. Calibration may be somewhat tedious. When permanent records are required, the display may be photographed.

With either of the above techniques it is possible to operate devices above their steady-state ratings for periods long enough to record the required data. This may be accomplished by using a waveform of short duty cycle as the driving function. By this technique it is possible to maintain a constant operating point and prevent effects resulting from nonisothermal conditions.

As has been shown, for devices with more than one port, one or more electrical quantity must be held constant while the independent variable traverses its required range, and the dependent variable is recorded.

For continuous line methods, this may be effected by judicious choice of source resistance. For example, if a current is to be held constant, its source resistance must be kept high compared to the resistance of the device over the entire range to be recorded.

1.4.3 The Stability Problem

Even if considerable care is taken to prevent thermal runaway, it is sometimes observed that the device exhibits electrical instability. Such instability may show up as double-valued points and failure to maintain a desired operating point, or in ringing and self-sustained oscillations. This behavior is a property of the device in conjunction with its terminating circuits and parasitic elements. In the majority of such cases it is possible to render the system non-oscillatory by an appropriate choice of terminating impedances.

Once the system has been rendered nonoscillatory, it is necessary to choose a technique for plotting the characteristic so as to obtain a single continuous curve. Consider some possible techniques for varying the voltage and current at any port of a device. Figure 1.6a illustrates the use of a constant-voltage source (impedance of the source negligibly small as compared to the device). Figure 1.6b shows a constant-current source (impedance of the device negligibly small as compared to the source). Figure 1.6c shows an intermediate value of impedance in series with a fixed voltage. Figure 1.6d shows a voltage source in series with a fixed intermediate value of impedance.

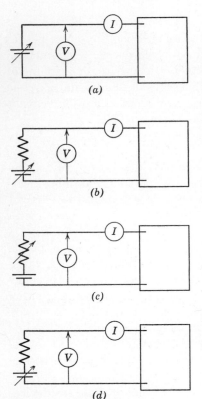

Fig. 1.6 Measurement techniques for static characteristics

The load lines resulting from these four techniques are shown in Figs. 1.7a, 1.7b, 1.7c, and 1.7d. For a constant-voltage source the load line is parallel to the current axis as in Fig. 1.7a. For a constant-current source the load line is parallel to the voltage axis as in Fig. 1.7b. For an intermediate impedance in series with a fixed voltage we have a load line that rotates about the value of this fixed battery voltage as in Fig. 1.7c. If the source impedance is intermediate to the constant-current and constant-voltage cases, the load line of Fig. 1.7d results. As long as our load line is chosen in such a manner that it never inter-

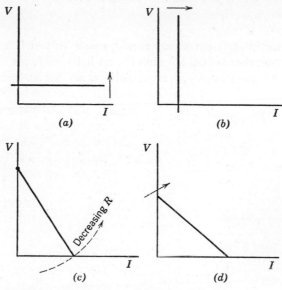

Fig. 1.7   Load lines for Fig. 1.6

sects the characteristic at more than one point at a time, a single continuous curve will be obtained.

To illustrate this, assume that a characteristic curve of a device is being plotted by the constant-current technique of Fig. 1.7b, and the curve appears as shown in Fig. 1.8a. This implies the presence of a

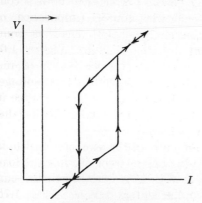

Fig. 1.8a   Constant-current plot of function double-valued in I

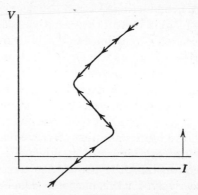

Fig. 1.8b   Constant-voltage plot of function double-valued in I

characteristic that is double-valued in I. Plotting this curve by the constant-voltage technique results in the required single continuous curve of Fig. 1.8b.

It should be pointed out that the load line of Fig. 1.7c would also be satisfactory provided its slope was such as to cut the curve at only one point at a time.

There are, fortunately extremely rarely, cases for which a device will exhibit a function that is double-valued in both V and I. It is extremely difficult to plot a satisfactory characteristic curve for such a device.

1.5   Physical Processes in Semiconductors

The treatment thus far has been limited to the electrical properties of the device as seen from its ports. Whereas such a treatment is in itself adequate for the solution of a circuit engineering problem, it is desirable that the engineer have some understanding of the physical principles of operation of the devices with which he is to work. In order to understand the operation of these devices, it is first necessary to present a brief outline of the physics of conduction processes in semiconductors. Detailed information of this type may be found in the references at the end of this chapter.

1.5.1   Conduction in Semiconductor Materials

Conductors are characterized by the presence of many electrons available for electrical conduction whereas *insulators* have very few. *Semiconductors* have current carriers in numbers between these extremes. *Germanium* and *silicon* are examples of commonly used semiconductor materials. Of particular importance in semiconductors is the fact that *charge carriers* may be *electrons* or may be *holes*, which can be thought of as conducting-electron deficiencies, each with a positive charge equal in magnitude to the negative electron charge. Both electrons and holes may contribute to current flow at the same time in the same material. If there are more electrons than holes, the semiconductor is known as *n-type*; if the number of holes predominates, it is *p-type*. Thus, *minority carriers* in *n*-type material, for example, are holes; *majority carriers* are electrons. It has been found that semiconductors such as germanium or silicon may be deliberately *doped* during manufacture by the addition of very small amounts of electron *donor* or electron *acceptor* impurities. Elements having one more or one less valence electron than the parent semiconductor crystal material are used, respectively, for this purpose. Donors and acceptors produce *n*-type and *p*-type material, respectively.

A semiconductor material, which is often a *single crystal*, offers electrical resistance to carrier flow due to forces acting in the crystal lattice. The carriers may move about owing to *diffusion* (a spreading out from a region of high carrier density), or under the influence of an *electric field* much as they do in an electron tube. The average velocity with which carriers move in the direction of a unit field is their *mobility*. The mobilities for holes and electrons in the same material are not generally equal. Some semiconductor devices utilize diffusion for their operation; others, field effects; still others, both mechanisms.

Minority carriers may be generated in semiconductors by *hole-electron pair* generation. This process corresponds to the release of an electron from its bound state in the crystal lattice by energy such as light or heat, producing an electron and a hole, both of which are free to contribute to electrical conduction. Excess minority carriers have a relatively short *lifetime*, and disappear by *recombination* with majority carriers. The *storage time* of minority carriers in a semiconductor is related to the lifetime and to the electric fields to which the carriers are subjected. One important influence of the presence of minority carriers is a reduction in the *resistivity* of the semiconductor in the neighborhood of the minority carriers as long as they are present.

Contacts are usually made to a semiconductor material by fusing or welding a metal to the semiconductor body. Such contacts may be either *ohmic* or *rectifying*, depending on the kind of metal used, the fabrication technique, etc. For an ohmic contact the magnitude of the total current flow is independent of the polarity of the applied voltage. The current through a rectifying contact depends strongly on the direction of the applied field.

1.6   Semiconductor Devices and Their Characteristics

The discussion given in the preceding section will now be applied to particular semiconductor devices. Characteristic curves for several representative devices will be given, and the physics of their operation explained in a general way. No attempt will be made to show the characteristics of the devices in all of the possible configurations or all the combinations of bias polarities. In general, the particular configuration chosen will either expedite the physical explanation or illustrate a particular characteristic of interest.

1.6.1   Junction Diode

A junction diode is a semiconductor device utilizing a single *p-n* junction. The magnitudes of the forward and reverse currents are dependent on the numbers of majority and minority carriers that are

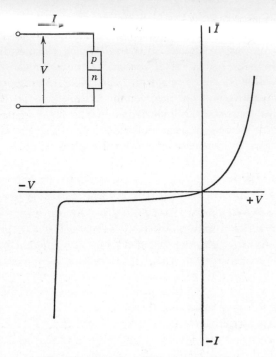

Fig. 1.9   Junction diode characteristic

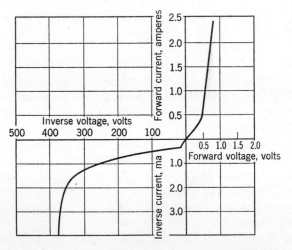

Fig. 1.10   Commerical diode characteristic (1N93)

present in the n and p regions.   Heat and light influence the number
of carriers available for conduction and hence the diode current for a
given applied voltage.   Figure 1.9 shows the V,I characteristic for such
a device.   Beyond a critical *inverse voltage*, the diode will exhibit *breakdown*.   The value of this breakdown voltage is largely dependent on
the physical constants of the semiconductor material and on the fabrication procedures used when making the diode; it is subject to reasonable production control during manufacture.   Figure 1.10 shows the
characteristic for a commercial device (type 1N93).

1.6.2   Junction Triode

Figure 1.11 shows a p-n-p junction triode or *transistor*.   The device
consists of two p-n junctions separated by a thin base region and is
usually constructed from single-crystal semiconductor material.   With
the biases as shown, holes are injected from the p region into the n region at the forward-biased junction J_1; they travel by diffusion as

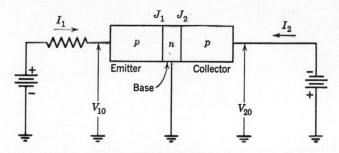

Fig. 1.11   Junction triode

minority carriers across the n region and are *collected* when they arrive
at the reverse-biased junction J_2.   In a properly designed transistor
most of the minority carriers are collected in this manner and contribute to *collector* current.

Since the emitter junction J_1 is biased in the forward direction, the
input curves for the transistor will closely resemble the forward characteristic of a junction diode.   The collector junction J_2 is biased in
the reverse direction, and, in the absence of emitter current I_1, its
characteristic will be analogous to that of a reverse-biased p-n junction.
The emitter-current bias I_1 has the effect of increasing the current in
the collector diode by almost this same amount.   Thus the output
characteristic of the transistor resembles that of a reverse-biased diode,

displaced along the current axis. The curves for the 2N43, shown in Fig. 1.12, illustrate this.

A similar explanation applies to the *n-p-n* transistor. For this device, the bias polarities are reversed, and the essential conduction process is by electrons rather than holes.

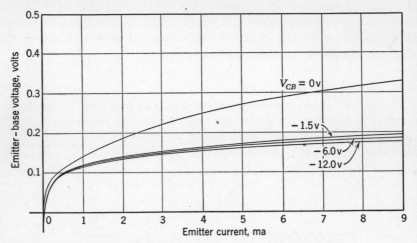

Fig. 1.12*a*   Common-base input characteristics (2N43)

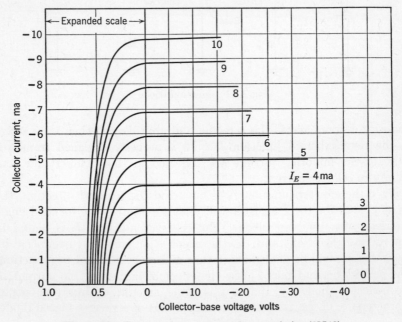

Fig. 1.12*b*   Common-base output characteristics (2N43)

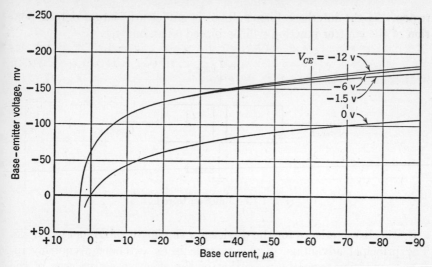

Fig. 1.12c   Common-emitter input characteristics (2N43)

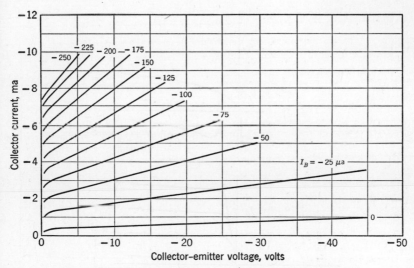

Fig. 1.12d   Common-emitter output characteristics (2N43)

1.6.3   Junction Tetrode

If an additional ohmic contact is attached appropriately to the base region of a junction triode, a junction tetrode is obtained as shown in Fig. 1.13. In normal operation, a bias voltage is impressed between base 1 and base 2. This establishes a potential gradient across the base region. If the interbase bias voltage is sufficiently large, only a portion of the emitter junction will be biased as an emitter.

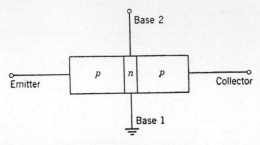

Fig. 1.13   Junction tetrode

Static characteristics for the device are similar to those for the triode. The principal advantage of the tetrode is an extended frequency response resulting from the reduction of the effective active area of the transistor when a d-c bias is applied between the two base contacts.

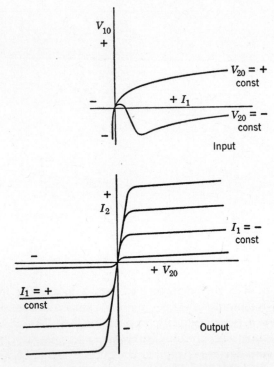

Fig. 1.14 p-n-p-n triode characteristics

It is also possible to use the tetrode as a grounded three-port device in applications such as mixing or modulation.

1.6.4   p-n-p-n Triode

The p-n-p-n transistor is a three-junction device; its curves are shown in Fig. 1.14. The operation of the device can be understood by considering it to consist of two transistors connected as shown in Fig. 1.15.

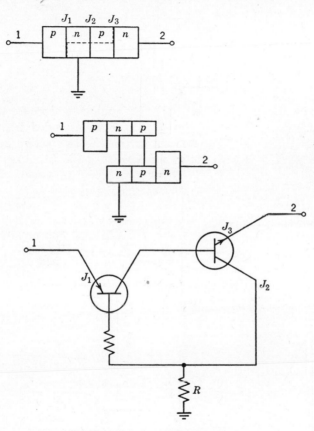

Fig. 1.15   Two-transistor representation of operation of p-n-p-n triode

The presence of R in the common lead results in positive feedback and causes a negative-input-resistance region as shown in the input characteristic. When a positive bias is applied between 2 and the common terminal, the functions of the electrodes J_2 and J_3 are reversed, the feedback becomes degenerative, and the output characteristic resembles that of the junction triode.

1.6.5 The Double-Base Diode (Unijunction Transistor)

A double-base diode is a semiconductor device with one p-n junction and two ohmic contacts (Fig. 1.16). Its characteristics are shown in Fig. 1.17. As seen from this figure, the input characteristic shows a region of negative resistance of the type exhibited by the p-n-p-n triode. The operation of the device is extremely complex, combining as it does

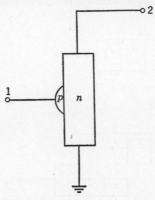

Fig. 1.16   Double-base diode

the mechanisms of injection and collection at the junction, field effects in the interbase region, and reduction of resistivity due to minority carriers in the region between the junction and the common base. For a complete treatment of the physical processes involved, the references listed at the end of the chapter may be consulted.

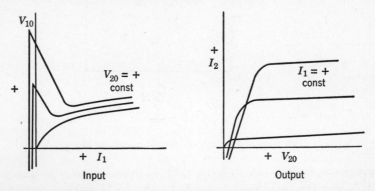

Fig. 1.17   Double-base diode characteristics

1.6.6 Field-Effect Transistor

The field-effect transistor utilizes two ohmic contacts and one p-n junction, as does the double-base diode (Fig. 1.16). In this device, however, the junction is always reverse-biased, producing an effective reduction of the cross section of the semiconductor bar. This controls the flow of current between the ohmic contacts resulting in the output characteristics shown in Fig. 1.18. The input characteristic is therefore that of a reverse-biased diode. The operation is analogous to that of an electron tube with a built-in grid leak resistor.

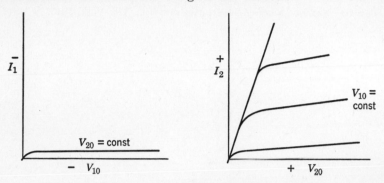

Fig. 1.18   Field-effect transistor characteristics

1.6.7   Point-Contact Triode

The characteristic curves for this device are similar to those for a junction triode except that considerable nonlinearity is present. A notable feature of this triode is that, unlike the conventional junction transistor, the incremental change in the collector current exceeds the incremental change in the emitter current. The theory of the operation of this device is complex and not well understood.

Bibliography

1. W. Shockley, "Transistor Electronics: Imperfections, Unipolar and Analog Transistors," *Proc. IRE, 40,* 1289 (1952).

2. J. S. Saby, "Fused Impurity *p-n-p* Junction Transistors," *Proc. IRE, 40,* 1358 (1952).

3. J. J. Ebers, "Four-Terminal *p-n-p-n* Transistors," *Proc. IRE, 40,* 1361 (1952).

4. W. Shockley, "A Unipolar 'Field Effect' Transistor," *Proc. IRE, 40,* 1365 (1952).

5. V. P. Mathis and J. S. Schaffner, "Quick Evaluation of Junction Transistor Characteristics by Oscilloscopic Display," *IRE Convention Record, 1,* pt. 9, 72 (1953).

6. I. A. Lesk and V. P. Mathis, "The Double-Base Diode: a New Semiconducting Device," *IRE Convention Record, 1,* pt. 6, 2 (1953).

7. N. Golden and R. Nielsen, "Oscilloscopic Display of Transistor Static Electrical Characteristics," *Proc. IRE, 40,* 1437 (1952).

8. G. L. Pearson and W. H. Brattain, "History of Semiconductor Research," *Proc. IRE, 43,* 1794 (1955).

9. J. L. Moll, "Junction Transistor Electronics," *Proc. IRE, 43,* 1807, (1955).

BOOKS

1. W. Shockley, *Electrons and Holes in Semiconductors*, Van Nostrand, New York, 1950.
2. D. A. Wright, *Semi-Conductors*, Wiley, New York, 1950.
3. H. C. Torrey and C. A. Witmer, *Crystal Rectifiers*, McGraw-Hill, New York, 1950.
4. F. Seitz, *Modern Theory of Solids*, McGraw-Hill, New York, 1940.

Chapter 2

Equivalent Circuits

2.1 Equivalent Representation of Devices

2.1.1 Two-Port Representation

We have seen that the behavior of many semiconductor devices may be studied by considering them as two-port devices. These ports, designated as the input and output ports, are the ones at which the be-

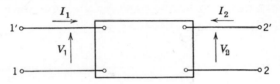

Fig. 2.1 Two-port network

havior of the device is to be studied, and we are interested in the electrical quantities that define this behavior.

Figure 2.1 shows a two-port network with the usual terminal markings and sign conventions. Currents I_1 and I_2 are defined as positive when flowing as indicated, into the network. Voltages V_1 and V_2 are defined as positive when the terminals 1' and 2' are at a higher potential than 1 and 2, respectively.

Such a device, then, is characterized by the relations existing between the currents and voltages, I_1, I_2 and V_1, V_2, respectively. If these relations can be expressed by a set of linear differential equations, we say the device is linear. For any fixed operating point and small-signal operation, this assumption is justified.

Any two of the four quantities I_1, I_2, V_1, V_2 may be given in terms of the remaining two. A study of the interrelations of these quantities is conveniently carried out with the aid of matrix algebra techniques. While a detailed analysis of these techniques is found elsewhere,[1-3] an

---

[1] Numbered references appear in the bibliography at the end of the chapter.

Introduction to the matrix algebra of two port devices has been given in the appendix.

In matrix notation, the sets of equations for two-port devices may be written as follows:

$$\begin{bmatrix} V_1 \\ V_2 \end{bmatrix} = \begin{bmatrix} z_{11}, z_{12} \\ z_{21}, z_{22} \end{bmatrix} \begin{bmatrix} I_1 \\ I_2 \end{bmatrix} \quad \text{and} \quad \begin{bmatrix} I_1 \\ I_2 \end{bmatrix} = \begin{bmatrix} y_{11}, y_{12} \\ y_{21}, y_{22} \end{bmatrix} \begin{bmatrix} V_1 \\ V_2 \end{bmatrix}$$

(2.1 and 2.2)

$$\begin{bmatrix} V_1 \\ I_2 \end{bmatrix} = \begin{bmatrix} h_{11}, h_{12} \\ h_{21}, h_{22} \end{bmatrix} \begin{bmatrix} I_1 \\ V_2 \end{bmatrix} \quad \text{and} \quad \begin{bmatrix} I_1 \\ V_2 \end{bmatrix} = \begin{bmatrix} g_{11}, g_{12} \\ g_{21}, g_{22} \end{bmatrix} \begin{bmatrix} V_1 \\ I_2 \end{bmatrix}$$

(2.3 and 2.4)

$$\begin{bmatrix} V_1 \\ I_1 \end{bmatrix} = \begin{bmatrix} a_{11}, a_{12} \\ a_{21}, a_{22} \end{bmatrix} \begin{bmatrix} V_2 \\ -I_2 \end{bmatrix} \quad \text{and} \quad \begin{bmatrix} V_2 \\ I_2 \end{bmatrix} = \begin{bmatrix} b_{11}, b_{12} \\ b_{21}, b_{22} \end{bmatrix} \begin{bmatrix} V_1 \\ -I_1 \end{bmatrix}$$

(2.5 and 2.6)

Given the elements of any one matrix, those of any other may be obtained. A table of such interrelations is given in the appendix.

2.1.2 Equivalent Circuits Based on Matrix Equations

Given a matrix equation for a two-port device, it is possible to construct any number of equivalent circuits for the network. Some of the

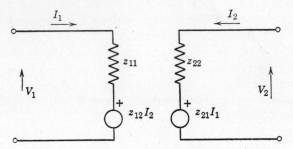

Fig. 2.2   Equivalent circuit using z parameters

$$V_1 = z_{11}I_1 + z_{12}I_2$$
$$V_2 = z_{21}I_1 + z_{22}I_2$$

simplest of these may be set up by inspection, as, for example, in Figs. 2.2 to 2.4.

Further equivalent circuits may be constructed by considering a possible equivalent network, and associating the elements of its matrix term-by-term with the elements of the device matrix.

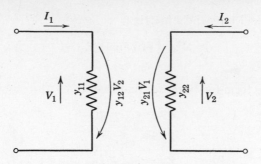

Fig. 2.3   Equivalent circuit using y parameters

$$I_1 = y_{11}V_1 + y_{12}V_2$$
$$I_2 = y_{21}V_1 + y_{22}V_2$$

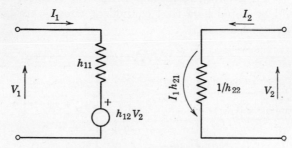

Fig. 2.4   Equivalent circuit using h parameters

$$V_1 = h_{11}I_1 + h_{12}V_2$$
$$I_2 = h_{21}I_1 + h_{22}V_2$$

Thus, consider the network of Fig. 2.5.   For this network,

$$\begin{bmatrix} V_1 \\ V_2 \end{bmatrix} = \begin{bmatrix} Z_1 + Z_2; & Z_2 \\ Z_2 + Z_4, & Z_3 + Z_2 \end{bmatrix} \begin{bmatrix} I_1 \\ I_2 \end{bmatrix} \qquad (2.7)$$

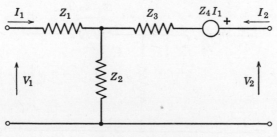

Fig. 2.5   Network

Defining our device by the z matrix,

$$\begin{bmatrix} z_{11}, z_{12} \\ z_{21}, z_{22} \end{bmatrix} \tag{2.8}$$

and comparing term-for-term, we find that

$$Z_1 = z_{11} - z_{12} \tag{2.9}$$

$$Z_2 = z_{12} \tag{2.10}$$

$$Z_3 = z_{22} - z_{12} \tag{2.11}$$

$$Z_4 = z_{21} - z_{12} \tag{2.12}$$

and the elements are known. In like manner, we can set up the equivalent circuit in a π-network form, and obtain the configuration of Fig. 2.6. It should be noted here that equivalent circuits are largely used

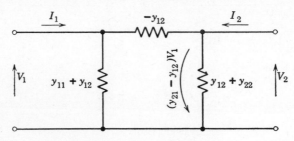

Fig. 2.6 π-network configuration
$$I_1 = y_{11}V_1 + y_{12}V_2$$
$$I_2 = y_{21}V_1 + y_{22}V_2$$

to provide an engineering concept of physical processes, and should therefore be preferably comprised of physically realizable elements.

Although the above equivalent circuits are the simplest types, it is possible to obtain many variations. Thus, voltage generators in series

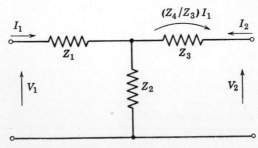

Fig. 2.7   Network equivalent to that of Fig. 2.5

with impedances may be replaced by current generators in shunt with admittances. By way of an example, the network of Fig. 2.5 is equivalent to that of Fig. 2.7, where the voltage generator $Z_4 I_1$ is replaced by the current generator $(Z_4/Z_3)I_1$.

Occasionally, more complex network configurations may be chosen. In this manner it is sometimes possible to isolate the separate elements of particular interest, at the price of redundancy.

2.2   General Considerations on Transistor Representation

2.2.1   Choice of Suitable Parameters

We have shown that the equations representing the behavior of a device may be given in any one of six different sets. The choice of sets will be dictated, among other things, by the ease with which measurements may be made on a device.

Consider, for example, eq. 2.2. Writing these equations in the usual form gives

$$I_1 = y_{11} V_1 + y_{12} V_2 \tag{2.13a}$$

$$I_2 = y_{21} V_1 + y_{22} V_2 \tag{2.13b}$$

Then

$$y_{11} = I_1/V_1 \quad \text{when} \quad V_2 = 0 \tag{2.14a}$$

$$y_{12} = I_1/V_2 \quad \text{when} \quad V_1 = 0 \tag{2.14b}$$

$$y_{21} = I_2/V_1 \quad \text{when} \quad V_2 = 0 \tag{2.14c}$$

$$y_{22} = I_2/V_2 \quad \text{when} \quad V_1 = 0 \tag{2.14d}$$

Thus y_{11} and y_{22} are the input and output short-circuit admittances, respectively, whereas y_{12} and y_{21} are the reverse and forward short-circuit transfer admittances. Consequently, the measurement of these four impedances in the laboratory imposes the conditions that the input and output be short-circuited successively. When these quantities are obtained, the equivalent circuit of Fig. 2.6 may be used.

By way of further example, consider the equations defined by eq. 2.3. In this case, h_{11} is the input impedance with the output short-circuited, h_{12} is the backward voltage transfer ratio with the input open, h_{21} is the forward current transfer ratio with the output short-circuited, and h_{22} is the output admittance with the input open.

The measurement of these parameters imposes the conditions that the input and output be open- and short-circuited, respectively, for the various measurements. These quantities result in the equivalent circuit of Fig. 2.4.

In like manner a z matrix characterization requires the measurement of the input, output, and transfer impedances under open-circuit con-

ditions, and results in the equivalent circuit of Fig. 2.7. When this circuit has the emitter for its input electrode, the collector for its output, and the base as the common electrode, the elements of the circuit are commonly labeled r_e, the emitter resistance; r_b, the base resistance; r_c, the collector resistance; and a, the multiplication factor for the internal current generator. The circuit may then be redrawn as illustrated in Fig. 2.8.

It has been mentioned in Chapter 1 that the equivalent input diode of a junction transistor is forward-biased (low resistance) while the

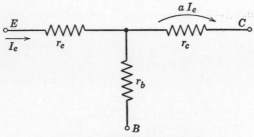

Fig. 2.8   T-equivalent circuit

equivalent output diode is reverse-biased (high resistance). For measurement purposes, it is very convenient to short-circuit a high resistance to alternating current by means of a capacitor, and to open-circuit a low resistance to alternating current by means of an inductor or a resistor. Thus, at low frequencies, laboratory measurements of junction transistors are most conveniently made in terms of the h parameters. Consequently, the h equivalent circuit is in common use. At higher frequencies, the z or y parameter measurements may become more convenient, and z or y equivalent circuits similar to those of Figs. 2.5 and 2.6 are often used. It is important to note that, at any operating frequency, at any operating point, and at any given temperature, any set of four independent measurements are sufficient to specify completely the behavior of the device.

2.2.2   Transistor Configurations

The h parameters have been shown to be the most convenient ones to measure at low frequencies. They result in the equivalent circuit of Fig. 2.9.

A transistor can be operated in three ways with a power gain in excess of unity. These are: (1) common-base, emitter input, collector output, (2) common-emitter, base input, collector output, and (3) common-collector, base input, emitter output. These are hereafter designated as the *common-base, common-emitter,* and *common-collector* configurations, respectively.

If the h parameters are known for any one configuration, they may be readily computed for the other configurations (see appendix). In order to distinguish between the different configurations, a letter sub-

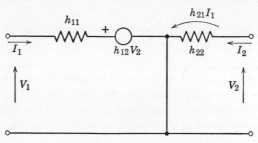

Fig. 2.9 h-equivalent circuit

script will be used to indicate the reference electrode. Thus, for example, h_{11b}, h_{21b}, y_{12b}, z_{22b} are common-base parameters, h_{11e}, h_{12e}, y_{22e}, z_{22e} are common-emitter parameters, and h_{11c}, h_{12c}, y_{11c}, z_{12c} are common-collector parameters.

2.3   Transistor Parameters and Equivalent Circuits

2.3.1   General Considerations

We have seen that the small-signal parameters of a transistor configuration can be determined by performing an appropriate set of four a-c measurements. This procedure gives adequate information for circuit design provided that the transistor is operated in the frequency range, at the d-c operating point and at the temperature at which the small-signal parameter measurements have been made. If, however, the transistor is used under different operating conditions, a new set of measurements is necessary to obtain the values of the parameters valid under these new conditions.

Consequently, if we desire to obtain complete information on the performance of the transistor, it becomes necessary to measure its small-signal parameters at all frequencies, d-c operating points, and temperatures of interest. This is feasible and, in some cases, where extreme accuracy is required, unavoidable, but is a rather laborious task. It is preferable to determine the fundamental quantities that govern the behavior of transistor small-signal parameters and the functional relationships existing between these quantities under different operating conditions. If this is done, the transistor can be character-

i̵n̵d̵ ̵b̵y̵ ̵a̵ ̵r̵e̵l̵a̵t̵i̵v̵e̵l̵y̵ ̵s̵m̵a̵l̵l̵ ̵n̵u̵m̵b̵e̵r̵ ̵o̵f̵ ̵q̵u̵a̵n̵t̵i̵t̵i̵e̵s̵,̵ ̵a̵n̵d̵ ̵i̵t̵s̵ ̵b̵e̵h̵a̵v̵i̵o̵r̵ ̵u̵n̵d̵e̵r̵
arbitrary operating conditions can be predicted without performing an
excessive number of measurements. The fundamental quantities and
their relationships are, however, related to the physical behavior of the
transistor. It is, therefore, necessary for the circuit design engineer to
gain a certain understanding of the physical processes involved in transistor operation.

Engineers engaged in the design of electron-tube circuits find it convenient that the relatively simple tube equivalent circuits (after inclusion of several parasitic reactances) are valid throughout a very wide
frequency range. Only at very high frequencies, where transit time
effects become important, does the representation of the tube become
complicated. Furthermore, the significance of the elements of the
equivalent circuit can be easily visualized in terms of the physical operation of the electron tube.

The situation is different for transistors. A large number of physical
processes take place in the transistor, and each of these exerts an influence on its circuit behavior. Therefore a complete transistor equivalent circuit valid throughout an extended frequency range includes a
great many circuit elements, some of which are lumped while others
have a distributed nature.

In view of the fact that there is practically no limit to refining a
transistor equivalent circuit to include the effects of additional physical
processes, no attempt will be made here to derive an exact one. An
approximate representation of the transistor will be shown; since, however, even this approximate representation would cause unnecessary
difficulties in many applications, further simplifications applicable to
specified frequency ranges will be carried out. More exact representations of transistors are available in the literature.[4]

2.3.2   Transistor Representation and Device Properties

2.3.2.1   The "Ideal" Transistor

In the p-n-p transistor triode shown in Fig. 2.10, all three semiconductor regions can be considered in the first approximation as equipotential, i.e. field-free. The applied voltages appear across the *barrier*
or *transition layers* separating emitter from base and collector from base,
respectively. (These barrier layers are also called *depletion layers*, since
the strong fields existing in the barrier layers tend to remove the carriers—holes and free electrons—from these regions.)

If a small incremental positive voltage is superimposed upon the
emitter-to-base d-c bias voltage, the emitter injects additional holes
into the base. The injected holes drift in the practically field-free base

region toward the collector by virtue of a density gradient. Some of the diffusing holes never reach the collector; they disappear by recombining en route with some of the numerous electrons existing in the base. However, a great majority of the injected holes reach the collector barrier, are swept across the barrier by the field, and enter the collector region.

In addition to this main diffusion process, there exist secondary effects of some importance. The applied incremental voltage across the emitter junction gives rise not only to a hole current from emitter to base but also to a smaller electron current from base to emitter. Fur-

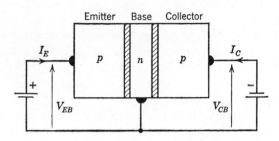

Fig. 2.10 p-n-p transistor

thermore, although the major part of the collector current consists of holes being swept across the collector barrier, some electrons traverse this barrier in the opposite direction and result in an increase of the collector current.

These diffusion processes can be treated mathematically, but no attempt will be made here to reproduce such calculations. The reader interested in the subject is referred to the classical paper by J. M. Early,[5] who has solved the diffusion equations related to the different current components for the "one-dimensional" transistor model. Since a transistor model based only on diffusion phenomena does not include unavoidable parasitic effects, it can be referred to as the *ideal transistor*.

Early's calculations express the small-signal parameters in terms of the physical properties of the transistor and result in the following approximate low-frequency common-base h parameters for the ideal transistor:

$$(h_{11b'})_0 = r_e \cong kT/qI_E \tag{2.15a}$$

$$(h_{12b'})_0 = \mu_0 \cong p'/[(q/kT) \sinh p \cosh p] \tag{2.15b}$$

$$(h_{21b'})_0 = -\alpha_{b0} \cong -\beta_0\gamma\alpha^* \cong -\gamma\alpha^*/\cosh p \tag{2.15c}$$

$$(h_{22b'})_0 = g_{cd} \cong p'I_E \sinh p/\cosh^2 p \tag{2.15d}$$

where r_ϵ = the *emitter diffusion resistance*

μ_0 = the *low-frequency reverse voltage transfer ratio*

α_{b0} = the *low-frequency short-circuit current amplification* (or forward current transfer ratio)

g_{cd} = the *collector diffusion conductance*

q = the charge of the electron (1.6×10^{-19} coulombs)

k = Boltzmann's constant (1.37×10^{-23} watt sec/°K)

T = the absolute temperature in degrees Kelvin

β = the *transport factor*, i.e. the ratio of holes reaching the collector to the total number of holes injected into the base (β is frequency-dependent, and β_0 is its low-frequency value.)

γ = the *emitter efficiency*, i.e. the ratio of emitter hole current to total emitter current †

α^* = the *collector multiplication factor*, i.e. the ratio of total collector current to collector hole current †

I_E = the d-c emitter current

p = w/L, where w is the width of the base region and L is the diffusion length of holes in the n-type base region, i.e. the net diffusion path of an average hole, in a region having properties similar to that of the base region, before recombination with an electron. (In order to have β_0 close to unity, w must be considerably smaller than L.)

p' = $\partial p/\partial V_{CB'} = (1/L)(\partial w/\partial V_{CB'})$ (The width of the collector barrier region and, consequently, that of the base region is a function of the collector-to-base voltage $V_{CB'}$. The derivative of this function is $\partial w/\partial V_{CB'}$.)

With increasing frequency the h parameters of the ideal transistor become complex. If we designate by τ the average lifetime of holes in the base region (i.e. the time during which the average hole can exist before recombination with an electron), and the frequency of the applied signal in radians per second by ω, the h parameters of the ideal transistor are

$$h_{11b}' \cong r_\epsilon \frac{\tanh [p(1 + j\omega\tau)^{1/2}]}{(1 + j\omega\tau)^{1/2} \tanh p} \qquad (2.16a)$$

$$h_{12b}' \cong \mu_0 \frac{\cosh p}{\cosh [p(1 + j\omega\tau)^{1/2}]} \qquad (2.16b)$$

† In eqs. 2.15 the effect of γ and α^* is neglected, except when $(h_{21b}')_0$ is considered. The error involved is small for $(h_{11b}')_0$ and $(h_{12b}')_0$ but may be considerable for $(h_{22b}')_0$, which can be appreciably larger than indicated by eq. 2.15d for transistors having relatively low emitter efficiency.

$$h_{21b'} = -\alpha_b \cong -\alpha_{b0} \frac{\cosh p}{\cosh [p(1 + j\omega\tau)^{\frac{1}{2}}]} \qquad (2.16c)$$

$$h_{22b'} \cong g_{cd} \frac{(1 + j\omega\tau)^{\frac{1}{2}} \tanh [p(1 + j\omega\tau)^{\frac{1}{2}}]}{\tanh p} \qquad (2.16d)$$

The equivalent circuit using these parameters is shown in Fig. 2.11.

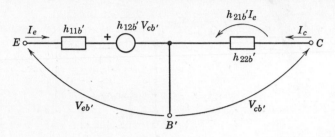

Fig. 2.11 h-type equivalent circuit of ideal transistor

2.3.2.2   Effect of Parasitic Elements

The computations leading to the h' parameters of expressions 2.16 are based on the mathematical treatment of the diffusion processes in the transistor. There exist, however, additional physical effects of considerable importance from the point of view of circuit performance. Taking these additional processes into account leads to circuit elements that must be added to the equivalent circuit of the ideal transistor in order to obtain an equivalent circuit representative of the performance of the *real transistor*.[5] Since the additional processes result in a deterioration of transistor performance, the corresponding equivalent-circuit elements are often referred to as *parasitic elements*.

In a real transistor, the base region is not equipotential, but exhibits an ohmic resistance to the flow of base current. This parasitic resistance is the *base-spreading resistance*,[6] usually designated by r_b'. (The designation base-spreading resistance is due to the shape of the base of an alloy junction transistor which "spreads out" as one progresses from the center of the junction to the periphery of the transistor.) r_b' can be incorporated into the equivalent circuit by connecting it between the *internal base B'* and the *base contact B*, as shown in Fig. 2.12. The base resistance is not always resistive; in the case of rate-grown n-p-n transistors r_b' is of a distributed nature (a transmission line) and must be associated at any higher frequency with a parallel capacitance.[7] In general, however, it will be assumed that r_b' is resistive. The existence of r_b' is objectionable since it contributes to the deterioration of transistor performance at high frequencies.

Since the barrier layers separating emitter from base and collector from base, respectively, are regions in which strong electric fields exist, this implies that these regions are associated with capacitances, the so-called *barrier capacitances* (often also called depletion-layer or transition capacitances). The barrier capacitance associated with the

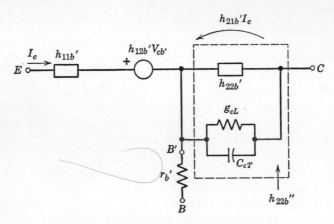

Fig. 2.12　Equivalent circuit of real transistor

emitter junction is usually negligible as compared to the emitter diffusion capacitance (i.e. the imaginary component of h_{11b}'), but the role of the collector-barrier capacitance C_{cT} is an important one. C_{cT} must be added to the equivalent circuit of the ideal transistor, in parallel with h_{22b}' (Fig. 2.12). [If one wants to be more rigorous, then, depending on the geometry of the particular transistor under consideration, it

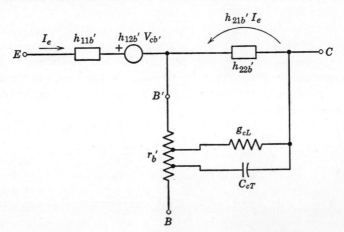

Fig. 2.13　More exact equivalent circuit of real transistor

should be connected between the collector terminal C and a tap on the base-spreading resistance r_b' (Fig. 2.13). However, this refinement is usually omitted.] The barrier capacitance is also a parasitic element; it results in considerable deterioration of high-frequency performance.

There exists a certain amount of leakage current from collector to base. This effect can be represented by a corresponding *leakage conductance* g_{cL} connected in parallel with h_{22b}' in Fig. 2.12. As with the barrier capacitance, this conductance should, depending on transistor geometry, be connected between the collector terminal C and a tap on r_b' (see Fig. 2.13), but, for the sake of simplicity, the arrangement of Fig. 2.12 is acceptable.

In some cases, the ohmic resistances of the emitter and collector regions and associated contacts are not negligible. These resistances will, however, be generally disregarded in small-signal applications.

Finally, the effect of parasitic interelectrode capacitances must often be considered.[8,9] For example, at high frequencies, in the common-emitter configuration, the collector-to-base capacitance may affect circuit performance.

2.3.2.3 The Real Transistor

Adding r_b', C_{cT}, and g_{cL} to the equivalent of the ideal transistor, we obtain a reasonably accurate equivalent circuit of the actual transistor, as shown in Fig. 2.12. (Since $V_{cb} \cong V_{cb'}$, the voltage generator is often indicated as being proportional to the measurable voltage V_{cb}.)

The common-base h parameters of the actual transistor corresponding to this equivalent circuit can now be computed. Since, with junction transistors (up to very high frequencies and at "normal" operating points), we have

$$h_{12b}' \ll 1 \tag{2.17}$$

$$r_b' h_{22b}'' \ll 1 \tag{2.18}$$

the expressions relating the h parameters of the "real" transistor to those of the "ideal" transistor can be written in simplified form. If we designate by

$$h_{22b}'' = h_{22b}' + g_{cL} + j\omega C_{cT} \tag{2.19}$$

we find the common-base h parameters of the real transistor:

$$h_{11b} \cong h_{11b}' + r_b'(1 + h_{21b}') \tag{2.20a}$$

$$h_{12b} \cong h_{12b}' + r_b' h_{22b}'' \tag{2.20b}$$

$$h_{21b} \cong h_{21b}' \tag{2.20c}$$

$$h_{22b} \cong h_{22b}'' \tag{2.20d}$$

These approximations are adequate for most purposes. In some cases however, assumption 2.18 is not permissible, especially when h_{12b} and h_{22b} are considered. Then the right-hand side of eqs. 2.20b and 2.20d must be multiplied by $1/(1 + r_b'h_{22b}'')$.

Substituting the h' parameters of the ideal transistor given by eqs. 2.16 into eqs. 2.19 to 2.20, we find the common-base h parameters of the real transistor. The common-emitter and common-collector h parameters can then be computed, using Table 4 of the appendix. The resulting expressions are quite involved but are of major importance; they represent the transistor in a general way and form the link between numerous, often seemingly independent, transistor representations. The circuit engineer is not expected to use these complicated expressions in practical circuit design. The following sections will show that, depending on the operating frequency, the expressions can be simplified considerably, and the simplified expressions do lend themselves to circuit calculations.

2.3.3 h Parameters in Various Frequency Ranges

2.3.3.1 The Low-Frequency Range

At low frequencies, the common-base h' parameters of the ideal transistor are given by r_e, μ_0, $-\alpha_{b0}$, and g_{cd} (see eqs. 2.15).

Owing to the existence of the collector-barrier capacitance, the phase shift of h_{22b}'' is not negligible at frequencies as low as a few kilocycles. It will be shown in Sec. 2.3.3.2 that we can write

$$h_{22b}'' \cong g_c + j\omega C_c \tag{2.21}$$

g_c being the *collector conductance* and C_c the *collector capacitance*.

The equivalent circuit of Fig. 2.12 now takes the form of Fig. 2.14.

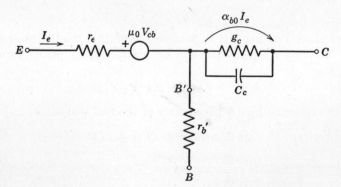

Fig. 2.14   Low-frequency equivalent circuit of transistor

Using eqs. 2.20, we find the h parameters corresponding to the three configurations (see Table 2.1).

Table 2.1

Approximate h Parameters in the Low-Frequency Range

Parameter	Configuration		
	Common-Base	Common-Emitter	Common-Collector
h_{11}	$r_\epsilon + r_b'(1 - \alpha_{b0})$	$r_b' + r_\epsilon/(1 - \alpha_{b0})$	$r_b' + r_\epsilon/(1 - \alpha_{b0})$
h_{12}	$\mu_0 + r_b'(g_c + j\omega C_c)$	$r_\epsilon(g_c + j\omega C_c)/(1 - \alpha_{b0}) - \mu_0$	1
h_{21}	$-\alpha_{b0}$	$\alpha_{b0}/(1 - \alpha_{b0})$	$-1/(1 - \alpha_{b0})$
h_{22}	$g_c + j\omega C_c$	$(g_c + j\omega C_c)/(1 - \alpha_{b0})$	$(g_c + j\omega C_c)/(1 - \alpha_{b0})$

Typical numerical values of the various h parameters can be calculated, if the typical values of their component quantities are kept in mind. For example, at 1 ma emitter current and 6 volts collector voltage, $r_\epsilon \cong 26$ ohms, $\mu_0 = 0.5 \times 10^{-4}$ to 5×10^{-4}, $\alpha_{b0} = 0.9$ to 1.0, $g_c = 0.1 \times 10^{-6}$ to 1×10^{-6} mho, $C_c = 2$ to 30 $\mu\mu$f, $r_b' = 30$ to 1000 ohms.

C_c can be disregarded whenever ωC_c is small compared to g_c; i.e. usually at low audio frequencies.

2.3.3.2 The Medium-Frequency Range

By medium-frequency range we designate the frequencies at which the imaginary components of the small-signal parameters cannot be neglected but where first-order approximations of the hyperbolic functions in eq. 2.16 are adequate.

The common-base short-circuit current amplification is given by eq. 2.16c:

$$\alpha_b \cong \alpha_{b0} \cosh p/\cosh [p(1 + j\omega\tau)^{\frac{1}{2}}] \tag{2.22}$$

The α_b cutoff frequency, $f_{\alpha b} = \omega_{\alpha b}/2\pi$ (sometimes referred to as the "α cutoff frequency") is defined as the frequency at which α_b is equal to 0.707 times its low-frequency value α_{b0}. Since $\omega_{\alpha b}$ can be measured easily, the frequency dependence of transistor parameters is usually described in terms of $\omega_{\alpha b}$. In general, $\omega_{\alpha b}$ is a function of p and τ. For practical transistors having α_{b0} close to unity, we have approximately

$$\omega_{\alpha b} \cong 2.5/p^2\tau \tag{2.23}$$

The hyperbolic functions of eq. 2.16 can then be written in first-order approximation:

$$\cosh [p(1 + j\omega\tau)^{\frac{1}{2}}] \cong (1 + j\omega\tau p^2/2) \cosh p$$

$$\cong (1 + j\omega/0.8\omega_{ab}) \cosh p \qquad (2.24)$$

$$\sinh [p(1 + j\omega\tau)^{\frac{1}{2}}] \cong (1 + j\omega\tau)^{\frac{1}{2}}(1 + j\omega\tau p^2/6) \sinh p$$

$$\cong (1 + j\omega\tau)^{\frac{1}{2}}(1 + j\omega/2.4\omega_{ab}) \sinh p \quad (2.25)$$

In the medium-frequency range the frequencies considered are considerably smaller than $(2.4\omega_{ab})$, and one can write

$$\tanh [p(1 + j\omega\tau)^{\frac{1}{2}}]$$

$$\cong (1 + j\omega\tau)^{\frac{1}{2}}[(1 + j\omega/2.4\omega_{ab})/(1 + j\omega/0.8\omega_{ab})] \tanh p$$

$$\cong (1 + j\omega\tau)^{\frac{1}{2}} \tanh p/(1 + j\omega/1.2\omega_{ab}) \qquad (2.26)$$

Consequently, using eqs. 2.16 and 2.19, we obtain (disregarding the effect of r_b')

$$h_{11b}' \cong r_\epsilon/(1 + j\omega/1.2\omega_{ab}) \qquad (2.27a)$$

$$h_{12b}' \cong \mu_0/(1 + j\omega/0.8\omega_{ab}) \qquad (2.27b)$$

$$h_{21b}' \cong -\alpha_{b0}/(1 + j\omega/0.8\omega_{ab}) \qquad (2.27c)$$

$$h_{22b}'' \cong g_{cd}(1 + j\omega\tau)/(1 + j\omega/1.2\omega_{ab}) + g_{cL} + j\omega C_{cT} \quad (2.27d)$$

In the expression for h_{22b}'' the term $j\omega C_{cT}$ is the dominant imaginary term, and, since

$$1/\tau \ll 1.2\omega_{ab}$$

we can write approximately

$$h_{22b}'' \cong g_{cd} + g_{cL} + j\omega(C_{cT} + g_{cd}\tau) \qquad (2.28)$$

Designating

$$g_c = g_{cd} + g_{cL} \qquad (2.29a)$$

$$C_c = C_{cT} + g_{cd}\tau = C_{cT} + C_{cd} \qquad (2.29b)$$

where $C_{cd} = g_{cd}\tau$ is the *collector diffusion capacitance*, we can simply write

$$h_{22b}'' \cong g_c + j\omega C_c \qquad (2.30)$$

g_o being the *collector conductance* and C_c the *collector capacitance*.

In many cases, especially at *lower* medium frequencies, the factors 1.2 and 0.8 in eqs. 2.27 can be neglected, resulting in the following simplified expressions for the h' parameters and h_{22b}'':

$$h_{11b}' \cong r_\epsilon/(1 + j\omega/\omega_{\alpha b}) \tag{2.31a}$$

$$h_{12b}' \cong \mu_0/(1 + j\omega/\omega_{\alpha b}) \tag{2.31b}$$

$$h_{21b}' \cong -\alpha_{b0}/(1 + j\omega/\omega_{\alpha b}) \tag{2.31c}$$

$$h_{22b}'' \cong g_c + j\omega C_c \tag{2.31d}$$

Depending on the desired degree of accuracy, eqs. 2.27 and 2.30 or eqs. 2.31 can now be used to represent the ideal transistor and can be substituted into eqs. 2.20. Thus, approximate expressions for the common-base h parameters of the real transistor can be obtained. The corre-

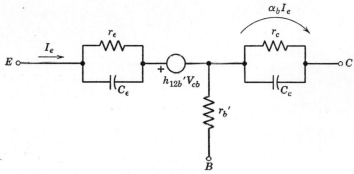

Fig. 2.15 Transistor equivalent circuit valid from low-through-medium frequencies

sponding equivalent circuit is shown in Fig. 2.15. The capacitance C_ϵ shunting r_ϵ is the *emitter diffusion capacitance* and is given by

$$C_\epsilon \cong 1/(1.2r_\epsilon\omega_{\alpha b}) \tag{2.32a}$$

Here again, the factor 1.2 is often omitted, and we write simply

$$C_\epsilon \cong 1/r_\epsilon\omega_{\alpha b} \tag{2.32b}$$

Table 2.2 shows the frequency-dependent h parameters of the three configurations, using eqs. 2.31 and 2.20. These expressions are approximately valid up to an appreciable fraction of $f_{\alpha b}$. (The frequency dependence of h_{12b}' is neglected in these expressions because, at higher frequencies, $h_{12b}' \ll r_b'h_{22b}''$.)

For many applications the behavior of the h parameters at audio frequencies is not too important, and we are interested in h parameter expressions that are valid only at medium frequencies, where $\omega \gg g_c/C_c$ and $h_{12b}' \ll j\omega C_c r_b'$. The equivalent circuit of Fig. 2.15 can then be

Table 2.2

Approximate h Parameters Valid throughout the Low- and Medium-Frequency Range

Parameter	Transistor Configuration		
	Common-Base	Common-Emitter	Common-Collector
h_{11}	$\dfrac{r_\epsilon}{1 + j\omega/\omega_{ab}} + r_b'(1 - \alpha_{b0})\dfrac{1 + j\omega/(1 - \alpha_{b0})\omega_{ab}}{1 + j\omega/\omega_{ab}}$	$r_b' + \left(\dfrac{r_\epsilon}{1 - \alpha_{b0}}\right)\left[\dfrac{1}{1 + j\omega/(1 - \alpha_{b0})\omega_{ab}}\right]$	$r_b' + \left(\dfrac{r_\epsilon}{1 - \alpha_{b0}}\right)\left[\dfrac{1}{1 + j\omega/(1 - \alpha_{b0})\omega_{ab}}\right]$
h_{12}	$\mu_0 + r_b'(g_c + j\omega C_c)$	$\dfrac{r_e(g_c + j\omega C_c)}{(1 - \alpha_{b0})[1 + j\omega/(1 - \alpha_{b0})\omega_{ab}]} - \mu_0$	1
h_{21}	$\dfrac{-\alpha_{b0}}{1 + j\omega/\omega_{ab}}$	$\left(\dfrac{\alpha_{b0}}{1 - \alpha_{b0}}\right)\left[\dfrac{1}{1 + j\omega/(1 - \alpha_{b0})\omega_{ab}}\right]$	$\left(\dfrac{-1}{1 - \alpha_{b0}}\right)\left[\dfrac{1 + j\omega/\omega_{a\alpha}}{1 + j\omega/(1 - \alpha_{b0})\omega_{ab}}\right]$
h_{22}	$g_c + j\omega C_c$	$\dfrac{(g_c + j\omega C_c)(1 + j\omega/\omega_{ab})}{(1 - \alpha_{b0})[1 + j\omega/(1 - \alpha_{b0})\omega_{ab}]}$	$\dfrac{(g_c + j\omega C_c)(1 + j\omega/\omega_{a\alpha})}{(1 - \alpha_{b0})[1 + j\omega/(1 - \alpha_{b0})\omega_{ab}]}$

Table 2.3

Approximate h Parameters in the Medium-Frequency Range

Parameter	Transistor Configuration		
	Common-Base	Common-Emitter	Common-Collector
h_{11}	$\dfrac{r_e}{1 + j\omega/\omega_{ab}} + r_b'(1 - \alpha_{b0})\dfrac{1 + j\omega/(1 - \alpha_{b0})\omega_{ab}}{1 + j\omega/\omega_{ab}}$	$r_b' + \left(\dfrac{r_e}{1 - \alpha_{b0}}\right)\left[\dfrac{1}{1 + j\omega/(1 - \alpha_{b0})\omega_{ab}}\right]$	$r_b' + \left(\dfrac{r_e}{1 - \alpha_{b0}}\right)\left[\dfrac{1}{1 + j\omega/(1 - \alpha_{b0})\omega_{ab}}\right]$
h_{12}	$j\omega C_e r_b'$	$\left(\dfrac{j\omega C_e r_e}{1 - \alpha_{b0}}\right)\left[\dfrac{1}{1 + j\omega/(1 - \alpha_{b0})\omega_{ab}}\right]$	1
h_{21}	$\dfrac{-\alpha_{b0}}{1 + j\omega/\omega_{ab}}$	$\dfrac{\alpha_{b0}/(1 - \alpha_{b0})}{1 + j\omega/(1 - \alpha_{b0})\omega_{ab}}$	$\left(\dfrac{-1}{1 - \alpha_{b0}}\right)\left[\dfrac{1 + j\omega/\omega_{ab}}{1 + j\omega/(1 - \alpha_{b0})\omega_{ab}}\right]$
h_{22}	$j\omega C_c$	$\left(\dfrac{j\omega C_c}{1 - \alpha_{b0}}\right)\left[\dfrac{1 + j\omega/\omega_{ab}}{1 + j\omega/(1 - \alpha_{b0})\omega_{ab}}\right]$	$\left(\dfrac{j\omega C_c}{1 - \alpha_{b0}}\right)\left[\dfrac{1 + j\omega/\omega_{ab}}{1 + j\omega/(1 - \alpha_{b0})\omega_{ab}}\right]$

simplified and results in the circuit of Fig. 2.16. The corresponding h parameters of the transistor are given in Table 2.3.

The expressions for the h parameters show that the transistor has three critical frequencies determining its performance. These are, in

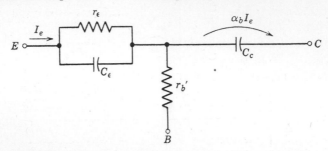

Fig. 2.16   Medium-frequency equivalent circuit of transistor

order of decreasing magnitude,

$$\omega_{ab}$$

$$\omega_{ae} \cong (1 - \alpha_{b0})\omega_{ab}$$

and $$\omega_c = g_c/C_c$$

Depending on the frequency range under consideration, therefore, the expressions for the h parameters and the corresponding equivalent circuits can be further simplified. For example, if the frequencies considered exceed considerably $(1 - \alpha_{b0})\omega_{ab}$ and are much smaller than ω_{ab}, h_{21e} can be written as

$$h_{21e} \cong -j\omega_{ab}/\omega \qquad (2.33)$$

Other parameters can be simplified in a similar manner.

Parasitic capacitances, which have not been taken into account in the above considerations and in the derivation of the expressions given in Tables 2.2 and 2.3, may affect circuit performance at medium and high frequencies. These capacitances are base-to-collector capacitance C_{bc}, emitter-to-collector capacitance C_{ec}, and emitter-to-base capacitance C_{eb}.

2.3.3.3   The High-Frequency Range

Some of the "medium-frequency" approximations made in the previous section cease to be valid as the frequency approaches f_{ab}, and it is necessary to work with better approximations of the h parameters which lead to increased complexities in calculations.

Various "almost exact" equivalent circuits of the transistor have been derived in the literature.[10, 11] These usually involve transmission lines and a large number of lumped circuit elements. Although such representations have contributed to a better understanding of transistor behavior, they do not lend themselves to practical circuit design methods.

Most transistor applications are in the field of the medium frequencies previously discussed, where the simplified first-order approximations apply. Transistors are also used in the frequency range extending up to even slightly above f_{ab}, where the first-order approximations no longer apply, but for which second-order approximations can easily be derived. Transistors are almost never used at frequencies of the order of several times f_{ab}, where very complicated equivalent circuits would be necessary, because their gain is insufficient at these frequencies.

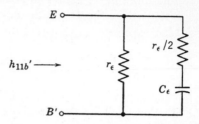

Fig. 2.17   Equivalent circuit of h_{11b}' used at high frequencies

The high-frequency representation of h_{11b}' can be improved by writing (according to eqs. 2.16a and 2.26)

$$h_{11b}' \cong r_\epsilon(1 + j\omega/2.4\omega_{ab})/(1 + j\omega/0.8\omega_{ab}) \tag{2.34}$$

The impedance corresponding to eq. 2.34 is shown in Fig. 2.17. This approximation is good up to about twice the α_b cutoff frequency.

The most significant error introduced by the first-order approximation was made in the expression for h_{21b}'. According to eq. 2.16c,

$$h_{21b}' \cong -\alpha_{b0} \cosh p/\cosh [p(1 + j\omega\tau)^{1/2}] \tag{2.16c}$$

and is 3 db down at the α_b cutoff frequency having a 57° phase shift. Using approximation 2.27c,

$$h_{21b}' \cong -\alpha_{b0}/(1 + j\omega/0.8\omega_{ab}) \tag{2.35}$$

we introduce a considerable amplitude error at frequencies close to ω_{ab} and a relatively small phase error. If, on the other hand, omitting the factor 0.8, we use

$$h_{21b}' \cong -\alpha_{b0}/(1 + j\omega/\omega_{ab}) \tag{2.36}$$

the amplitude of α_b is correct at ω_{ab}, the phase shift, however, is 45° instead of 57°. The approximation can be improved materially by considering a second-order expansion of α_b which leads to

$$h_{21b}' \cong -\alpha_{b0}/(1 + j\omega/\omega_{ab})(1 + j\omega/4\omega_{ab}) \tag{2.37}$$

This approximation given satisfactory results up to and even well beyond $f_{\alpha b}$.

Since the frequency-independent barrier capacitance is usually the dominant term in h_{12b} and h_{22b}, the medium-frequency approximations of these parameters can be used up to very high frequencies.

The more exact expressions 2.34 and 2.37 for h_{11b}' and h_{21b}' can be substituted in the h parameters of the three configurations. The resulting expressions are useful up to frequencies well beyond $f_{\alpha b}$.

2.3.4 Other Equivalent Representations

Transistor performance can be analyzed conveniently, using the frequency-dependent h parameters and the corresponding equivalent circuits discussed in the previous section. There are, however, many

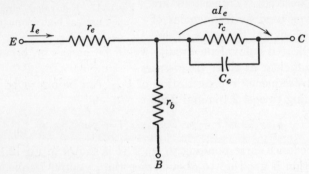

Fig. 2.18   Low-frequency T-type equivalent circuit of transistor

other equivalent circuits adequately describing the circuit behavior of transistors.

The T-type equivalent circuit of Fig. 2.18 is often used at low frequencies, and, in the specification sheets of some manufacturers, low-frequency transistors are characterized by the elements of this circuit. When using this circuit it is important not to confuse the base-spreading resistance r_b' with the *equivalent low-frequency base resistance* r_b; r_b is usually considerably larger than r_b'. Similarly one should distinguish between the emitter diffusion resistance r_e and the *equivalent emitter resistance* r_e. The *collector resistance* r_c is approximately equal to $1/g_c$ and $a \cong \alpha_b$.

Several equivalent circuits can be used to represent the transistor at medium frequencies (i.e. at frequencies smaller than $f_{\alpha b}$). The elements constituting these circuits can be expressed in terms of the parameters used throughout the preceding sections. (Note: The equivalent circuits shown in Figs. 2.19 to 2.23 can be justified by computing the T- or π-type equivalent circuits of the ideal transistor in common-base and common-emitter configuration, using eqs. 2.15 and 2.16 and subsequently adding the parasitic elements.   Equations 2.38 to 2.42 relating the circuit elements of these equivalent circuits to the quantities used in preceding sections are quite accurate if one assumes in eq. 2.15c that $\gamma = \alpha^* = 1$.   Then we have $\alpha_{b0} = \beta_0$ and $h_{21b}' = -1/\cosh [p(1 + j\omega\tau)^{1/2}]$, and, furthermore, r_{ϵ}, μ_0, α_{b0}, and g_{cd} are related by $\mu_0(1 - \alpha_{b0}^2) = \alpha_{b0}r_{\epsilon}g_{cd}$.   However, for transistors having relatively low emitter efficiency or significant collector current multiplication, several of the relationships of eqs. 2.38 to 2.42 may be considerably in error.)

The equivalent circuit of Fig. 2.19a (or its simplified version [6] of Fig. 2.19b) may be used in dealing with common-base circuits.   It contains

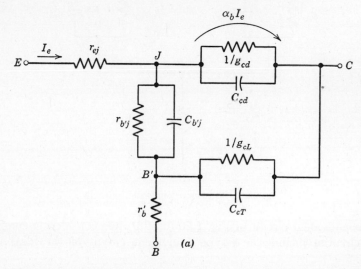

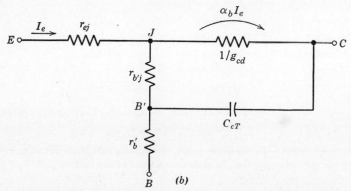

Fig. 2.19   Transistor equivalent circuit and its simplified form

a T-type equivalent of the ideal transistor. We have

$$r_{ej} \cong r_{\epsilon}/2 \qquad (2.38a) \; *$$

$$r_{b'j} \cong r_{\epsilon}/2(1 - \alpha_{b0}) \qquad (2.38b) \; *$$

$$C_{b'j} \cong 2/r_{\epsilon}\omega_{\alpha b} \qquad (2.38c)$$

$$\alpha_b \cong \alpha_{b0}/(1 + j\omega/\omega_{\alpha b}) \qquad (2.38d)$$

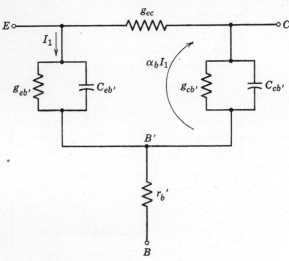

Fig. 2.20   Transistor equivalent circuit

The equivalent circuit of Fig. 2.20 (useful when considering common-base circuits) includes a π-type equivalent circuit of the ideal transistor: [12]

$$g_{eb'} \cong 1/r_{\epsilon} \qquad (2.39a)$$

$$C_{eb'} \cong C_{\epsilon} \cong 1/r_{\epsilon}\omega_{\alpha b} \qquad (2.39b)$$

$$g_{cb'} \cong g_c \qquad (2.39c)$$

$$C_{cb'} \cong C_c \qquad (2.39d)$$

$$g_{ec} \cong \mu_0/r_{\epsilon} \qquad (2.39e)$$

$$\alpha_b \cong \alpha_{b0}/(1 + j\omega/\omega_{\alpha b}) \qquad (2.39f)$$

* r_{ej} is equal to r_e of the equivalent circuit of Fig. 2.18. If the emitter efficiency is low (on the order of the transport factor β_0), r_{ej} may be much smaller than indicated by eq. 2.38a and is shunted by an appreciable capacitance. Then $r_{b'j}$ is larger than indicated by eq. 2.38b. On the other hand, due to physical effects not discussed here, r_{ej} may be larger than $r_{\epsilon}/2$ and, in some cases, even larger than r_{ϵ}.

The equivalent circuit of Fig. 2.21 is similar to that of Fig. 2.20 but has a current generator proportional to the emitter current. Its cir-

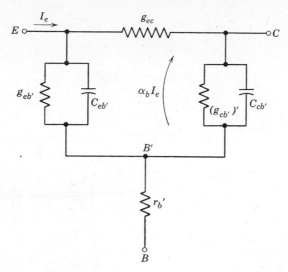

Fig. 2.21   Modified version of the equivalent circuit of Fig. 2.20

cuit elements are identical to those of eq. 2.39 with one exception:

$$(g_{cb'})' \cong g_c - \mu_0/r_\epsilon \qquad (2.40)$$

$[(g_{cb'})'$ is usually negative.]

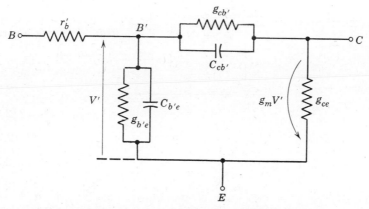

Fig. 2.22   "Hybrid" π-type equivalent circuit of transistor

The "hybrid π-type" equivalent circuit of Fig. 2.22 is often used to represent the common-emitter configuration: [13]

$$g_{b'g} \cong (1 - \alpha_{b0})/r_\epsilon \qquad (2.41a)$$

$$C_{b'e} \cong C_\epsilon \cong 1/r_\epsilon \omega_{\alpha b} \qquad (2.41b)$$

$$g_{ce} \cong \mu_0/r_\epsilon \qquad (2.41c)$$

$$g_{cb'} \cong g_c - g_{cd}/2 \cong g_c \qquad (2.41d)$$

$$C_{cb'} \cong C_c - C_{cd}/2 \cong C_c \qquad (2.41e)$$

$$g_m \cong \alpha_{e0}/r_\epsilon \qquad (2.41f)$$

The circuit of Fig. 2.23 is a modification of that of Fig. 2.22, and has a current generator proportional to the base current rather than to the

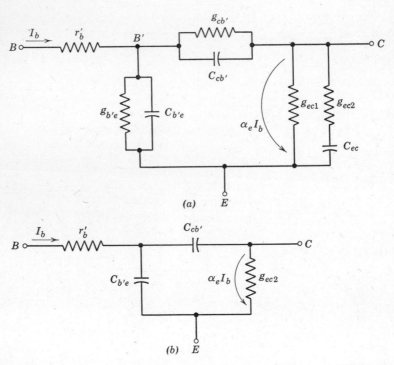

(a)   E

(b)   E

Fig. 2.23 Modified version of the equivalent circuit of Fig. 2.22 and its high-frequency approximation

internal voltage V'. Its circuit elements are identical with those given by eqs. 2.41, with the following exceptions:

$$g_{ec1} \cong y_c/(1 - \alpha_{b0}) \qquad (2.42a)$$

$$g_{ec2} \cong C_c[\omega_{\alpha b} - \omega_c/(1 - \alpha_{b0})] \qquad (2.42b)$$

$$C_{ec} \cong C_c/(1 - \alpha_{b0}) \tag{2.42c}$$

$$\alpha_e \cong \alpha_{e0}/(1 + j\omega/\omega_{\alpha e}) \tag{2.42d}$$

These equivalent circuits can often be simplified greatly when considering specific frequency ranges. For example, if $\omega_{\alpha e} < \omega < \omega_{\alpha b}$, the circuit of Fig. 2.23a can be represented approximately by that of Fig. 2.23b.

2.4   Parameters as Functions of Operating Point and Temperature

Equations 2.15 show that the h parameters of the transistor are functions of the d-c operating point.

r_ϵ is inversely and g_{cd} is directly proportional to I_E. p' is independent of I_E but varies with V_{CB}:

$$p' = p'(1)V_{CB}^{-m} \tag{2.43}$$

$p'(1)$ designates the value of p' at 1 volt collector-to-base voltage. The value of the exponent m depends on the nature of the collector junction. In alloy-junction transistors m is close to $\frac{1}{2}$.

The collector barrier capacitance is independent of I_E but is a function of V_{CB}:

$$C_{cT} = C_{cT}(1)V_{CB}^{-n} \tag{2.44}$$

$C_{cT}(1)$ designates the value of C_{cT} at 1 volt collector-to-base voltage. The exponent n is again a function of the nature of the collector junction. For diffused junction transistors n is close to $\frac{1}{2}$.

Consequently, the common-base h parameters can be written in the following schematic form:

$$h_{11b} \cong K_1/I_E + r_b'(1 - \alpha_b) \tag{2.45}$$

$$h_{12b} \cong K_2 V_{CB}^{-m} + r_b'[K_3 I_E V_{CB}^{-m} + g_{cL} + j\omega C_{cT}(1)V_{CB}^{-n}] \tag{2.46}$$

$$h_{21b} \cong -\alpha_b \tag{2.47}$$

$$h_{22b} \cong K_3 I_E V_{CB}^{-m} + g_{cL} + j\omega C_{cT}(1)V_{CB}^{-n} \tag{2.48}$$

where K_1, K_2, and K_3 are expressions independent of I_E and V_{CB}.

From eq. 2.47 it appears that h_{21b} is not a function of the emitter current. In reality this is true only over a restricted range of emitter currents: h_{21b} decreases at small and large values of I_E. [14] It is, however, relatively independent of the collector-to-base voltage. (In some transistors h_{21b} rises slightly with V_{CB}.)

h_{11b} decreases as the emitter current is increased. Owing to the variation of α_b with I_E which causes an even stronger variation of

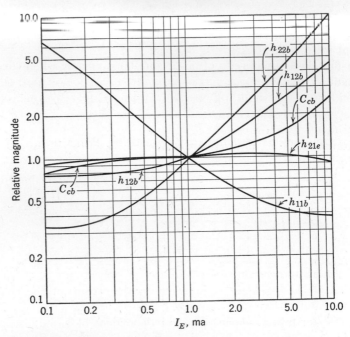

Fig. 2.24   Transistor parameters as functions of the emitter current

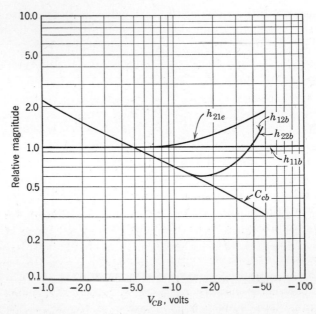

Fig. 2.25   Transistor parameters as functions of the collector voltage

$(1 - \alpha_b)$, the second term in eq. 2.45 is not constant; however, the principal variation comes from the first term. h_{11b} is practically independent of the collector-to-base voltage.

The first term constituting h_{22b} is the diffusion term. This term is dominant at low frequencies (and is resistive), provided that the leakage conductance is small. Consequently the collector conductance increases with the emitter current. At high frequencies the term containing C_{cT} is most important, and the variation of the total collector capacitance with I_E at moderate values of I_E is rather small. Both collector conductance and capacitance decrease as V_{CB} is increased.

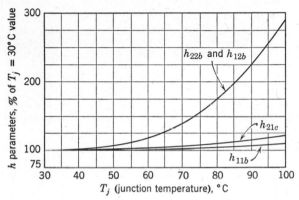

Fig. 2.26   Transistor parameters as functions of the temperature

$$V_{CB} = 5 \text{ v}, I_E = 1 \text{ ma}$$

(If V_{CB} approaches the breakdown voltage of the collector junction, h_{22b} increases with increasing V_{CB}.)

At low frequencies $K_2 V_{CB}^{-m}$ is the dominant term of h_{12b}. Consequently, h_{12b} decreases as V_{CB} is increased and increases only moderately with increasing emitter current. At high frequencies the term containing C_{cT} prevails, and h_{12b} behaves similarly to h_{22b}.

The variation of the h parameters with I_E and V_{CB} is illustrated by Figs. 2.24 and 2.25.

As was mentioned earlier, $f_{\alpha b}$ is approximately $2.5/p^2 \tau$, where $p = w/L$. In transistors with narrow base width w might be significantly affected by variations of V_{CB}; w decreases as V_{CB} is increased. This causes $\omega_{\alpha b}$ to increase with increasing V_{CB}.

The temperature variation of the h parameters is shown schematically in Fig. 2.26. h_{22b} and h_{12b} show the strongest variation with temperature: both parameters increase as the temperature is increased.

Many transistors exhibit a slight increase in h_{21b} as the temperature is increased. This may imply a considerable increase in h_{21e}.

Problems

1. Compute the y and z parameters of the "ideal transistor" in the common-base configuration using eqs. 2.15 to 2.16. Assume $\alpha_{b0} = \beta_0 = 1/\cosh p$ and $\gamma = \alpha^* = 1$. Construct T- and π-type equivalent circuits, using first-order approximations of the parameters and add $r_b{}'$, C_{cT}, and g_{cL}. Compare with the circuits of Figs. 2.19 to 2.21 and eqs. 2.38 to 2.40.

2. Compute the y parameters of the "ideal transistor" in the common-emitter configuration with the assumptions of problem 1. Construct a "first-order" equivalent circuit, adding $r_b{}'$, C_{cT}, and g_{cL}. Compare with Figs. 2.22 and 2.23 and eqs. 2.41 and 2.42.

3. Evaluate the effect of a parasitic collector-to-base capacitance C_{cb} on the h parameters of the common-emitter circuit from low to high frequencies.

4. Evaluate the effect at high frequencies of (a) a parasitic emitter-to-base capacitance C_{eb} on h_{21b} and of (b) a parasitic collector-to-emitter capacitance C_{ce} on h_{22b}.

5. Compute common-base and common-emitter h parameters valid from low frequencies up to a considerable fraction of f_{ab}, using eqs. 2.20 and 2.31. Sketch the frequency response of these parameters. (Use "broken line" representation.)

6. Compute approximate expressions for the common-base and common-emitter h parameters valid for $\omega_{ae} < \omega < \omega_{ab}$.

7. Evaluate and discuss the variation of common-emitter h parameters with varying I_E and V_{CB}: (a) at low frequencies and (b) at high frequencies.

8. The load of a common-collector stage is a high resistance. Consequently, the input impedance is approximately z_{11c}. Compute this parameter, and discuss its frequency dependence.

9. Consider the approximate high-frequency equivalent circuit of Fig. 2.16. Transistor 1 has $r_b{}' = 3000$ ohms and transistor 2 has $r_b{}' = 100$ ohms. Both transistors have $C_c = 20\mu\mu f$ and $\alpha_b = 0.98/(1 + j\omega/6 \times 10^7)$. What will be the effect of $r_b{}'$ and C_c on h_{21b} at high frequencies in the two cases?

Bibliography

1. E. A. Guillemin, *Communication Networks*, Vol. II, Wiley, New York, 1935.

2. R. F. Shea, et al., *Principles of Transistor Circuits*, Wiley, New York, 1953.

3. L. A. Pipes, "The Matrix Theory of Four Terminal Networks," *Phil. Mag.*, *30*, 370 (1940).

4. R. L. Pritchard, "Electric-Network Representation of Transistors—a Survey," *IRE Trans.*, *CT-3*, 5–21 (1956).

5. J. M. Early, "Design Theory of Junction Transistors," *Bell System Tech. J.*, *32*, 1271–1312 (1953).

6. J. M. Early, "Effects of Space-Charge Widening in Junction Transistors," *Proc. IRE*, *40*, 1401–1405 (1952).

7. R. L. Pritchard and W. N. Coffey, "Small-Signal Parameters of Grown-Junction Transistors at High Frequencies," *IRE Convention Record*, *2*, pt. 3, 89–93 (1954).

8. R. L. Pritchard, "Effect of Base-Contact Overlap and Parasitic Capacitance on Small-Signal Parameters of Junction-Transistors," *Proc. IRE*, *43*, 38–40 (1955).

9. A. P. Stern, C. A. Aldridge, and W. F. Chow, "Internal Feedback and Neutralization of Transistor Amplifiers," *Proc. IRE, 43*, 838–847 (1955).

10. R. L. Pritchard, "Frequency Variations of Junction Transistor Parameters," *Proc. IRE, 42*, 786–799 (1954).

11. H. Statz, E. A. Guillemin, and R. A. Pucel, "Design Considerations of Junction Transistors at Higher Frequencies," *Proc. IRE, 42*, 1624 (1954).

12. R. J. Turner, "Surface Barrier Transistor Measurements and Applications," *Tele-Tech, 13*, 78 (Aug. 1954).

13. L. J. Giacolletto, "The Study and Design of Alloyed-Junction Transistors," *IRE Convention Record, 2*, pt. 3, 102 (1954).

14. W. M. Webster, "On the Variation of Junction-Transistor Current-Amplification Factor with Emitter Current," *Proc. IRE, 42*, 914–920 (1954).

Chapter 3

Bias and Its Stabilization

3.1 Introduction

The variation of the a-c parameters of a transistor with operating point and with temperature has been discussed in Chapter 2. In general, when such variations are of importance, the manufacturer will supply curves showing the values of all parameters of interest over the

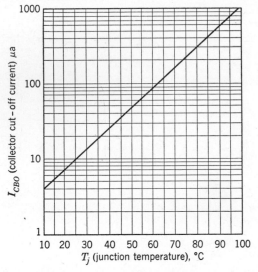

Fig. 3.1   Variation of I_{CBO} with junction temperature

recommended range of operating conditions.   An additional characteristic that is required for the design of bias circuits is shown in Fig. 3.1.   This figure shows the saturation current of the collector-to-base diode, I_{CBO} (reverse collector current with the emitter open, also frequently labeled I_{CO}), as a function of temperature.   For silicon transistors, the variation of parameters with operating conditions is of the

52

same order of magnitude as for germanium. It should be noted, however, that the value of I_{CBO} for a silicon device is three to four orders of magnitude below that for germanium.

In view of the large variation of some transistor parameters with operating conditions, it is desirable to develop techniques for maintaining the collector voltage and emitter current within prescribed limits in the range of operating conditions of interest. Both linear and nonlinear techniques may be used to achieve this result.

3.2 Physical Aspects of the Bias Problem

Changes in the ambient temperature to which a transistor is subjected will result in a shift in the operating point. In extreme cases this shift is cumulative, and will result in a runaway condition, leading to the ultimate destruction of the transistor.

The mechanisms contributing to a shift in the operating point are two in number. These will now be discussed with the aid of Fig. 3.2.

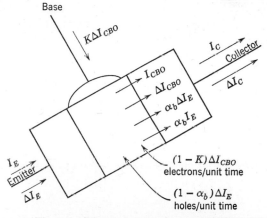

Fig. 3.2   Direct currents in a transistor

Figure 3.2 shows a p-n-p transistor in an arbitrary circuit configuration. The first effect is due to the fact that, with increasing temperature, the saturation current I_{CBO} increases, resulting in a hole current from the base to the collector and an electron current from the collector to the base. The base region thus becomes an electron-excess region; some of these excess electrons will be removed by way of the ohmic base contact, and base current will result. The magnitude of this base current will depend on the nature of the external circuit. If, in unit time, only a fraction of the electrons are removed from the base, corresponding to a base current of $K\Delta I_{CBO}$, a number of electrons corresponding to a current of $(1 - K) \Delta I_{CBO}$ are left in the base region. This will cause holes to be injected from the emitter, resulting in an increase of emitter current. Of these holes, a fraction α_b will be collected at the collector, and $(1 - \alpha_b)$ will combine with the electrons in the base region. Thus the increase in emitter current will be of such a magnitude that

$$\Delta I_E (1 - \alpha_b) = (1 - K) \Delta I_{CBO} \tag{3.1}$$

or
$$\Delta I_E = (1 - K) \Delta I_{CBO} / (1 - \alpha_b) \tag{3.2}$$

This emitter current will result in further collector power dissipation, resulting in a further increase in I_{CBO}, and the cycle is repeated. Whether the final outcome of this process is stabilization at some elevated temperature or whether the device will experience thermal runaway will depend on the effectiveness of the cooling technique.

A second factor that contributes to the thermal sensitivity of the device is that the forward conduction current of the emitter-to-base diode increases exponentially with temperature.[1] For most germanium and silicon devices this increase is of the order of 8% per °C. This results in a further increase of emitter current. The amount of this increase will depend on the circuit configuration and on the impedance levels at which the base and emitter are maintained.

At low temperatures, the change in I_{CBO} becomes very slight; thus the effect of the first mechanism diminishes rapidly, and the shift in operating point is almost entirely due to the second effect.

The techniques that may be used to reduce or eliminate ΔI_E are indicated by the above analysis. It is seen that stabilization is improved if (a) the base is fed from a low-impedance point $(K \rightarrow 1)$, (b) the emitter is fed from a high-impedance point $(\Delta I_E \rightarrow 0)$, (c) the emitter-to-base diode forward resistance is stabilized with temperature.

Of these it would appear that nonlinear techniques must be utilized for the last condition to be met. Indeed, in many applications where the current variation with temperature must be held to a minimum (as in d-c amplifiers), such techniques must be used. For most applications, however, if we meet the condition that the emitter is fed from a high-impedance source, the nonlinear characteristic of the emitter-to-base diode is effectively swamped, together with its variation with temperature. Linear stabilization techniques will be considered first.

3.3   Design Requirements

The design requirements for a bias circuit may be simply stated if we consider the V_{CB}, I_E plane. The first of the design requirements is to operate the transistor at a desired point in this plane, and the second is to maintain it within a desired neighborhood of this point over the entire temperature range of interest. The selection of the operating point, as well as its permissible variation limits are determined by factors such as (a) maximum signal voltage and current swings, (b) required overload capacity of the stage, (c) location and slopes of the d-c and a-c load lines.

The variation of I_{CBO} over this same range of temperature is obtained from the manufacturer's data, such as that shown in Fig. 3.1.

Let ΔI_{E1} and ΔI_{E2}, ΔV_{CB1} and ΔV_{CB2} be the changes in I_E and V_{CB} for changes in I_{CBO} of ΔI_{CBO1} and ΔI_{CBO2}, respectively, above and below the normal value. Then, define *current stability factors* S_{I1} and S_{I2}, as the respective ratios of the changes in emitter current to the changes in I_{CBO}. Thus:

$$S_{I1} = \Delta I_{E1}/\Delta I_{CBO1} \cong dI_{E1}/dI_{CBO1} \qquad (3.3)$$

$$S_{I2} = \Delta I_{E2}/\Delta I_{CBO2} \cong dI_{E2}/dI_{CBO2} \qquad (3.4)$$

In like manner, define *voltage stability factors* as the ratios of collector-to-base voltage changes to the changes in I_{CBO}:

$$S_{V1} = \Delta V_{CB1}/\Delta I_{CBO1} \cong dV_{CB1}/dI_{CBO1} \qquad (3.5)$$

$$S_{V2} = \Delta V_{CB2}/\Delta I_{CBO2} \cong dV_{CB2}/dI_{CBO2} \qquad (3.6)$$

Since linear-circuit techniques require that

$$dI_{E1}/dI_{CBO1} = dI_{E2}/dI_{CBO2} \qquad (3.7)$$

and $$dV_{CB1}/dI_{CBO1} = dV_{CB2}/dI_{CBO2} \qquad (3.8)$$

we choose the numerically smaller * of the two current and voltage stability factors as the basis for the design. Call these S_I and S_V, respectively. It may be shown that, for the single stage,

$$S_I \geq 0 \qquad (3.9)$$

and $$S_V \leq 0 \qquad (3.10)$$

Example. Compute the stability factors for the following stage.

$$V_{CB} = 5 \text{ volts}, \qquad I_E = 1 \text{ ma at } 20° \text{ C}$$

$$I_{CBO} \text{ at } 20° \text{ C} = 7 \text{ } \mu\text{a}$$

Operating range from 10 to 80° C. All temperatures are junction temperatures.

Total allowable variation in V_{CB} is +0.05 volt, −0.5 volt. Total allowable variation in I_E is +0.1 ma, −0.01 ma.

---

* This is the more stringent requirement.

Referring to Fig. 3.1,

$$I_{CBO} \text{ at } 20° \text{ C} = 7 \ \mu a$$

$$I_{CBO} \text{ at } 10° \text{ C} = 4 \ \mu a$$

$$I_{CBO} \text{ at } 80° \text{ C} = 300 \ \mu a$$

Therefore ΔI_{CBO} is $+293 \ \mu a$ and $-3 \ \mu a$. ΔI_E is $+100 \ \mu a$ or $-10 \ \mu a$. Since $S_I \geq 0$,

$$S_I = 100/293 \text{ or } 10/3$$

$$= 0.34 \text{ or } 3.3$$

V_{CB} is $+50$ mv or -500 mv.
Since $S_V \leq 0$,

$$S_V = -500 \times 10^3/293 \text{ or } -50 \times 10^3/3$$

$$\cong -1710 \text{ ohms or } -16,700 \text{ ohms}$$

Then $S_I = 0.34$, $S_V \cong -1710$ ohms are the stability factors to be used in this case.

3.4   Bias-Circuit Analysis

Figure 3.3 shows a general circuit for biasing a transistor. The circuit is general in that it may represent any configuration, depending on the

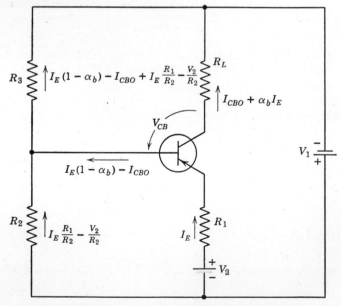

Fig. 3.3   General transistor bias circuit

points of entry and exit of the signal. It is also general since, by either removing components or short-circuiting them, the circuit may be used for the one-battery or two-battery bias schemes which follow. With transformer- or choke-coupled stages, appropriate resistances are made essentially zero. A linear analysis of this circuit may be made by neglecting the voltage drop across the emitter-to-base diode. In a practical circuit R_1 is normally chosen large enough that it swamps the emitter-to-base diode, and so this assumption is a valid one. We may show that

$$S_I = G_1/[G_2 + G_3 + G_1(1 - \alpha_b)] \tag{3.11}$$

and

$$S_V = -[S_I R_1 + R_L(1 + \alpha_b S_I)] \tag{3.12}$$

where G is used to represent the reciprocal of R. Various special cases may now be investigated.

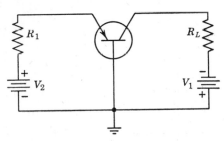

Fig. 3.4   Common-base stage with two-battery bias

(a) *Common-Base, Two-Battery (Fig. 3.4)*. Here, $R_2 = 0$, $R_3 = \infty$; whence $S_I = 0$. This is the case where current stabilization is ideal.

(b) *Common-Emitter Stage, Two-Battery Transformer-Coupled Input (Fig. 3.5)*. Here $R_2 = 0$; whence $S_I = 0$.

(c) *Common-Emitter, One-Battery (Fig. 3.6)*. Here $V_2 = 0$ and

$$S_I = G_1/[G_2 + G_3 + G_1(1 - \alpha_b)]$$

Since $\alpha_b \cong 1$,

$$S_I \cong G_1/(G_2 + G_3)$$

Here, S_I is the ratio of the base-to-ground d-c source resistance to R_1.

(d) *Zero Emitter Resistance, Non-zero R_2 and R_3*. Here $G_1 = \infty$; whence

$$S_I \cong 1/(1 - \alpha_b) \tag{3.13}$$

This is the worst case. Furthermore, setting R_1 equal to zero allows the emitter-to-base diode variation to raise the value of S_I still further.

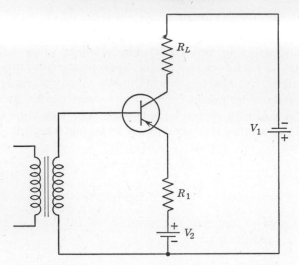

Fig. 3.5   Common-emitter stage with two-battery bias

In all cases, we again see that S_I is improved (reduced in magnitude) if (a) R_1 is increased, (b) R_2 is decreased, (c) R_3 is decreased; i.e. S_I is improved if we allow a majority of the ΔI_{CBO} to flow by way of the base

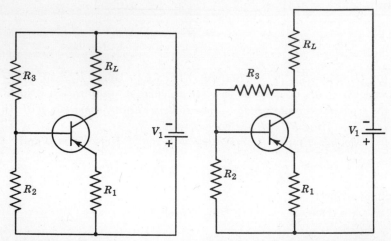

Fig. 3.6   Common-emitter stage with one-battery bias

Fig. 3.7   Common-emitter feedback stage with one-battery bias

lead.   This conclusion was arrived at earlier in the discussion of the mechanisms contributing to a shift in the operating point.   A study of eq. 3.12 shows that an improvement in S_I always results in an improvement in S_V. For the ideal case when S_I is zero, a limiting value is reached where $S_V = -R_L$. If such a stage is transformer-coupled on the output side ($R_L = 0$), the voltage stability factor is reduced to an ideal value of zero.

3.5 Bias-Circuit Design

We now proceed to the design details for the different biasing techniques. The common-emitter configuration will be used throughout since it has the most widespread use in practical circuitry.

3.5.1 One-Battery Circuit

If $V_2 = 0$ in the circuit of Fig. 3.3, we have a bias scheme requiring only one battery. This is shown in Fig. 3.6. The design for such a circuit allows the specification of four design requirements (V_{CB}, I_E, S_V, S_I) with the aid of five parameters (R_1, R_2, R_3, R_L, V_1). Consequently, any one of these parameters may be chosen independently. Since R_1 must be chosen * so as to swamp the emitter-to-base diode, we shall choose this as the independent variable. With this in mind, the design is given in Table 3.1 at the end of the chapter.

A study of the equation for the total battery power dissipated shows that once the operating point and stability factors are chosen this power is fixed and is independent of the circuit constants.

3.5.2 Two-Battery Circuit

This is the original circuit of Fig. 3.3. The design for this circuit allows the independent choice of two circuit components. As before, one of these is chosen as R_1. Analysis of this circuit shows that, for any choice of R_1, the power-supply drain is a minimum when R_3 is made infinite. Using this condition, i.e. setting R_3 at infinity, the design is carried out as in Table 3.2 at the end of the chapter. A study of the expression for battery power dissipated shows that it is (a) a function of R_1, (b) always less than that for the equivalent one-battery case.

3.5.3 One-Battery Feedback Circuit

The circuit shown in Fig. 3.7 may also be used for setting up the bias of a transistor. As before, an independent choice of one component, say R_1, may be made and the design carried out as in Table 3.3 at the end of the chapter. For any given operating point and stability factors, a study of the expression for total battery power dissipated shows that, for this circuit also, the battery drain is independent of the circuit

---

* The choice of R_1 in all the designs is limited by the restriction that the design must result in positive values for the resistances R_2, R_3, and R_L.

parameters. Furthermore, it is identical with that obtained for the one-battery configuration of Sec. 3.5.1. We may conclude therefore that, once the operating point and the stability factors are chosen, the power drain from the supply is independent of the type of one-battery configuration used. It should be mentioned, however, that this drain is always in excess of that for the two-battery configuration of Sec. 3.5.2.

3.5.4 Direct-Coupled Stages

The possibility of using direct-coupled stages is an attractive one since it eliminates the coupling capacitors. It may be shown that, if a chain of direct-coupled stages is used, the current and voltage stability factors alternate in sign from stage to stage. This is due to the fact that the incremental change in the collector voltage of one stage produces an incremental change in the base current of the following stage. The net changes in collector current and voltage are primarily due to this effect. Furthermore, it is possible to show that, for an infinite chain of identical stages, all the current and voltage stability factors are identically equal to zero. Such an amplifier, though possible in theory, would require that (*a*) each stage be biased to the same operating point even though the signal is increasing in amplitude from stage to stage, and (*b*) two independent voltage supplies be furnished for each stage—one for the emitter, and one for the collector. In addition, it would require that the value of the voltage sources vary with each stage.

A practical circuit, involving some compromises suggested by the principles above, is the direct-coupled pair shown in Fig. 3.8. For this

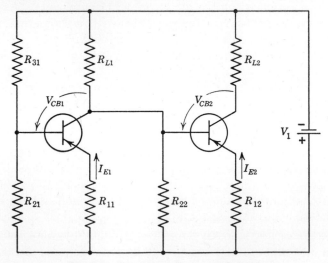

Fig. 3.8 Two-stage direct-coupled pair

circuit, there are a total of eight design requirements (V_{CB1}, V_{CB2}, I_{E1}, I_{E2}, S_{I1}, S_{I2}, S_{V1}, S_{V2}). In order that these design requirements be met, it is necessary that R_{22} be included in the circuit, resulting in a total of eight circuit parameters (R_{11}, R_{12}, R_{21}, R_{22}, R_{L1}, R_{L2}, R_{31}, V_1). Clearly, none of these may be chosen arbitrarily. As a result, the battery power drain is also fixed. The design equations are given in Table 3.4 at the end of the chapter.

3.6   Comparison of Bias Techniques

A comparison of the various techniques may now be made. Aside from the different physical features of each scheme, (number of batteries, resistors, etc.), the battery drain, the variation of operating point with supply voltage, and the a-c current-transfer ratio are factors that may form a basis of comparison. If low battery power drain is the primary consideration, the two-battery bias scheme is used. For the same operating point, the power required by this stage is less than that required by either single-battery technique, and depends on the value of resistor R_1. The drawback is that two batteries (or a tapped battery) are required. It is not possible to include the direct-coupled pair of Sec. 3.5.4 in this comparison, as it is unique with respect to the other techniques.

The one-battery schemes will be compared with the assumption that both the feedback and the nonfeedback stages have the same operating points and the same stability factors.

(a) *Battery Power Drain.* This has been shown to be identical for both stages.

(b) *Sensitivity to Change of Supply Voltage.* It may be shown that, for either stage,

$$dV_{CB}/V_{CB} \cong dV_1/V_1 \qquad (3.14)$$

and that

$$dI_E/I_E \cong dV_1/V_1 \qquad (3.15)$$

Thus, the relative change in V_{CB} and in I_E is the same as the relative change in the supply voltage, regardless of the stabilization technique used.

(c) *Current-Transfer Ratio.* It may be shown that the current-transfer ratio is nearly the same for both configurations. If the load resistance of the stage is very much larger than the input impedance of the next stage, A_i is usually about 0.5 db larger for the feedback case. The reverse is true if these two resistances are comparable.

A minor difference between the circuits is that the feedback circuit requires a somewhat larger supply voltage than the alternative single-battery circuit. If this is important, it may form the basis of selection.

The feedback circuit also supplies a small amount of degeneration to the signal. This is, however, usually too slight to produce much beneficial effect.

The engineering reasons for choosing one of these circuits in preference to the other are quite weak. The circuit designer is therefore free to choose a design, perhaps on the basis of simplicity of analysis and ready visualization of the effect of changes in circuit parameters. It is for this reason that the one-battery circuit without feedback is most often chosen in practical circuitry.

3.7 Nonlinear Compensation Techniques

Whereas in the majority of cases adequate biasing of transistor circuits may be obtained by the linear techniques discussed earlier, a number of important specialized circuit applications arise where nonlinear techniques may be used to advantage. Some of the specialized applications of nonlinear compensation techniques arise when:

(a) Very accurate control of the operating point is required, such as in frequency standards.

(b) Stabilization is required over extreme ranges of temperature without the attendant extremes of power dissipation and a-c losses. An example of this is to be found in some high-power output stages.

(c) Stabilization of the transistor operating point is required with respect to power-supply variations.

(d) It is necessary to eliminate the external resistance for other circuit considerations, for example, to improve supply voltage economy.

3.7.1 Breakdown Diode Applications

A principal factor in stabilization of the transistor operating point is a stable collector-voltage supply. One of the simplest methods of obtaining such a supply is with the aid of a diode biased into breakdown in the reverse direction (so-called Zener diode), such that it exhibits very low resistance. In this region the voltage drop across the diode is essentially constant for considerable variation of the load current; hence it can be used as a standard voltage reference. Figure 3.9a shows such a simple arrangement and Fig. 3.9b its current-voltage characteristic.

Silicon breakdown diodes may have characteristics ranging from 4 to 6 volts at 10 ma with a dynamic resistance of 5 to 10 ohms, to 40 to 60 volts at 10 μa with a dynamic resistance of approximately 1000 ohms.

It has been observed that breakdown diodes have a positive temperature coefficient depending on the slope and the breakdown voltage.[2] This coefficient may be on the order of +0.1% per °C. In order to compensate for this temperature effect, it is necessary to operate the break-down diode in series with a temperature-sensitive element having a negative temperature coefficient. It has been shown [3] that a forward-biased diode has such a negative temperature coefficient. Under constant-current conditions, the variation in the voltage drop across the diode is about -2.0 mv per °C for germanium and -1.8 mv per

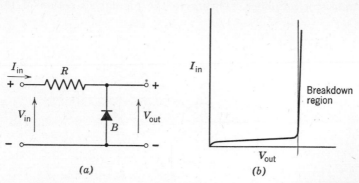

Fig. 3.9   (a) Voltage regulator.   (b) Performance curve for the circuit of Fig. 3.9a.

°C for silicon. By connecting one or more diodes biased in the forward direction in series with the reversed-biased breakdown diode, we can obtain a near-zero temperature coefficient for the combination. Figure 3.10 shows this type of arrangement consisting of a breakdown diode B, and three forward-biased diodes, all connected in series. In this particular example, the breakdown diode alone has a temperature coefficient of approximately $+6.0$ mv per °C. The forward-biased diodes

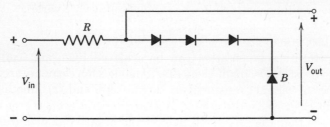

Fig. 3.10   Temperature-compensated voltage regulator

have a temperature coefficient of -2.0 mv per °C each; so the total temperature coefficient of the network will be approximately equal to zero. The addition of a few forward-biased diodes in series with the breakdown diode does not cause any appreciable change of the regulated voltage, since the forward-voltage drop across the diodes is usually very small.

The breakdown diode can also be used as a part of the transistor amplifier as shown in Fig. 3.11. In this circuit R_L is the regulating resistance for the breakdown diode B. B is connected from the collector of the transistor to ground through an inductance L, which limits the shunting effect of the breakdown diode on the output of the transistor amplifier. The regulating resistance can also serve as an a-c load to the transistor amplifier. Owing to the regulating action of the $R_L B$

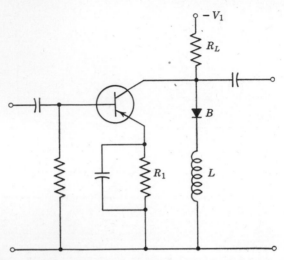

Fig. 3.11   Temperature-compensated stage using a breakdown diode

combination, the transistor collector voltage will remain practically constant as either temperature or supply voltage V_1 varies.

3.7.2   Temperature-Sensitive Resistance Applications

Temperature compensation can be achieved by using temperature-sensitive resistors as circuit elements. Among such elements are: (a) special types of ceramic resistors, (b) thermistors, and (c) junction diodes biased in the reverse direction. A characteristic property of all these elements is that they have relatively large negative temperature coefficients (on the order of 2 to 8% per °C).

Figure 3.12 shows an amplifier stage using a thermistor for temperature stabilization. The emitter of this stage is connected to ground through R_1, and to the d-c source through a thermistor R_4.

The resistance of the thermistor changes with temperature according to the relationship

$$R = R_0 \exp B(1/T - 1/T_0) \tag{3.16}$$

where T_0 is the reference temperature in degrees Kelvin (for room temperature $1/T_0 = 0.00335$), T is the temperature of the resistance in degrees Kelvin, R_0 is the resistance at temperature T_0, and B is a temperature constant which may have a value of several thousand degrees Kelvin. Equation 3.16 shows that the resistance of a thermistor de-

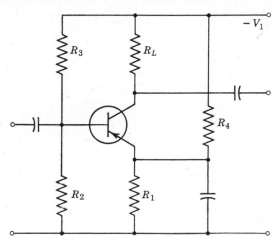

Fig. 3.12   Compensated stage using a temperature-sensitive resistance

creases with temperature.   Figure 3.13 shows a typical temperature characteristic.   In a conventional transistor circuit the emitter current increases as the temperature of the transistor is raised.   On the other hand, in the amplifier of Fig. 3.12 the emitter current will decrease as resistance R_4 decreases with increasing temperature.   Thus in this circuit the variation of temperature has two opposite effects on the emitter current.   By proper choice of the temperature characteristic of the resistance R_4, those effects can be made to cancel so that the emitter current remains practically constant over a wide range of ambient temperatures.   One of the features of the circuit is that the compensation network does not interfere with the a-c operation of the amplifier stage, since it is connected only to those parts of the circuit that are at a-c ground potential.

Different types of temperature-sensitive elements may also be used, such as semiconductor diodes biased in the reverse direction.   The proper characteristics can be obtained from various temperature-sensitive elements by using them in conjunction with special shaping networks.[4]

The use of junction diodes as temperature-sensitive elements is attractive, since their temperature-dependent properties are similar to those

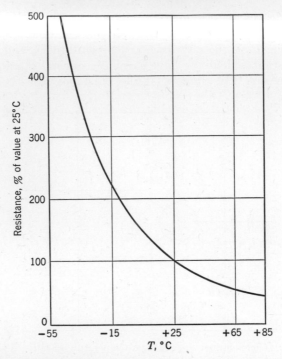

Fig. 3.13   Characteristic of a temperature-sensitive resistance

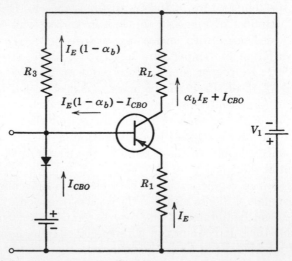

Fig. 3.14   Stage using a reverse-biased diode as the temperature-sensitive element

of the p-n junctions that comprise the junction transistor. Figure 3.14 shows a circuit that may be used for bias stabilization. This circuit is identical with that of Fig. 3.6, except that R_2 is replaced by a junction diode biased in the reverse direction. If the junction diode is selected so that its reverse current is equal to I_{CBO} for the transistor, this equality will hold over a wide range of temperatures. As a consequence, any increase in the I_{CBO} of the transistor with increasing temperature will be

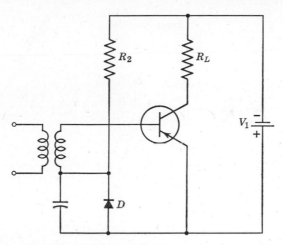

Fig. 3.15   Stage using a forward-biased diode as the temperature-sensitive element

supplied by the base circuit, and the emitter current will remain unchanged. The value of R_3 required for the operation of the circuit is given by

$$R_3 = (V_1 - I_E R_1)/I_E(1 - \alpha_b) \qquad (3.17)$$

Since R_3 is a function of $1/I_E(1 - \alpha_b)$, the operating point of this stage will depend both on the value of $1/(1 - \alpha_b)$, and on its temperature variation.

This circuit only compensates for the behavior of the collector-to-base diode, and it is still necessary to include resistance R_1 to swamp the temperature-dependent effects of the emitter-to-base diode.

Figure 3.15 shows a circuit for a temperature-compensated detector [5] stage in which resistance R_1 is eliminated. In this circuit, the forward-biased diode D provides a variable voltage across the emitter-to-base diode. With increasing temperature, the voltage across this diode decreases in such a manner that the emitter current is held constant.

Table 3.1

One-Battery Bias Stabilization

Note: In all of the equations below, *absolute values* of all quantities have been used. (In practice the *signs* of the voltages and currents will be determined by the type of transistor used, i.e. *p-n-p* or *n-p-n*. S_I will always be a positive number, and S_V will always be a negative number.)

Exact Formulas

Design Procedure

1. Select R_1.
2. $R_L = (S_V - S_I R_1)/(1 + \alpha_b S_I)$
3. $V_1 = [S_I V_{CB} + S_V I_E - R_L(I_E - S_I I_{CBO})]/S_I$
4. $R_3 = S_I V_1/(I_E - S_I I_{CBO})$
5. $G_2 = G_1[1 - S_I(1 - \alpha_b)]/S_I - G_3$
6. $P_D = I_E[V_{CB}(1 + \alpha_b S_I) + S_V(I_{CBO} + \alpha_b I_E)]/S_I$

Analysis Procedure

1. $S_I = G_1/[G_2 + G_3 + G_1(1 - \alpha_b)]$
2. $S_V = S_I R_1 + R_L(1 + \alpha_b S_I)$
3. $I_E = S_I(V_1 + I_{CBO}R_3)/R_3$
4. $V_{CB} = V_1 - I_E R_1 - R_L(\alpha_b I_E + I_{CBO})$

Approximate Formulas

$\alpha_b \cong 1; S_I I_{CBO} \ll I_E; S_I(1 - \alpha_b) \ll 1;$
$\quad G_1(1 - \alpha_b) \ll G_2 + G_3$

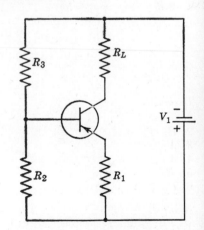

Design Procedure

1. Select R_1.
2. $R_L \cong (S_V - S_I R_1)/(1 + S_I)$
3. $V_1 \cong [S_I V_{CB} + I_E(S_V - R_L)]/S_I$
4. $R_3 \cong S_I V_1/I_E$
5. $G_2 \cong (G_1/S_I) - G_3$
6. $P_D \cong I_E[V_{CB}(1 + S_I) + S_V I_E]/S_I$

Analysis Procedure

1. $S_I \cong G_1/(G_2 + G_3)$
2. $S_V \cong S_I R_1 + (1 + S_I)R_L$
3. $I_E \cong S_I V_1/R_3$
4. $V_{CB} \cong V_1 - I_E(R_1 + R_L)$

Table 3.2

Two-Battery Bias Stabilization

Note: In all of the equations below, *absolute values* of all quantities have been used. (In practice, the *signs* of the voltages and currents will be determined by the type of transistor used, i.e. *p-n-p* or *n-p-n*. S_I will always be a positive number, and S_V will always be a negative number.)

Exact Formulas

Design Procedure

1. Select R_1. (Note that $R_3 = \infty$.)
2. $R_L = (S_V - S_I R_1)/(1 + \alpha_b S_I)$
3. $V_2 = R_1(I_E - S_I I_{CBO})/[1 - S_I(1 - \alpha_b)]$
4. $V_1 = [S_I V_{CB} + S_V I_E - R_L(I_E - S_I I_{CBO})]/S_I - V_2$
5. $R_2 = S_I R_1/[1 - S_I(1 - \alpha_b)]$

6. $P_D = P_{D(\text{one-battery case})} - \dfrac{I_E - S_I I_{CBO}}{S_I[1 - S_I(1 - \alpha_b)]} \times$

$$\{R_L(I_E - S_I I_{CBO}) + V_{CB}[1 - S_I(1 - \alpha_b)] - S_V[I_E(1 - \alpha_b) - I_{CBO}]\}$$

Analysis Procedure

1. $S_I = G_1/[G_2 + G_1(1 - \alpha_b)]$
2. $S_V = S_I R_1 + R_L(1 + \alpha_b S_I)$
3. $I_E = V_2[1 - S_I(1 - \alpha_b)]/R_1 + S_I I_{CBO}$
4. $V_{CB} = V_1 + V_2 - R_L I_{CBO} - I_E(R_1 + \alpha_b R_L)$

Approximate Formulas

$\alpha_b \cong 1; S_I I_{CBO} \ll I_E; S_I(1 - \alpha_b) \ll 1;$
    $G_1(1 - \alpha_b) \ll G_2 + G_3$

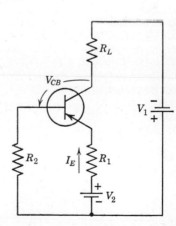

Design Procedure

1. Select R_1. (Note that $R_3 = \infty$.)
2. $R_L \cong (S_V - S_I R_1)/(1 + S_I)$
3. $V_2 \cong R_1 I_E$
4. $V_1 \cong (S_I V_{CB} + S_V I_E - I_E R_L)/S_I - V_2$
5. $R_2 \cong S_I R_1$
6. $P_D \cong (V_1 + V_2)I_E$

Analysis Procedure

1. $S_I \cong R_2/R_1$
2. $S_V \cong S_I R_1 + R_L(1 + S_I)$
3. $I_E \cong V_2/R_1$
4. $V_{CB} \cong V_1 + V_2 - I_E(R_1 + R_L)$

Table 3.3

One-Battery Feedback Stabilization

Note: In all of the equations below, *absolute values* of all quantities have been used. (In practice the *signs* of the voltages and currents will be determined by the type of transistor used, i.e. *p-n-p* or *n-p-n*. S_I will always be a positive number, and S_V will always be a negative number.)

Exact Formulas

Design Procedure

1. Select R_1.
2. $V_1 = (S_I V_{CB} + S_V I_E)/S_I$
3. $R_3 = S_I V_1/(I_E - S_I I_{CBO})$
4. $P_D = I_E[V_{CB}(1 + \alpha_b S_I) + S_V(I_{CBO} + \alpha_b I_E)]/S_I$
5. $R_L = V_1 I_E(S_V - S_I R_1)/P_D S_I$
6. $R_2 = V_1 I_E R_1/(P_D - V_1 I_E)$

Analysis Procedure

1. $S_I = G_1/[G_2 + G_3 + G_1(1 - \alpha_b) + G_3(G_1 + G_2)/G_L]$
2. $S_V = S_I[R_1 + R_L(1 + R_1/R_2)]$
3. $I_E = S_I(V_1 + R_3 I_{CBO})/R_3$
4. $V_{CB} = V_1 - S_V I_E/S_I$

Approximate Formulas

$\alpha_b \cong 1; S_I I_{CBO} \ll I_E; S_I(1 - \alpha_b) \ll 1;$
$\quad G_1(1 - \alpha_b) \ll G_2 + G_3$

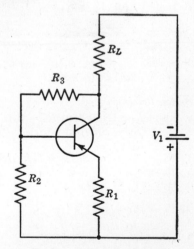

Design Procedure

1. Select R_1.
2. $V_1 \cong (S_I V_{CB} + S_V I_E)/S_I$
3. $R_3 \cong S_I V_1/I_E$
4. $P_D \cong I_E[V_{CB}(1 + S_I) + S_V I_E]/S_I$
5. $R_L \cong V_1 I_E(S_V - S_I R_1)/P_D S_I$
6. $R_2 \cong S_I R_1 V_1/V_{CB}$

Analysis Procedure

1. $S_I \cong G_1/[G_2 + G_3 + G_3(G_1 + G_2)/G_L]$
2. $S_V \cong (R_3 I_E - S_I V_{CB})/I_E$
3. $I_E \cong S_I V_1/R_3$
4. $V_{CB} \cong S_I V_1 R_1/R_2$

Table 3.4

Direct-Coupled Pair

Note: In all of the equations below, *absolute values* of all quantities have been used. (In practice the *signs* of the voltages and currents will be determined by the type of transistor used, i.e. *p-n-p* or *n-p-n*. S_{I1} and S_{V2} will always be positive numbers, and S_{V1} and S_{I2} will always be negative numbers.)

Approximate Formulas

$$\alpha_{b1} \cong \alpha_{b2} \cong \alpha_b \cong 1; \; I_{CBO1} \cong I_{CBO2} \cong I_{CBO}$$
$$I_{E1} \gg S_{I1}I_{CBO}; \; I_{E2} \gg I_{CBO};$$
$$G_{31} + G_{21} \gg G_{11}(1 - \alpha_b); \; G_{22} + G_{L1} \gg G_{12}(1 - \alpha_b)$$

Design Procedure

$$R_{11} \cong (S_{V1}I_{E2} - S_{I2}V_{CB1})/(S_{I1}I_{E2} + S_{I2}I_{E1})$$
$$R_{12} \cong (V_{CB1} + I_{E1}R_{11})/I_{E2}$$
$$R_{L2} \cong (S_{V2} - R_{12}S_{I2})/(S_{I2} - 1)$$
$$V_1 \cong V_{CB2} + I_{E2}(R_{12} + R_{L2})$$
$$R_{L1} \cong V_1S_{I2}/(I_{E1}S_{I2} + I_{E2}S_{I1})$$
$$R_{31} \cong S_{I1}V_1/I_{E1}$$
$$R_{21} \cong R_{31}R_{11}S_{I1}/(R_{31} - R_{11}S_{I1})$$
$$R_{22} \cong R_{12}R_{L1}S_{I2}/(R_{L1}S_{I1} - R_{12}S_{I2})$$

Analysis Procedure

$$S_{I1} \cong G_{11}/(G_{21} + G_{31})$$
$$S_{I2} \cong S_{I1}R_{L1}/R_{12}(1 + R_{L1}/R_{22})$$
$$S_{V1} \cong R_{11}S_{I1} + R_{12}S_{I2}$$
$$S_{V2} \cong S_{I2}(R_{12} + R_{L2}) - R_{L2}$$
$$I_{E1} \cong S_{I1}V_1/R_{31}$$
$$I_{E2} \cong S_{I2}(V_1 - I_{E1}R_{L1})/S_{I1}R_{L1}$$
$$V_{CB1} \cong R_{12}I_{E2} - R_{11}I_{E1}$$
$$V_{CB2} \cong V_1 - I_{E2}(R_{12} + R_{L2})$$

$$\left[\begin{array}{c} \text{Note:} \\ \text{see} \\ \text{Fig. 3.8.} \end{array} \right]$$

Problems

1. Given $V_{CB} = -10$ volts, $I_E = 2$ ma, $S_V = -47,000$ ohms, $S_I = +7$, $R_1 = 1000$ ohms, design a bias circuit using the two-battery configuration.

2. Repeat problem 3, using the one-battery configuration.

3. Repeat problem 3, using the one-battery feedback configuration. Compare the supply voltage required with that of problem 4.

4. Design a direct-coupled pair with $V_{CB1} = -1.0$ volt; $V_{CB2} = -5.0$ volts; $I_{E1} = 0.5$ ma; $I_{E2} = 2.0$ ma; $S_{I1} = +4$; $S_{I2} = -4$; $S_{V1} = -10,000$ ohms, $S_{V2} = +10,000$ ohms.

Bibliography

1. W. Shockley, "The Theory of p-n Junctions in Semiconductors and p-n Junction Transistors," *Bell System Tech. J.*, *28*, 435–439 (1949).

2. D. H. Smith, "Silicon Alloy Junction Diode as a Reference Standard," *Commun. & Electronics*, 645–651 (Jan. 1955).

3. J. S. Schaffner and R. F. Shea, "The Variation of the Forward Characteristics of Junction Diodes with Temperature," *Proc. IRE*, *43*, 101 (1955).

4. E. Keonjian and J. S. Schaffner, "The Shaping of the Characteristics of Temperature-Sensitive Elements," *Elect. Eng.*, *73*, 933–936 (Oct. 1954).

5. II. C. Lin and A. A. Barco, "Temperature Effects in Circuits Using Junction Transistors," "Transistors, I," *RCA Lab. Publ.*, 369–402 (1956).

Chapter 4

Audio Amplifiers

4.1 Introduction

The specifications for an audio amplifier usually state that a required amount of power must be delivered to a specified load from a specified signal source. Thus the problem of audio-amplifier design consists essentially of the design of the series of amplifier stages necessary to match this signal to the load. We may think of each of these stages as an individual power amplifier working at a level intermediate to the stages preceding and following it. Those stages in which the transistors operate well below their permissible dissipation may be termed *low-level* or *signal* stages. *High-level* or *power* stages are those in which the transistors operate near their dissipation limits. Thus, an amplifier may consist entirely of signal stages, entirely of power stages, or of some of each.

In this chapter we shall take up in turn, the engineering principles that may be applied to the analysis and design of both low-level and high-level stages. Some circuits, notably the direct-coupled circuits, may involve more than one stage, and are discussed separately. Throughout most of the treatment, *p-n-p* transistors will be considered; the analysis is identical for *n-p-n* transistors except that all battery polarities must be reversed. Although an exhaustive treatment of audio amplifiers is given elsewhere in the literature,[1] the material presented here will be adequate for most applications.

4.2 Low-Level Stages

In this section we shall consider the basic amplifier stage, and the manner in which its performance is affected by the bias and interstage coupling networks associated with it. In the various illustrative examples that will follow, we shall consider a typical transistor with the low-frequency circuit parameters of Table 4.1. These are for an operating point of 5 volts and 1 ma.

Table 4.1

Parameter	Configuration		
	Common-Base	Common-Emitter	Common-Collector
h_{11}	40 ohms	2000 ohms	2000 ohms
h_{12}	4×10^{-4}	16×10^{-4}	1
h_{21}	-0.98	49	-50
h_{22}	1×10^{-6} mho	50×10^{-6} mho	50×10^{-6} mho
Δ^h	4.32×10^{-4}	216×10^{-4}	50.1

4.2.1 The Basic Amplifier Stage

A single amplifier stage is shown in Fig. 4.1. Here a transistor is fed from a source resistance R_g, and terminated in a load R_l. The transistor is represented by a black box whose h parameters are known for the particular configuration. The performance of such a stage may be

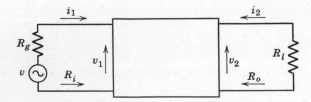

Fig. 4.1   Four-terminal network

readily computed with the aid of the matrix interrelations for the terminated two-port network (see appendix). Since audio frequencies are considered, all terms will be resistive.

Input resistance,

$$R_i = (h_{11} + \Delta^h R_l)/(1 + h_{22}R_l) \qquad (4.1)$$

Output resistance,

$$R_o = (h_{11} + R_g)/(\Delta^h + h_{22}R_g) \qquad (4.2)$$

Current ratio,

$$i_2/i_1 = A_i = h_{21}/(1 + h_{22}R_l) \qquad (4.3)$$

and power gain,

$$G = (i_2/i_1)^2 (R_l/R_i) = h_{21}{}^2 R_l/(1 + h_{22}R_l)(h_{11} + \Delta^h R_l) \qquad (4.4)$$

The behavior of these various quantities may now be studied in more detail.

(a) *Input Resistance.*

If $R_l = 0,$ $R_i = h_{11}$ (4.5)

$R_l = \infty,$ $R_i = \Delta^h/h_{22}$ (4.6)

$= h_{11} - (h_{12}h_{21}/h_{22})$ (4.7)

Thus the input impedance of a transistor stage is h_{11} when the output is short-circuited, and $h_{11} - (h_{12}h_{21}/h_{22})$ when the output is open. Figure 4.2 shows this behavior for the "typical" transistor. Note that the input impedance of the common-base and the common-collector stages increases for increasing R_l whereas the input impedance of the

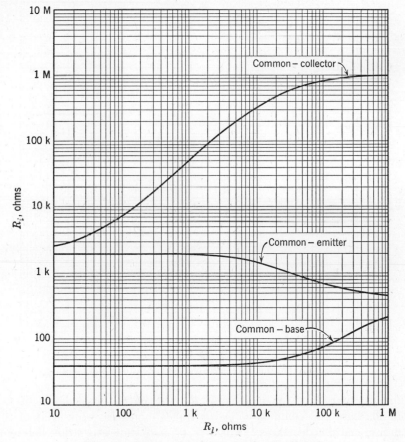

Fig. 4.2   Input resistance versus load resistance

common-emitter configuration decreases with increasing R_l. A study of the parameters shows that this is due to the negative value of h_{21b} and h_{21c}, as opposed to the positive value of h_{21e}.

(b) *Output Resistance.*

If $\qquad R_g = 0, \qquad R_o = h_{11}/\Delta^h$ $\qquad\qquad$ (4.8)

$$= 1/[h_{22} - (h_{12}h_{21}/h_{11})] \qquad (4.9)$$

If $\qquad R_g = \infty, \qquad R_o = 1/h_{22}$ $\qquad\qquad$ (4.10)

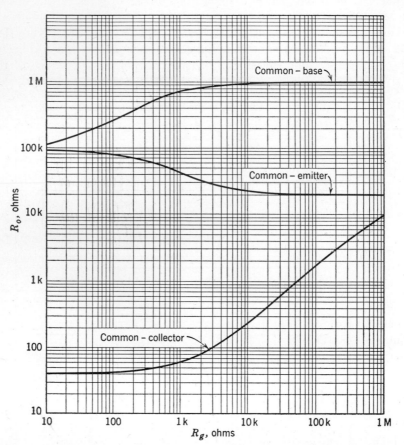

Fig. 4.3   Output resistance versus generator resistance

Thus we find that, for increasing R_g, the output impedance of the common-base and common-collector stages increases, while that of the common-emitter decreases. For our typical transistor, this behavior is shown in Fig. 4.3.

(c) *Current-Transfer Ratio.*

If $\qquad\qquad R_l = 0, \qquad\quad A_i = h_{21}$ $\qquad\qquad$ (4.11)

If $\qquad\qquad R_l = \infty, \qquad\quad A_i = 0$ $\qquad\qquad\quad$ (4.12)

Thus the current-transfer ratio for all configurations is h_{21} for $R_l = 0$, and decreases with increasing R_l. Figure 4.4 shows the variation of A_i with R_l.

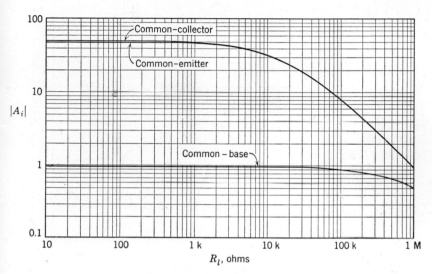

Fig. 4.4   Current amplification versus load resistance

(d) *Power Gain.* The power gain is zero for the open- and short-circuit conditions. A study of eq. 4.4 shows that the power gain attains a maximum value given by

$$G_m = h_{21}{}^2/(\sqrt{h_{11}h_{22}} + \sqrt{\Delta^h})^2 \qquad (4.13)$$

at a value of R_l given by

$$R_l = \sqrt{h_{11}/h_{22}\,\Delta^h} \qquad (4.14)$$

Figure 4.5 shows this behavior for our typical transistor. From these curves we see that in order to realize maximum gain from a transistor in the common-base or common-emitter configuration, the load resistance must be approximately 300 or 43 kilohms, respectively. This results in limited high-frequency response since the effects of the output capacitance become important. Such operation is consequently to be avoided. Even though adequate high-frequency response is realized when the common collector is used under conditions of maximum power gain, this matched gain is still small. In fact, for our typical transistor, the maximum gain of the common-collector stage is 13.5 db below that of the gain of the common-emitter stage working into the same load.

The maximum gain of a transistor stage is often specified by the manufacturers. A reason for its importance lies perhaps in the fact that

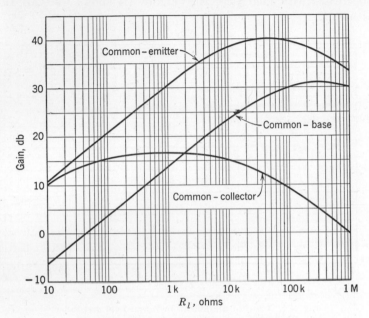

Fig. 4.5   Power gain versus load resistance

it is a function of the transistor parameters alone, and also results in the largest figure of theoretically realizable gain. At audio frequencies, this specification is of little engineering value, and should not be used as the basis of choice of transistor type.

(e) *Transducer Gain.* The transducer gain G_t is defined as the ratio of the power delivered to the load to the maximum available power from the generator.

Referring to Fig. 4.1,

$$v_1 = vR_i/(R_i + R_g) \qquad (4.15)$$

Maximum available power from the generator $= v^2/4R_g$ (4.16)

Combining eqs. 4.1, 4.4, 4.15, and 4.16 yields

$$G_t = 4R_gR_lh_{21}{}^2/[R_g(1 + h_{22}R_l) + h_{11} + \Delta^hR_l]^2 \qquad (4.17)$$

Since the transducer gain is a function of the parameters of the amplifier and of its terminating impedances, it is sometimes used as a basis of comparison of the performance of amplifiers driven from identical sources.

4.2.2   The Intermediate Stage

The majority of transistor amplifiers are multistage; therefore the study of the intermediate stage becomes an extremely important one. The principal characteristic that distinguishes the intermediate stage is that the effects of the preceding stage, and of the succeeding stage must be considered in its design.   The intermediate stage may be either transformer-coupled or resistance-capacitance-coupled.   These will be considered in turn.   The choke-coupled stage has very limited application, and will not be discussed.

4.2.2.1   Transformer-Coupled Stages

Transformer-coupled stages permit any degree of match between the source and load; although perfect match is hardly ever used, any improvement does result in increased gain.   Since we have control over the source and load impedances, the performance of such a stage may be computed directly from the equations of Sec. 4.2.1.   The design of the stage consists mainly in the specification of such transformer properties as (a) primary and secondary impedance levels, (b) direct current in windings, (c) frequency response, and (d) transmission loss.   Since isolation is obtained with a transformer, this results in simplified circuitry for coupling as well as for feedback.   We have already seen in Chapter 3 that the use of transformers improves the bias stability of the stage considerably, and also reduces the necessary battery power.

The disadvantages of transformer coupling are many.   Miniature transformers which are ordinarily used have substantial transmission loss, and are extremely poor in their frequency response.   Their phase characteristics are even worse, resulting in considerable difficulty in designing a feedback loop.   They are still the heaviest component in the circuit, notwithstanding the advances that have been made in miniaturization techniques in recent years.

4.2.2.2   Design of a Transformer-Coupled Stage

An example illustrating the design of a transformer-coupled stage follows. A 400-cycle transducer has a source impedance of 600 ohms and a maximum available power of 2×10^{-8} watts. Design a single-stage two-battery amplifier to supply the maximum power to a 600-ohm load. Since maximum gain is desired from the stage, and high-frequency response is unimportant, the configuration of Fig. 4.6 will be used. The terminations will be 600 ohms. As a first attempt, select a collector operating point at 5 volts, 1 ma.

Choosing R_1 large compared to the emitter-to-base diode resistance, as outlined in Chapter 3, let

$$R_1 = 1500 \text{ ohms}$$

Then $$V_1 = 1.5 \text{ volts}$$

Using our typical transistor of Table 4.1, maximum power gain is realized for a load of 43 kilohms. This is the primary load impedance to be

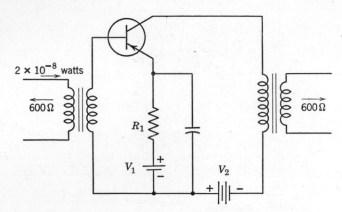

Fig. 4.6   Transformer-coupled amplifier stage

presented by the output transformer. Then the input impedance of the amplifier is 930 ohms (see eq. 4.1). This is the secondary impedance of the input transformer.

A reasonable value of d-c primary resistance for this type of output transformer is 1000 ohms. Then the d-c drop in this winding and R_1 is 2.5 volts. Therefore

$$V_2 = 7.5 \text{ volts}$$

Check:

Signal current in primary of input transformer

$$= (2 \times 10^{-8}/600)^{1/2} \text{ amperes}$$

$$= 5.77 \ \mu\text{a rms}$$

Signal current in transistor base $= 5.77\sqrt{600/930} \ \mu\text{a} = 4.65 \ \mu\text{a rms}$

Current amplification of transistor $= 15.5$ (see eq. 4.3).

Signal current in collector circuit $= 15.5 \times 4.65 = 72 \ \mu a$ rms

$$\equiv 102 \ \mu a \text{ peak}$$

Signal voltage at collector $= 43,000 \times 102 \times 10^{-6}$

$$= 4.39 \text{ volts peak}$$

This is plotted on the output curves of the transistor as in Fig. 4.7. The excursion of the operating point is observed to be within the linear operating region. The overall power gain will be somewhat less than

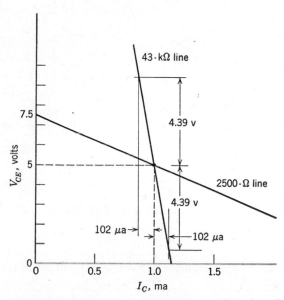

Fig. 4.7   Output curves for circuit of Fig. 4.6

the maximum figure of 40 db, owing to loss in the transformers. The direct current in the output transformer primary coil is 1 ma; the direct current in the input transformer secondary coil is negligible.

The specifications may now be rounded out to convenient values, and the circuit rechecked. If desired, the value of the operating current may be reduced by as much as 750 μa and the stage redesigned using new values of parameters corresponding to the new operating current.

4.2.2.3   RC-Coupled Stages

With this form of connection, the designer is more restricted in his choice of the source and load impedances. In general, both d-c and a-c power losses will occur in the resistances, and there will be a further a-c loss as a result of the mismatch between stages.

Notwithstanding these losses, such stages are most commonly used, owing to the small size and low cost of the components involved. Consider a chain of n transistor stages, as shown in Fig. 4.8. Since the input impedance of each stage is a function of its load, a computation of the input impedance of any one stage would require the computation of the input impedance of all the stages following it. It is possible to show, however, that except for the last few stages, the input impedance of

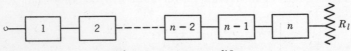

Fig. 4.8　n-stage amplifier

each stage becomes nearly equal to that of the stage preceding it. Such a stage may be called an iterative stage. The iterative input impedance may now be computed by setting $R_l = R_i$ in eq. 4.1 and solving the resulting quadratic equation. Neglecting all terms of the second and higher orders, we have

$$R_i \text{ (common-base)} \cong h_{11b} \tag{4.18}$$

$$R_i \text{ (common-emitter)} \cong h_{11e} \tag{4.19}$$

$$R_i \text{ (common-collector)} \cong -h_{21c}/h_{22c} \tag{4.20}$$

It is important to know at which point in a chain of stages it is possible to designate a stage as "iterative." In general, for an n-stage amplifier, all but the last stage may be considered as iterative for the common-

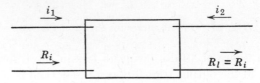

Fig. 4.9　Iterative stage

emitter or common-base configuration, whereas all but the last two stages of a common-collector chain are iterative. The iterative stage thus becomes an extremely important one to analyze. Consider the iterative stage of Fig. 4.9. Since $R_l = R_i$, the iterative power gain is given by

$$G_i = i_2{}^2 R_l / i_1{}^2 R_i = (i_2/i_1)^2 \tag{4.21}$$

$$= h_{21}{}^2 / (1 + h_{22} R_l)^2 \tag{4.22}$$

Substituting the iterative input impedance for R_l, we have

$$G_i \text{ (common-base)} \cong (h_{21b})^2 \qquad (4.23)$$

$$G_i \text{ (common-emitter)} \cong (h_{21e})^2 \qquad (4.24)$$

$$G_i \text{ (common-collector)} \cong 1 \qquad (4.25)$$

For our typical transistor, the iterative stage gains are

$$\text{Common-base} \cong 0 \text{ db}$$

$$\text{Common-emitter} \cong 33.5 \text{ db}$$

$$\text{Common-collector} \cong 0 \text{ db}$$

It is now possible to draw conclusions as to the choice of stage. The common-emitter stage should be used in almost all cases; for those applications where special terminations are required at either end of the amplifier the common-base or common-collector stage may sometimes be used. Thus, the common-base stage may be used if its low input impedance or high output impedance is necessary, whereas the common-collector stage may be used for its high input and low output impedances.

The above conclusions have been arrived at on the basis of an analysis of the iterative stage. If an amplifier has only two or three stages, each stage may be analyzed by the equations given earlier (eqs. 4.1 to 4.4). For such an amplifier it is possible to analyze various combinations of

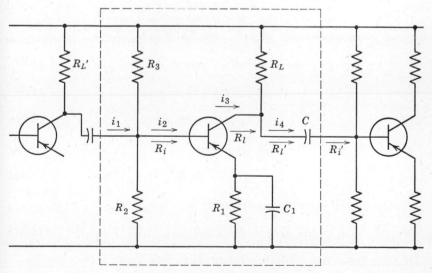

Fig. 4.10   RC coupled amplifier

configurations in order to realize the optimum gain for the generator and load conditions that pertain. In general, the common-emitter chain results either in the maximum power gain, or in a figure of gain that is so close to the maximum that it is not worth the detailed analysis required for this optimization.

A complete analysis of a common-emitter stage will now be undertaken, to indicate the principles of design involved. Figure 4.10 shows such a stage with its associated bias and coupling elements. In the midband, the reactance of the capacitances is neglected.

In the following design procedure it will be assumed that the operating point and the bias-stability factors defined in Chapter 3 have been chosen. Let R_i be the input impedance of the transistor, exclusive of R_2 and R_3; R_l' the impedance of the load, exclusive of R_L; and R_l the parallel impedance of R_L and R_l'.

Then
$$R_i = (h_{11e} + \Delta^h{}_e R_l)/(1 + h_{22e}R_l) \qquad (4.26)$$

Since
$$h_{11e} \gg \Delta^h{}_e R_l,$$

$$R_i \cong k h_{11e} \qquad (4.27)$$

where
$$k = 1/(1 + h_{22e}R_l) \qquad (4.28)$$

In general, if the load consists of another transistor,

$$k \cong 1$$

If S_I is the current stability factor, the parallel impedance of R_2 and R_3 is given approximately as $S_I R_1$ (see Table 3.1). Then

$$i_2/i_1 \cong S_I R_1/(S_I R_1 + R_i) \qquad (4.29)$$

$$\cong S_I R_1/(S_I R_1 + h_{11e}) \qquad (4.30)$$

Now,
$$i_3/i_2 = h_{21e}/(1 + h_{22e}R_l) \qquad (4.31)$$

$$\cong h_{21e} \qquad (4.32)$$

Also,
$$i_4/i_3 = R_L/(R_L + R_l') \qquad (4.33)$$

Then the overall current-transfer ratio is

$$i_4/i_1 \cong [R_L/(R_L + R_l')][S_I R_1 h_{21e}/(S_I R_1 + h_{11e})] \qquad (4.34)$$

If S_V is the voltage stability factor, then (see Table 3.1)

$$R_L \cong -(S_V + S_I R_1)/(1 + S_I) \qquad (4.35)$$

Substituting in equation 4.34,

$$\frac{i_4}{i_1} = \frac{h_{21e}S_I R_1 (S_I R_1 + S_V)}{S_I^2 R_1^2 + S_I R_1 [S_V + h_{11e} - R_l'(1 + S_I)] + h_{11e}[S_V - R_l'(1 + S_I)]}$$

$$(4.36)$$

Whereas eq. 4.36 is too unwieldy for use in design, a study of the expression shows that the overall current-transfer ratio is zero at the two extreme values of R_1 given by

$$R_1 = 0 \quad \text{and} \quad R_1 = -S_V/S_I \ * \qquad (4.37 \text{ and } 4.38)$$

and therefore a value for R_1 exists at which the overall current-transfer ratio is a maximum.

For the condition

$$h_{11e} = R_l'(1 + S_I) \qquad (4.39)$$

we may show that the maximum current-transfer ratio occurs at

$$R_1 = -S_V/2S_I \qquad (4.40)$$

In general, a sharply defined maximum does not occur, and a range of values for R_1 lying between $-S_V/4S_I$ and $-3S_V/4S_I$ results in a value of current-transfer ratio that is not far removed from the maximum.

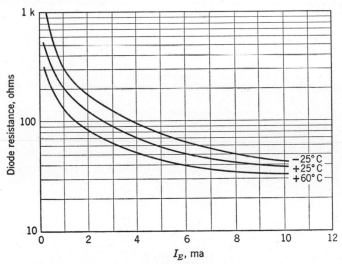

Fig. 4.11   Diode resistance versus emitter current

In a practical design, a lower limit of R_1 is set such that its value must be large compared with the d-c resistance of the emitter-to-base diode. Figure 4.11 shows approximate values of this resistance as a function of

* If $R_1 > -S_V/S_I$, R_L becomes negative.

emitter current for germanium transistors, and may be used as a basis for design. A few alternate designs should be carried out, using different values of R_1. As has been shown in Chapter 3, the choice of R_1 automatically fixes the values of the battery voltage, the current-transfer ratio, and the circuit components. If a suitable selection cannot be

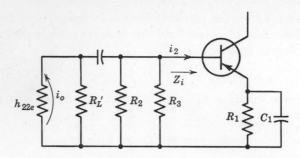

Fig. 4.12   Equivalent circuit of the transistor input

made, it may be necessary to alter the original choice of the operating point and the stability factors.

The value of the emitter bypass capacitor C_1 may be computed with the aid of the equivalent circuit of Fig. 4.12 as follows:

$$Z_i \cong h_{11e} + (1 + h_{21e})R_1/(1 + j\omega C_1 R_1) \qquad (4.41)$$

Whence

$$\frac{i_2}{i_o} \cong K_1(1 + j\omega C_1 R_1)/\left[1 + j\omega C_1 R_1\left(\frac{R_g + h_{11e}}{R_g + h_{11e} + R_1(1 + h_{21e})}\right)\right] \qquad (4.42)$$

where i_o is the internal current generator of the previous stage, K_1 is a constant, and R_g is the parallel combination of R_2, R_3, and the output circuit of the preceding stage.

Equation 4.42 shows that the frequency response is 3 db down at

$$\omega_1 \cong \frac{1}{R_1 C_1}\left[\frac{R_g + h_{11e} + R_1(1 + h_{21e})}{R_g + h_{11e}}\right] \qquad (4.43)$$

Ordinarily,

$$R_1(1 + h_{21e}) \gg R_g + h_{11e} \qquad (4.44)$$

whence

$$\omega_1 \cong (1 + h_{21e})/C_1(R_g + h_{11e}) \qquad (4.45)$$

Thus the time constant determining the cutoff frequency is that of the shunt combination of C_1 and $(R_g + h_{11e})/(1 + h_{21e})$ (4.46)

It is interesting to note that the value of R_1 does not appear in this expression.

At a low frequency, given by

$$\omega_o = 1/R_1C_1 \tag{4.47}$$

there is a rise in the frequency response curve; this has little significance in the design.

If the emitter bypass capacitor C_1 is chosen so that ω_1 is well below the low-frequency cutoff of the amplifier, the effect of degeneration in the emitter resistance may be ignored.

The value of the coupling capacitance C may be found with the aid of the equivalent circuit of Fig. 4.13. The output impedance of the pre-

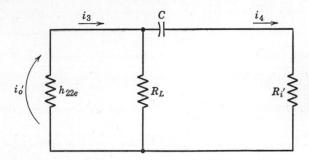

Fig. 4.13　Equivalent circuit of the transistor output

ceding stage is given approximately as kR_L where k is as defined in eq. 4.28. If we write R_i' as the input resistance of the succeeding transistor and its associated bias network, the current amplification is down 3 db, owing to C at

$$\omega_2 = 1/C(kR_L + R_i') \tag{4.48}$$

Then, at ω_2, the effective resistance in series with C is $kR_L + R_i'$.

The high-frequency response of the stage will be limited by the output capacitance of the transistor as well as by the decrease of h_{21e} with frequency. These two effects have been combined to give the design curve of Fig. 4.14.

In order to use this curve, let R_L' be the parallel resistance of all the external elements of the load.

Let

$$x = h_{22e}R_L' \tag{4.49}$$

Let C_o be the output capacitance of the stage. This is approximately equal to $1/(1 + h_{21b})$ times that for the common-base connection. Let

$$u = \omega_{\alpha e}C_o/h_{22e} \tag{4.50}$$

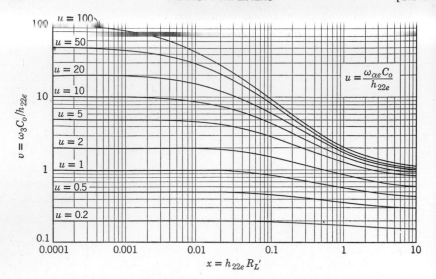

Fig. 4.14   High-frequency response design curve

Let ω_3 be the frequency at which the response of the stage is down 3 db. Then

$$v = \omega_3 C_o / h_{22e} \qquad\qquad (4.51)$$

4.2.2.4   Example of RC Amplifier Design

Design an amplifier with the following specifications:

Input signal $= 0.5 \ \mu a$ peak

Output signal $= 1$ volt peak

Design for single-battery operation at normal ambient temperature of 30° C.   Allowable temperature variation is 10 to 60° C ambient. Assume that the parameters are reasonably constant with temperature, and that $1/h_{11e}$ and h_{22e} vary directly with I_E.

In general, the design is started with a rough estimate of the number of stages.   Since 60° C operation is required, assume an input-circuit loss of, say, 50% for sufficient bias stability.   Then

Signal current entering first transistor $\cong 0.25 \ \mu a$ peak

Output current $\cong 0.25 \times 49 \cong 12.5 \ \mu a$ peak

For a single stage, the load resistance would have to be about 80,000 ohms for an output of 1 volt peak.   This is unreasonably large, if adequate frequency response is desired, and so a second stage is indicated.

Again, assuming an input loss of 50% for the second stage:

$$\text{Input current} \cong 6.25 \ \mu a \text{ peak}$$

$$\text{Output current} \cong 313 \ \mu a \text{ peak}$$

$$\text{Load resistance} \cong 3200 \text{ ohms}$$

This will result in adequate high-frequency performance. Thus a two-stage amplifier will suffice. A simple preliminary design is now initiated, using arbitrary choices of circuit variables. From such a design, an idea is obtained of the orders of magnitude involved, and the design corrected by successive approximations. Particular care has been taken in this example to insure mathematical accuracy as an aid to the understanding of the design procedure. It should be emphasized that in normal engineering design such precision is entirely unnecessary. For brevity, the initial approximations in the design are omitted here. Let

$$I_{E1} = 0.5 \text{ ma for the input stage}$$

Then $R_{i1} \cong h_{11e1} \cong 2000/0.5 \cong 4000 \text{ ohms}$

Assume that the shunt combination of R_{21} and R_{31} (see Fig. 4.15) is 6000 ohms.

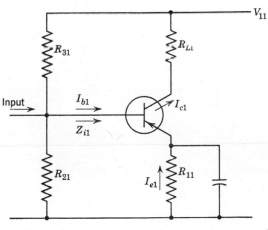

Fig. 4.15   Transistor stage

Then, the signal current entering the transistor, $I_{b1} = (6/10)0.5 = 0.3$ μa peak.

Since $h_{21e} \cong 49,$

$$I_{c1} \cong 0.3 \times 49 \cong 14.7 \ \mu a \text{ peak}$$

Choose I_{E2} as 2 ma for the second stage. Then $R_{i2} = 2000/2 = 1000$ ohms. This, in shunt with the bias elements and the load resistance, will constitute the a-c load resistance R_{l1} of the first stage.

Choose $\qquad\qquad\qquad R_{l1} = 565$ ohms

Then $\qquad\qquad\qquad V_{c1} \cong 7.74$ mv peak

$\qquad\qquad\qquad\qquad\; I_{c1} \cong 14.7\ \mu a$ peak

Therefore $\qquad\qquad\; I_{e1} \cong 14.7\ \mu a$ peak

For the purposes of design, the slight error resulting from setting $I_{E1} \cong I_{C1}$ and $I_{e1} \cong I_{c1}$ may be neglected. Furthermore we may assume that $V_{CE} \cong V_{CB}$.

Set the operating point at

$$(V_{CB1})_0 = 1 \text{ volt} \quad \text{and} \quad (I_{C1})_0 = 0.5 \text{ ma}$$

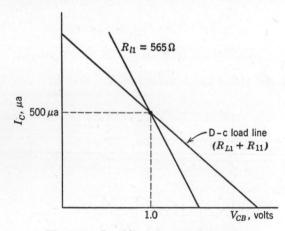

Fig. 4.16   Load lines for transistor stage

This is illustrated in Fig. 4.16. For the transistor, let

$$I_{CO1} \text{ at } 30° \text{ C} = 10\ \mu a$$

From the manufacturer's curves,

$$I_{CO1} \text{ at } 10° \text{ C} = 3\ \mu a$$

$$I_{CO1} \text{ at } 60° \text{ C} = 60\ \mu a$$

Then ΔI_{CO1} is $+50\ \mu a$ and $-7\ \mu a$. Since the collector dissipation is only 0.5 mw, the junction temperature will not rise appreciably above ambient. With changing temperature, the operating point moves along the d-c load line, and the peak signal voltage and current swings will determine the permissible shift of the operating point. With increasing temperatures, it may be shown that

$$\Delta V_{CB1} \cong -[(V_{CB1})_0 - V_{c1}] \tag{4.52}$$

$$\Delta I_{C1} \cong [(V_{CB1})_0 - V_{c1}]/(R_{L1} + R_{11}) \tag{4.53}$$

For decreasing temperatures,

$$\Delta V_{CB1} = [(I_{C1})_0 - I_{c1}](R_{L1} + R_{11}) \tag{4.54}$$

$$\Delta I_{C1} = -[(I_{C1})_0 - I_{c1}] \tag{4.55}$$

Assuming that $R_{L1} + R_{11} = 3100$ ohms, we have

$$\Delta V_{CB1} \cong -992 \text{ mv and } +1505 \text{ mv}$$

$$\Delta I_{C1} \cong \Delta I_{E1} = +320 \ \mu\text{a and } -485 \ \mu\text{a}$$

$$\Delta I_{CO1} \cong +50 \ \mu\text{a and } -7 \ \mu\text{a}$$

Using the procedure outlined in Chapter 3 gives

$$S_{V1} = \Delta V_{CB1}/\Delta I_{CO1} = -19{,}850 \text{ ohms and } -215{,}000 \text{ ohms}$$

$$S_{I1} = \Delta I_{C1}/\Delta I_{CO1} = 6.4 \text{ and } 69.5$$

Of these, the lesser values give the maximum permissible stability factors,

$$S_{V1} = -19{,}850 \text{ ohms}, \qquad S_{I1} = +6.4$$

In order to include a margin of safety, we select the actual stability factors as

$$S_{V1} = -14{,}000 \text{ ohms}, \qquad S_{I1} = +4$$

The design of the bias circuit follows the outline of Table 3.1.

Select $R_{11} = 1500$ ohms

Using $(V_{CB1})_0 = 1$ volt, $(I_{E1})_0 = 0.5$ ma

$$S_{I1} = 4, \text{ and } S_{V1} = -14{,}000 \text{ ohms}$$

we have (see Fig. 4.15)

$$R_{L1} = 1600 \text{ ohms}, \qquad R_{21} = 8500 \text{ ohms}, \qquad R_{31} = 20{,}400 \text{ ohms}$$

$$V_{11} = 2.55 \text{ volts}$$

Then the parallel impedance of R_{21} and R_{31} is 6000 ohms, as was assumed earlier. Furthermore, the d-c load line is given approximately by $R_{11} + R_{L1}$, and is 3100 ohms, as was assumed.

The design of the second stage may now be started. With reference
to the circuit of Fig. 4.1b, but using the subscript 2 to designate the
second stage, we have

$$R_{i2} = 1000 \text{ ohms}$$

since I_{E2} has been chosen as 2 ma. Assume that the shunt combination
of R_{22} and R_{32} is 7000 ohms,

$$I_{c1} = 14.7 \ \mu\text{a peak}$$

Then the current entering the second transistor is

$$I_{b2} = 8.31 \ \mu\text{a peak}$$

$$h_{21e} \cong 49$$

For an operating point of 2 ma, $h_{22e} \cong 2 \times 5 \times 10^{-5} = 10^{-4}$ mho.
Assuming that $R_{L2} = 5000$ ohms,

$$1/(1 + h_{22e}R_{L2}) = 0.667 \tag{4.56}$$

Then $I_{c2} = 8.31 \times 49 \times 0.667 = 272 \ \mu\text{a}$ peak (see eq. 4.31), and
$V_{c2} = 1.36$ volts peak. This meets the 1-volt requirement.

Assume an operating point at 10 volts and 2 ma, and a d-c load line
of 6 kilohms. Using the method applied to the first stage, and recalling
that

$$R_{l2} = R_{L2} = 5 \text{ kilohms}$$

we have $$\Delta V_{CB2} = -8.64 \text{ and } +10.4 \text{ volts}$$

$$\Delta I_{C2} \cong \Delta I_{E2} = +1.44 \text{ ma and } -1.73 \text{ ma}$$

The collector dissipation is 20 mw. Assuming a temperature rise of
0.5° C per mw, this corresponds to an increase of 10° C in the junction
temperature.

From the manufacturer's curves,

$$I_{CO2} \text{ at } 70° \text{ C} = 130 \ \mu\text{a}$$

Then $$\Delta I_{CO2} = +120 \ \mu\text{a and } -7 \ \mu\text{a}$$

Therefore $$S_{V2} = -72,000 \text{ ohms and } -1,493,000 \text{ ohms}$$

$$S_{I2} = +12 \text{ and } +249.0$$

Whence maximum permissible stability factors are

$$S_{V2} = -72,000, \qquad S_{I2} = +12$$

Including a reasonable safety margin,

$$S_{V2} = -47{,}000 \text{ ohms}, \qquad S_{I2} = +7$$

Since this stage does not feed into another transistor, the load resistance R_{L2} is also the a-c load, and the choice of R_{12} is relatively free, as long as it stabilizes the emitter-to-base diode adequately. In this case R_{12} should be chosen so as to result in a commonly available battery voltage, and a value of R_{L2} that would not adversely affect the high-frequency performance of the stage.

Select $\qquad\qquad R_{12} = 1000 \text{ ohms}$

Then $\qquad\qquad R_{L2} = 5000 \text{ ohms}$

whence the d-c load line is 6000 ohms as assumed. Also,

$$V_1 = 22 \text{ volts}$$

$$R_{32} = 77{,}000 \text{ ohms}$$

$$R_{22} = 7700 \text{ ohms}$$

The shunt combination of R_{22} and R_{32} is 7000 ohms as previously assumed.

The complete circuit is shown in Fig. 4.17. A battery of 22.5 volts is necessary, and a bleeder network is used to supply the first stage. Available component values should now be selected and the design rechecked.

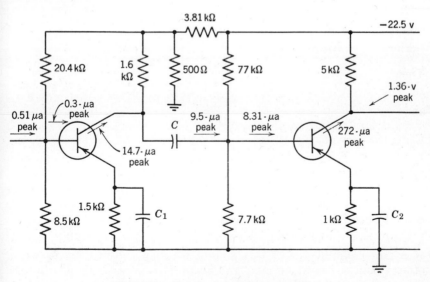

Fig. 4.17 Circuit of transistor amplifier

The values of the various capacitors may be computed as follows.
Effective resistance in shunt with C_1 is given from eq. 4.48 as 200 ohms.

$$\text{If } f = 30 \text{ cps, } C_1 = 26 \ \mu f$$

Effective resistance in shunt with C_2 is 46 ohms.

$$\text{If } f = 30 \text{ cps, } C_2 = 125 \ \mu f$$

The coupling capacitor is computed as follows. Neglecting the output admittance of the first stage, the effective resistance in series with C is given from eq. 4.48 as 2475 ohms.

$$\text{If } f = 30 \text{ cps, } C = 2.19 \ \mu f$$

If flat response to 30 cps is required, the capacitance values should be well in excess of those computed. Since the majority of the capacitance is in the emitter bypass, it is usually more practical to increase the coupling capacitor so that its effect may be ignored, and to increase the bypass capacitors as much as is necessary to obtain the desired low-frequency cutoff. It is unnecessary to check the high-frequency performance of the first stage since it is terminated in a load of 565 ohms. The high-frequency performance of the output stage may be computed as follows:

From the manufacturer's specifications,

$$f_{\alpha e} = 32 \text{ kc}$$

$$C_o = 1000 \ \mu\mu f$$

Since $\qquad R_{l2} = 5000 \text{ ohms}$

Then $\qquad x = 10^{-4} \times 5000 = 0.5$

and $\qquad u = \dfrac{2\pi \times 32{,}000 \times 1000 \times 10^{-12}}{10^{-4}} \cong 2.0$

Using the curve of Fig. 4.14,

$$v = 1.0$$

and the 3-db down point occurs at a frequency of 16 kc.

4.3 Special Low-Level Circuits

Up to now we have discussed the low-level stage primarily in its role of a power amplifier. In this section we shall consider stages where other conditions must be met, and where factors other than gain may assume primary importance.

4.3.1 Low-Noise Stages

The lower limit of input signal power at which an amplifier will operate is determined largely by the noise generated within it. Since the noise generated in the input stage is amplified by all succeeding stages, it is important that this noise level be low, so as to give an acceptable signal-to-noise ratio. The noise due to the other stages may usually be neglected.

We define the noise figure F of an amplifier as the ratio of the total noise power in the output (disregarding the noise in the load impedance)

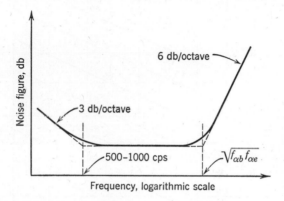

Fig. 4.18   Noise figure versus frequency

to that portion of the output noise resulting from thermal agitation in the source resistance. If we define P_{ni} as the equivalent transistor noise power referred to the input of the amplifier, and P_{ng} as the available noise power due to thermal agitation in the source resistance, then

$$P_{ni} = FP_{ng} \tag{4.57}$$

For any specified signal-to-noise ratio, the value of the maximum permissible noise power may be computed and the minimum acceptable noise figure determined.

The character of transistor noise is shown in Fig. 4.18. At low frequencies,[2] the noise figure varies inversely with frequency at the rate of 3 db per octave, and then levels off from 500 cycles to 1 kc to a value comparable to the thermal and shot noise. At a frequency given by $(f_{\alpha b} f_{\alpha e})^{1/2}$, there is a rise in the noise figure at 6 db per octave. This is due to the fall-off in power gain of the amplifier as well as to an increase in the generated noise. This rise occurs beyond the audio range, and may usually be disregarded in audio amplifier design.

If the transistor is to operate over the frequency range from zero to 1000 cps, such as in d-c or servo amplifiers, the curve of Fig. 4.19 may be used to obtain some idea of the minimum acceptable noise figure of the device. By way of example, if the power input to a transistor is 1.0×10^{-10} watt, and the required signal-to-noise ratio is 60 db, the input noise power P_{ni} is 1.0×10^{-16} watt. If the amplifier band pass is 10 to 1000 cps, $f_2/f_1 = 100$. This requires a transistor with a maximum noise figure of approximately 9 db.

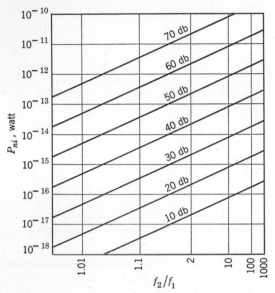

Fig. 4.19   Noise power versus frequency ratio

The noise figure of the input stage may be reduced to a minimum by selection of transistor type and proper choice of operating conditions. If the source impedance is maintained at 100 to 1000 ohms; and if the device is operated at a collector voltage of less than 1.5 volts and a collector current of less than 1 ma, the noise figure for a given transistor will be minimized. In some cases, it is even possible to operate transistors at zero [3] or slightly reversed collector-to-base voltages, resulting in an extremely low noise figure. However, an additional consequence of such a mode of operation is that the stage has relatively limited gain.

4.3.2   Gain Controls

The function of an ideal gain control is to adjust the gain of an amplifier from zero to its maximum value. This must be effected without any other change in the performance of the amplifier.

Since the power gain of a transistor is approximately equal to the square of the current-transfer ratio, it is usually sufficient to control the input current to the transistor. Two basic techniques present themselves: series control and shunt control (see Fig. 4.20a and b, respectively). Whereas the series control circuit is relatively frequency-independent, it suffers from the disadvantage that the gain cannot be set to zero, since this would require that R be infinite.

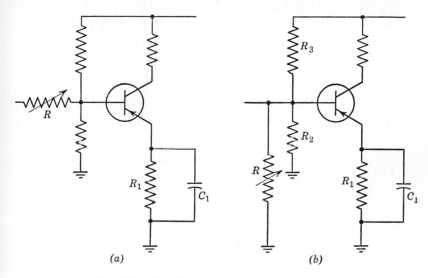

(a)　　　　　　　　　　　　　　　(b)

Fig. 4.20　Unsatisfactory volume-control circuits

In the circuit of Fig. 4.20b, gain control is effected by bypassing part or all of the input current to ground. This circuit does allow gain control down to zero, when R goes to zero. With decreasing gain however, the source impedance feeding the transistor is rapidly reduced, resulting in a deteriorated low-frequency response characteristic (see Sec. 4.2.2.3).

For example, if the circuit of Fig. 4.20b is fed from a constant-current source, and $R_1 = 4$ kilohms, $R_2 = 20$ kilohms, $R_3 = 80$ kilohms, $R = 20$ kilohms, and $C_1 = 25$ μf, the low-frequency cutoff occurs at 30 cycles with R set for maximum gain, and 100 cycles when the current-transfer ratio is reduced by 50%.

If, in the circuit of Fig. 4.20b, the ground end of R is tied directly to the emitter, this element does not shunt the emitter bias network, and the control no longer deteriorates the low-frequency response. Such a circuit is shown in Fig. 4.21. Two coupling capacitors are used to isolate the control from the biasing circuits. This also helps to reduce the noise produced by direct current in the control.

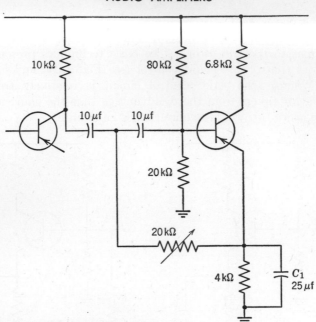

MATCH

Fig. 4.21 Satisfactory volume-control circuit

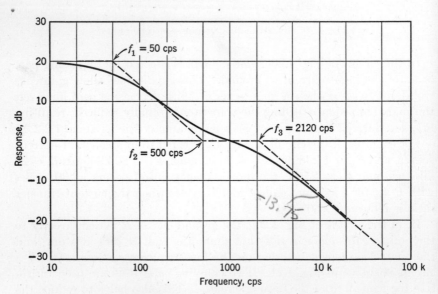

Fig. 4.22   RIAA playback characteristic

Various other satisfactory gain controls are possible using ganged elements, such as T, L, and H pads. The design of such controls is straightforward, and will not be discussed here.

4.3.3 Equalization Networks

It is often desirable to shape the frequency response of the amplifier to a prescribed characteristic. This may be done by a method similar to that used in the design of the gain control circuit discussed in

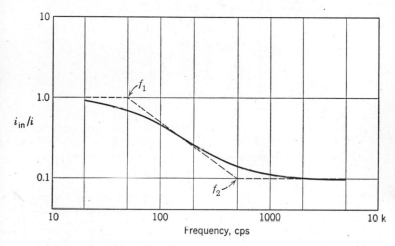

Fig. 4.23   RIAA playback characteristic at low frequencies

Sec. 4.3.2, except that the gain control R must be replaced by a combination of frequency-dependent elements. An example will illustrate the design procedure.

Example. It is required to compensate the amplifier of Sec. 4.2.2.4 for the RIAA * playback characteristic for microgroove records. The preamplifier is to operate from a variable-reluctance cartridge having the following specification: peak output at 1 kc = 50 mv; terminating resistance for a high-frequency roll-off at 2120 cycles = 6200 ohms. Figure 4.22 shows the RIAA playback characteristic.

Since the high-frequency roll-off is obtained by terminating the cartridge in a 6200 ohms load, it is only necessary to design a compensating network for the response characteristic of Fig. 4.23. We choose to place the compensation networks in the first stage in order to obtain a minimum operating dynamic range for the transistors.

* Record Industry Association of America.

The circuit will take the form of Fig. 4.24. The equivalent circuit is shown in Fig. 4.25a, with R_{21}, R_{31}, and the 6200 ohms resistance combined in parallel in a common term R_g.

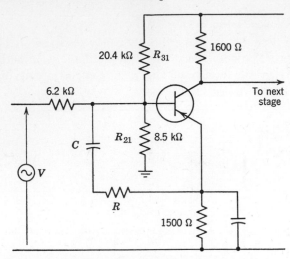

Fig. 4.24   Compensation network

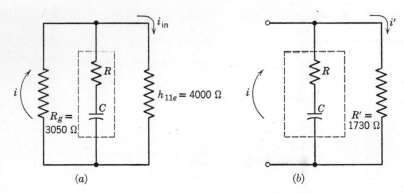

(a)   (b)

Fig. 4.25   Equivalent circuits for Fig. 4.24

This may be further redrawn in the form of Fig. 4.25b where R' is the parallel combination of R_g and h_{11e}.

Then $R_g = 3.05$ kilohms

$R' = 1.73$ kilohms

At high frequencies, the output is down to 0.1 of its initial value.   Therefore

$$R/(R + R') = 0.1$$

or
$$R = R'/9 = 192 \text{ ohms}$$

The frequency f_2 occurs when R is equal to the reactance of the capacitor; whence $C = 1.7$ μf. Since

$$i_{in}/i' = R_g/(h_{11e} + R_g) \tag{4.58}$$

the current entering the transistor has the same frequency characteristic as i', and the design is complete.

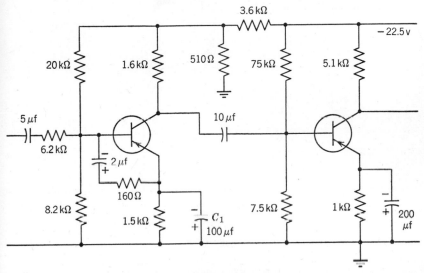

Fig. 4.26   Amplifier with frequency compensation

A study of the playback characteristic of Fig. 4.22 shows that the location of f_2 determines the amount of bass boost over the entire low-frequency range, whereas the location of f_1 determines only the gain at very low frequencies. Thus, while f_1 may be varied considerably without much apparent effect, it is important that the location of f_2 be maintained critically. This will be accomplished if the product of R and C is maintained constant. With this restriction in mind, minor changes in C are permissible. In general, it is preferable to increase C since this will lower f_1 slightly. In the final design, this may result in a reduction in the size of the emitter bypass capacitance. The final version is shown in Fig. 4.26.

The decrease in the equivalent resistance in shunt with C_1 due to the finite source impedance resulted in a selection of C_1 well in excess of the original design value. Using this input circuit, we may compute a peak input current of 0.5 μa. The original circuit design of the example of Sec. 4.2.2.4 is therefore satisfactory.

4.3.4   Tone Controls

The function of tone controls is to provide frequency-selective amplification. In general, circuits similar to those used in electron-tube amplifiers cannot be used, since the frequency-dependent characteristic must be made a function of the signal current, rather than of the volt-

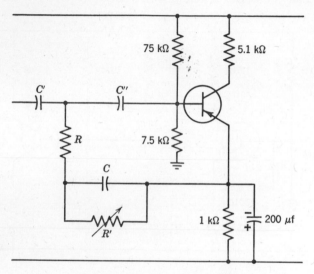

Fig. 4.27   Bass-boost tone control

age. The two types of control that are most frequently used are the bass-boost and treble-cut controls.

A satisfactory control giving low-frequency boost is shown in Fig. 4.27. This control is similar to the low-frequency compensation network of Sec. 4.3.3, except for the addition of a variable resistance across the capacitor. This resistance serves to control the amount of bass boost.

Example. Design a bass-boost control for the second stage of the amplifier of Fig. 4.26. Design requirements are as follows.

$$\text{Low-frequency turnover} = 800 \text{ cps}$$

$$\text{Bass boost} \qquad = 20 \text{ db}$$

The design procedure is as follows.   Referring to Fig. 4.26,

Input impedance of second stage and bias network = 875 ohms

For a 20-db boost at low frequencies, $R = 875/9$ ohms

$$= 97.3 \text{ ohms}$$

For a 800-cps turnover, $C = 2 \ \mu f$

R' must be chosen to keep the loss at low frequencies down to a negligible amount.

If $R' \geq 10 \times 875$ ohms, say 10,000 ohms, this loss is about 1 db.

The coupling capacitor is broken into two sections to prevent interference with the transistor bias, and to keep direct current out of the

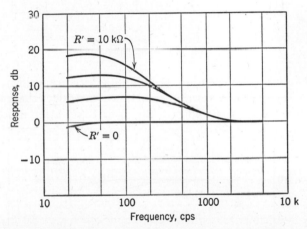

Fig. 4.28   Response versus frequency for circuit of Fig. 4.27

bass control.   The minimum value of the series combination of C' and C'' should be about 10 μf, and C'' must be large compared to C.   For a practical design, choose $C' = 15 \ \mu f$ and $C'' = 30 \ \mu f$.   Figure 4.28 shows the response of such a tone control.   The control element should have a logarithmic taper.

The function of bass boost is in reality one of attenuating the midband by a constant amount.   In general, an additional stage must be used to make up for this loss.   Since the function of "treble-cut" results in attenuation at high frequencies, it is extremely desirable that the control circuit introduce no additional midband loss.   With this in

mind, a simple form of treble control, for use in conjunction with a magnetic cartridge, may take the form of Fig. 4.29.

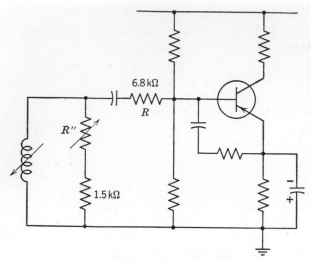

Fig. 4.29   Treble-cut tone control

Typical values will depend on the manufacturer's specification for his
cartridge.   For the G.E. variable-reluctance cartridge, the values given
in the figure are adequate and provide up to 12 db attenuation at 16 kc

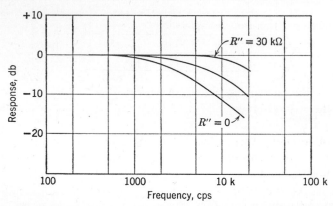

Fig. 4.30   Response versus frequency for circuit of Fig. 4.29

beyond that required for the compensation function.   The resistance R
may be increased to 6800 ohms to compensate for the shunting effect of
the treble tone control.   If R is increased further, the treble control will
perform the additional function of boost.   The compensation network

would require redesign, however, and the midband gain would then be reduced.

Figure 4.30 shows the frequency response for various settings of the treble control. In each case, the variations due to playback compensation have been subtracted to illustrate the effect of the control alone.

4.4 High-Level Stages

The high-level stage has been defined as one in which the transistor is operated near its dissipation limits. Although the principles discussed in the preceding sections are still applicable, the design of a high-level stage will present many special problems of its own. Here the excursions of the bias voltages and currents may approach the absolute limits of operation of the transistor. Therefore, the selection of the operating point and load become of paramount importance.

In most audio amplifiers, high-level operation will occur only in the output stage, or in those stages immediately preceding it. Thus the discussion of the high-level stage is essentially that of the output stage.

The choice of the transistor configuration and mode of operation of the output stage will be influenced by many factors, some of which are noted below: (a) power output, (b) d-c power requirement, (c) power gain, (d) nonlinear distortion, (e) frequency response.

The modes of operation that may be utilized are class A and class B. These will be analyzed in turn, and related to the requirements above.

4.4.1 Choice of Transistor Configuration

The power gain of a transistor stage is given by

$$G = P_o/P_{in} = A_i^2 R_l/R_i \tag{4.59}$$

where A_i is the current amplification of the stage, R_i is the input resistance of the loaded stage, and R_l is the load resistance required by a specified output power and supply voltage.

The common-emitter configuration provides the greatest ratio of A_i^2/R_i and is thus the optimum choice if maximum power gain is required from the stage.

Owing to the relatively linear transfer characteristic of the common-base stage, even up to very high collector currents, and also owing to its relatively higher permissible inverse voltage, this stage may be chosen if maximum power output is required at a specified harmonic distortion level. The power gain will, however, be reduced by a factor of h_{21e} compared to that of the common-emitter stage.

The common-collector stage is usually chosen only when greatly simplified circuit design is desired. For example the common-collector configuration sometimes results in the elimination of a transformer or other coupling network, or in the possibility of using a single untapped power supply. The power gain in this configuration is again reduced compared to that of the common-emitter stage.

4.4.2 Choice of Operating Conditions

Figure 4.31 shows a pair of transfer characteristics for a transistor in the common-emitter configuration. It will be noted that, over the same

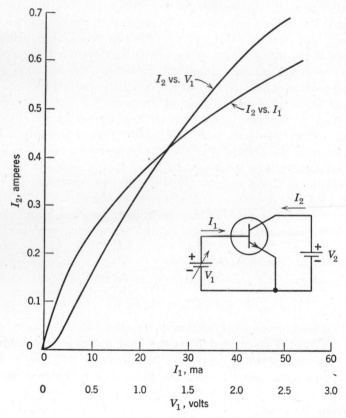

Fig. 4.31   Transfer characteristics

range of I_2, the V_1 versus I_2 curve is considerably more linear than the I_1 versus I_2 curve. The reason for this lies in the fact that at high currents the nonlinearities of the input diode are partially compensated by the nonlinearities of the current-transfer characteristic.

Quite the opposite effect is noted in the transfer characteristics for the common-base configuration. For this configuration, the current-transfer characteristic is itself linear and the previously compensating nonlinearities of the input diode are to be avoided.

4.4.3 Class-A Operation

In class-A operation, the transistor conducts over the entire cycle, and the output waveform is a reasonable facsimile of the input signal. It is therefore possible to utilize a single transistor for a class-A stage.

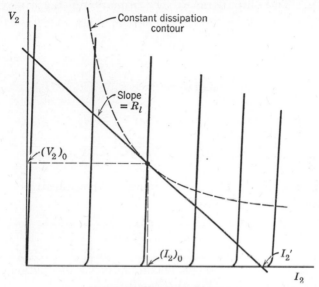

Fig. 4.32   Class-A operation

.The operation of such a stage is readily visualized with the aid of the output characteristic for the configuration of interest.

Figure 4.32 shows the output characteristics of a transistor. On this curve is shown also the hyperbola for maximum permissible collector dissipation for a specified cooling technique and a specified ambient temperature.

If the transistor is to be operated at this value of collector dissipation, the operating point must be located on this hyperbola. For any such operating point, a load line may be constructed tangential to this curve. This line will be bisected at the point of tangency. The extremities of the load line are subject to the restriction that the voltage swing must not exceed the permissible peak inverse voltage, and also that the current swing must be limited to a reasonably linear portion of the output characteristics. Ordinarily, a transistor output stage operates into a load resistance well below that value required for maximum gain (as given by eq. 4.14). Thus, it is advantageous to operate the stage with as high a load resistance as possible, since this will result in the highest power gain. This condition is realized when we choose the highest permissible supply voltage. Maximum supply voltage corresponds to minimum collector current and confines the collector-current swing to the most linear part of the output characteristic.

Consider a transformer-coupled stage. Let the operating point be at $(V_2)_0, (I_2)_0$. The output-transformer primary resistance may be neglected, and so the supply voltage will also be $(V_2)_0$. Then the maximum possible voltage swing is $2(V_2)_0$.

Referring to Fig. 4.32,

$$\text{Load resistance } R_l \cong (V_2)_0/(I_2)_0 \qquad (4.60)$$

$$\text{Maximum a-c power output } P_o \cong (I_2)_0(V_2)_0/2 \qquad (4.61)$$

$$\text{D-c battery power } P_{dc} = (V_2)_0(I_2)_0 \qquad (4.62)$$

This is also the standby dissipation power of the transistor.

Collector efficiency η is given by

$$\eta = P_o/P_{dc} \cong 50\% \qquad (4.63)$$

In class-A operation, however, maximum power dissipation occurs for the zero-signal condition. For this condition,

$$P_{diss} = (V_2)_0(I_2)_0 \qquad (4.64)$$

whence $\qquad\qquad\qquad P_o = 0.5\,P_{diss} \qquad\qquad\qquad (4.65)$

Ordinarily, a class-A stage is driven only a fraction of its total possible output swing, say k, where $k \leq 1$. Then

$$P_o \cong k^2(V_2)_0(I_2)_0/2 \qquad (4.66)$$

and $\qquad\qquad\qquad \eta \cong k^2(50)\% \qquad\qquad\qquad (4.67)$

4.4.3.1 Class-A Push-Pull Operation

If a larger power output is required than can be obtained by a single class-A stage, two transistors may be connected in class-A push-pull.

The input signals for the two transistors must be phased 180° apart, and any of the phase-inversion techniques discussed later may be used for this purpose.

The push-pull connection has the advantage that each transistor may be driven much harder and even into its nonlinear operating region. When the two signals are combined in the load, all even-harmonic distortion resulting from the nonlinearities is canceled if the transistors are evenly matched in transfer characteristics and frequency response. In general, the distortion for a class-A push-pull stage will always be less than that for a comparative class-B stage. However, the high standby power requirements for a class-A stage will still hold for the push-pull connection.

4.4.3.2 Distortion in Class-A Stages

The presence of nonlinear distortion components in the output of a transistor stage is primarily due to a combination of nonlinearity (a) in the transfer characteristic, (b) in the input characteristic.

The interrelation of these two nonlinearities must be considered in analyzing the distortion of the stage. The method outlined below is suitable for computing the second- and third-harmonic distortion components. Either the V_1 versus I_2 or I_1 versus I_2 curve may be used in conjunction with the V_1 versus I_1 characteristic. By way of example, the current-transfer characteristic is used.

Figure 4.33 shows the two sets of characteristics, with a common abscissa I_1. Let the operating point be set at $(I_2)_0$, and correspondingly $(I_1)_0$. Let the source resistance be R_g. Draw $P'P$ at a slope of $-R_g$. Let PB and PC be the peak swings of V_1 about P. Draw BB' and CC' parallel to PP'.

Draw $B'B''$, $P'P''$ and $C'C''$ parallel to the ordinate to intersect the current transfer characteristic in B'', P'', and C''.

Draw $B''B'''$, $P''P'''$, $C''C'''$ parallel to the abscissa. Then $B'''P'''$ and $C'''P'''$ are the output-current swings, respectively.

Let D and F be chosen such that $DP = FP = BP/\sqrt{2}$.

Using the above construction, the points D''' and F''' may be obtained. Then

$$\text{2nd harmonic} \cong \frac{P'''B''' - P'''C'''}{C'''B''' + \sqrt{2}F'''D'''} \times 100\% \qquad (4.68)$$

$$\text{3rd harmonic} \cong \frac{C'''B''' - \sqrt{2}F'''D'''}{C'''B''' + \sqrt{2}F'''D'''} \times 100\% \qquad (4.69)$$

In the design of an amplifier stage, it may be desirable to choose a few values of R_g in order to pick the one resulting in minimum distortion. The above analysis assumes that both input and transfer characteristics are independent of the output voltage. This is a reasonably good assumption.

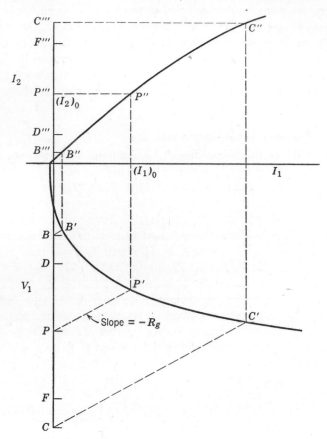

Fig. 4.33 Graphical construction for distortion analysis

As indicated by the graphical analysis, distortion in a class-A stage is a function of the source impedance. In general, the common-emitter stage will require a low source impedance compared to the transistor-input impedance, corresponding to a voltage drive, if the distortion is to be minimized. A common-base stage, on the other hand, requires a relatively high source impedance compared to that of the transistor-impedance, corresponding to a current drive.

Degenerative feedback circuits may be used for the reduction of distortion. However, the high-frequency response of many available power transistors is so poor that there is considerable phase shift at audio frequencies. As a result, the use of large quantities of negative feedback will often result in increased distortion at high frequencies. It is possible, however, to use local degenerative feedback with considerable success, for example, an unbypassed resistance in the emitter circuit, or a shunt path from collector to base. The common-collector configuration is an extreme application of the technique, and is frequently used.

Class-A push-pull operation results in some cancellation of even-order harmonics. If the transistors are matched, this cancellation is complete.

4.4.3.3   Design of a Class-A Output Stage

Example. Design a common-emitter stage with the following specifications.

$$\text{Power output} \quad = 3 \text{ watts}$$
$$\text{Transformer } \eta \quad = 75\%$$
$$\text{Overload capacity} = 25\%$$
$$\text{Supply voltage} \quad = 28 \text{ volts}$$

For an output of 3 watts, the stage must supply 4.0 watts to the primary winding of the transformer. For an overload capacity of 25%, the stage must be capable of 5 watts output. Then

$$\text{Collector dissipation} = 10 \text{ watts}$$
$$(V_{CE})_0 = 28 \text{ volts}$$

Therefore
$$(I_C)_0 = 0.36 \text{ ampere}$$

Therefore   Load resistance $= 28/0.36 = 78$ ohms (from eq. 4.60)

Overall output circuit η at full output $= \frac{3}{10} = 30\%$

$$\text{Overload capacity} = 25\%$$
$$k = \sqrt{1/1.25} \cong 0.9$$

Therefore actual collector voltage and current swings are 25.2 volts and 0.324 ampere, respectively.

We select a transistor that is capable of 10 watts dissipation for the given ambient conditions, and has a permissible peak inverse voltage in excess of 56 volts. The output characteristics for such a transistor are

shown in Figure 4.34. Note that both input voltage and input curren⸱
are shown as parameters.

Using this information, we compute the input power and input impedance as approximately 10 mw and 40 ohms, respectively. Whence

$$\text{Power gain} = 4.0/(10 \times 10^{-3})$$

$$= 26 \text{ db}$$

For optimum power transfer, the source impedance should be 40 ohms.

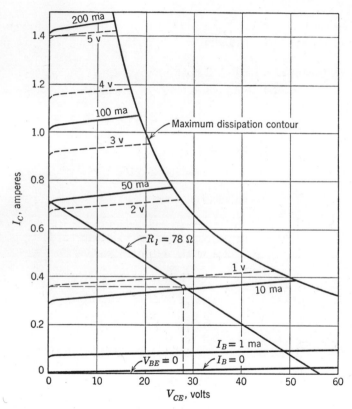

Fig. 4.34 Transistor output characteristics

However, a 10 ohm source impedance may be preferable in order to
keep the distortion at a low value. A possible circuit configuration is
shown in Fig. 4.35. At the operating point, the bias values on the
emitter-base diode are

$$I_E = 0.38 \text{ ampere} \quad \text{and} \quad V_{EB} = 0.9 \text{ volt}$$

For stabilization, we may use a 4.5-volt emitter supply and a resistance of $(4.5 - 0.9)/0.38 = 9.5$ ohms. The value of this resistance may have to be adjusted to give the required operating point. D-c power from emitter battery = 1.7 watts.

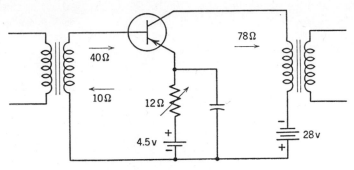

Fig. 4.35   Class-A output stage

4.4.4   Class-B Operation

In class-B operation the transistor conducts for only one half of the cycle, and it is therefore necessary to use push-pull operation in order

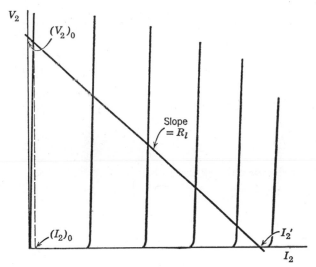

Fig. 4.36   Class-B operation

to amplify the entire waveform. The class-B analysis may be undertaken on the basis of a single transistor. Figure 4.36 shows the appropriate output characteristics for this stage.

The operating point of a class-B stage is set approximately on the voltage axis, corresponding to minimum standby current, and the load line is drawn next. It may be shown that, if the stage is transformer coupled to the load, the maximum inverse voltage that is impressed on the transistor is twice the supply voltage. This limits the operating point to no more than one-half the permissible peak inverse voltage. The other restriction that is placed on the load line is that the peak current swing shall be in the region where the curves are reasonably linear. As with the class-A stage, a high battery voltage is desirable.

Let the operating point be set at $(V_2)_0, (I_2)_0$ and the peak current swing be at I_2'. Then $(V_2)_0$ is the battery voltage to a close approximation, and $(I_2)_0$, the standby current, may be neglected in comparison with I_2'. Then the load impedance per transistor is

$$R_l \cong (V_2)_0/I_2' \tag{4.70}$$

Since this is the impedance of one half of a center-tapped primary winding, the total primary impedance is

$$4(V_2)_0/I_2' \tag{4.71}$$

The output signal consists of a train of half-waves of voltage and current, of peak value $(V_2)_0$ and I_2', respectively.

The a-c power output per transistor is given by

$$P_o \cong (V_2)_0 I_2'/4 \cong (V_2)_0^2/4R_l \tag{4.72}$$

Neglecting leakage, the collector current corresponds to an average d-c value of approximately I_2'/π amperes.

Battery power per transistor is

$$P_{dc} \cong I_2'(V_2)_0/\pi \tag{4.73}$$

and

$$\eta = P_o/P_{dc} \cong 78\% \tag{4.74}$$

The power dissipation per transistor is given by

$$P_{diss} = P_{dc} - P_o \cong 0.272 I_2'(V_2)_0/4 \tag{4.75}$$

$$\cong 0.272 P_o \tag{4.76}$$

Whence

$$P_o \cong 3.68 P_{diss} \tag{4.77}$$

If the stage is driven to a fraction k of its total swing,

$$P_o \cong k^2(V_2)_0 I_2'/4 \tag{4.78}$$

$$P_{dc} \cong k(V_2)_0 I_2'/\pi \tag{4.79}$$

$$\eta \cong k(78)\% \tag{4.80}$$

It should be noted that, although the efficiency of a class-A stage varies as k^2, that for a class-B stage varies as k.

4.4.4.1 Effect of Resistance in the Output Circuit

In the analysis of Sec. 4.4.3, it was assumed that the resistance of the primary winding of the output transformer was negligible. A practical transformer primary winding may be represented by a resistance in series with an ideal winding. If we denote this loss resistance by R_{dc} and the reflected load impedance by R_{ac}, the power delivered per transistor to the primary winding is (eq. 4.72)

$$(V_2)_0{}^2/4R_l \quad \text{where} \quad R_l = R_{dc} + R_{ac} \tag{4.81}$$

The power transferred to the secondary side will be $R_{ac}/(R_{ac} + R_{dc})$ times the power delivered to the primary side. Under this condition, it may be shown that the maximum inverse voltage on the transistor is reduced to $(V_2)_0(1 + R_{ac}/R_l)$. Furthermore, under full load, the average collector voltage falls from $(V_2)_0$ to $(V_2)_0(1 - R_{dc}/\pi R_l)$.

The above analysis also holds for the extreme case where a resistive load is connected directly to the output stage. Under this condition, $R_{dc} = R_l$, and the total power delivered per transistor to the load is $(V_2)_0{}^2/4R_{dc}$.

If the load takes the form of a center-tapped loudspeaker, the push-pull class-B stage may be used without an output transformer. Since the impedance of a moving-coil loudspeaker is almost entirely resistive, such an analysis may be applied to this case.

4.4.4.2 Effect of Power-Supply Regulation

In practice, unfortunately, the voltage of the power supply will vary with the load. Owing to the fact that transistor operation is not affected over a wide range of collector voltage, such variations may be tolerated. The effect of power-supply regulation may be included in the design as follows. Referring to Fig. 4.37, let $(V_2)_0$ be the supply voltage for zero current. Let $(V_2)_L$ be the supply voltage for a current I_L.

Then the effective source impedance of the power supply is

$$R_S = [(V_2)_0 - (V_2)_L]/I_L \tag{4.82}$$

Writing

$$R_l' = R_S + R_{dc} + R_{ac} \tag{4.83}$$

It may be shown that

$$\text{Power in } R_l' = (V_2)_0{}^2/4R_l' \tag{4.84}$$

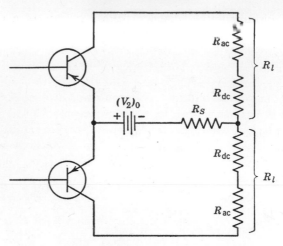

Fig. 4.37   Effect of loss resistance in the transformer

Power transferred to the transformer secondary is

$$[R_{ac}/(R_S + R_{dc} + R_{ac})](V_2)_0{}^2/4R_l' \qquad (4.85)$$

Under full load, the average collector voltage falls from

$$(V_2)_0 \quad \text{to} \quad (V_2)_0[1 - (R_S + R_{dc})/\pi R_l']$$

The inverse voltage that is applied to the transistor during its off half-cycle is given by

$$(V_2)_0\{1 + [(R_{ac} - R_S)/R_l'] \sin \omega t\} \qquad (4.86)$$

If $\qquad\qquad\qquad R_{ac} < R_S \qquad\qquad\qquad (4.87)$

the maximum inverse voltage is $(V_2)_0$ and occurs when the supply current is zero, both at standby and at those points in the cycle at which the transistor current goes to zero.

If $\qquad\qquad\qquad R_{ac} > R_S \qquad\qquad\qquad (4.88)$

the maximum inverse voltage applied to the nonconducting transistor is

$$(V_2)_0[1 + (R_{ac} - R_S)/R_l'] \qquad (4.89)$$

and occurs when the conducting transistor is passing its peak current.

In conclusion, we note that the effect of resistance in the power supply is to reduce the power delivered to the load. Owing to the reduction in peak inverse voltage that results from the power-supply resistance, it is possible to utilize supply voltages as great as the permissible inverse voltage of the transistor. It should be noted that the standby dissipation in the transistor is doubled for this condition. However, dissipation is ordinarily not the limiting factor in the design of a class-B stage.

Example. A transformer-coupled class-B amplifier is designed to operate from a 25-volt supply. The a-c load impedance is 100 ohms per transistor. It is desired to operate this amplifier from an existing 100-volt d-c supply.

Solution. With the original 25-volt supply, the maximum inverse voltage on the transistor is 50 volts. Then a 50-volt supply may be utilized, and, if the source resistance of the supply is made 100 ohms or more, the maximum inverse voltage on the transistor will not exceed 50 volts.

For the supply resistance of 100 ohms, the power output of the amplifier is seen to remain unchanged (see eq. 4.85), and a satisfactory bleeder across the supply takes the form of Fig. 4.38.

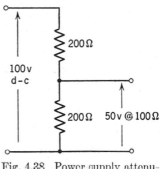

Fig. 4.38   Power supply attenuator

4.4.4.3 Distortion in Class-B Stages

The effect of source impedance on the distortion of a class-B stage is similar to that obtained with a class-A stage. The same general conclusions also hold: in order to minimize distortion, a common-emitter output stage should be fed from a low source resistance compared to its input impedance and a common-base stage fed from a high resistance compared to the input.

Since each transistor contributes to one half of the output waveform, it is highly desirable that the transistors be matched in their current-transfer characteristics. It is generally unnecessary to seek a match in the input characteristics also, since transistors with matched current-transfer characteristics will usually have reasonably matched input characteristics. The graphical analysis follows the lines of that for the class-A stage, except that the excursion is only to one side of the operating point. Since the output transistors are assumed to be matched, only third-harmonic distortion may be obtained from the curves.

The precautions and recommendations concerning the use of negative feedback in class-A stages should be stressed even more highly for class-B stages. This is due to the fact that the gain of a class-B amplifier changes appreciably with signal amplitude. If such a stage is part

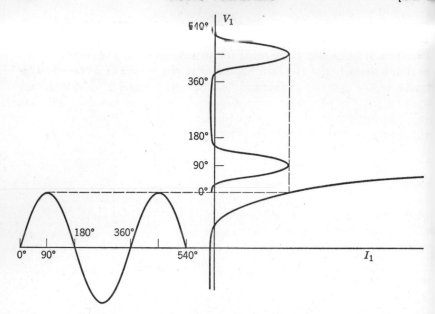

Fig. 4.39   Input voltage and current in a class-B stage

of a feedback loop, stability must be insured at all signal levels that will be encountered.

In addition to the above, the class-B stage must be operated in such a manner that the switching of the transistors occurs smoothly so as to minimize cross-over distortion. Figure 4.39 shows a graphical construction for the input current of a common-emitter stage fed from a con-

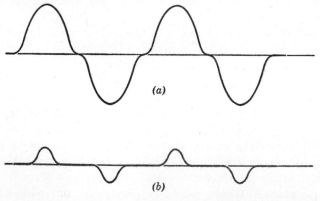

Fig. 4.40   (a) Cross-over distortion at high levels.   (b) Cross-over distortion at low levels.

tant-voltage source. If the input is unbiased, it is seen from the input-current waveform that the transistor conducts for less than one half of the cycle, resulting in an operation somewhat similar to class-C. The resultant output waveform for the stage is shown in Fig. 4.40a for large signals and Fig. 4.40b for small signals. With such a waveform, the

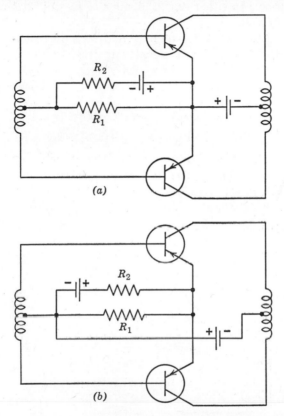

Fig. 4.41   Bias circuits for class-B operation

percentage distortion *increases* with decreasing signal. It is therefore extremely important that cross-over distortion be eliminated at low levels. This is done by prebiasing the stage slightly into the class-A region, resulting in class-AB operation. With germanium transistors the amount of this bias will be about 0.1 to 0.2 volt; with silicon units the bias is about 0.6 to 1 volt.

A resistive bias network is normally used in the input circuit of the transistor, as shown in Figs. 4.41a and 4.41b. This will reduce the power entering the transistor somewhat.

Let R be the parallel combination of R_1 and R_2. If R is made equal to the input impedance of the transistor, the power-drive requirements will be increased by 3 db. If R is placed as in Fig. 4.41a, the input impedance to be considered is the common-emitter impedance. If R is placed as in Fig. 4.41b, it must be chosen relative to the common-base input impedance. In either case, the value of R_2 will be determined by the bias supply voltage.

The bias resistors must not be bypassed with a capacitor. If this is done, the half-waves of input signal will decrease the charge on the capacitor, the bias on the transistors will decrease with increasing signal level, and the stage may even be driven into class-C operation.

4.4.4.4   Design of Transformer-Coupled Class-B Stage

Example.   Design for the following specifications.

$$
\begin{aligned}
\text{Load power} &= 10 \text{ watts} \\
\text{Transformer } \eta &= 80\% \\
\text{Overload capacity} &= 25\% \\
\text{Supply voltage} &= 28 \text{ volts}
\end{aligned}
$$

The design proceeds as follows.

Load power	$= 10$ watts
Transformer η	$= 80\%$

Therefore

Power delivered to transformer	$= 12.5$ watts
Overload capacity	$= 25\%$
Stage should be capable of	
12.5×1.25	$= 15.6$ watts
	$= 7.8$ watts per transistor
Supply voltage	$= 28$ volts
Maximum inverse voltage	$= 56$ volts
Peak current swing	$= 7.8 \times 4/28 \cong 1.11$ amperes
Load resistance	$\cong 28/1.11 = 25$ ohms

This corresponds to a primary impedance of 100 ohms. Overload capacity $= 25\%$.

Therefore $k^2 = 1/1.25$ and $k = 0.896$

Full-load current swing $\cong 0.896 \times 1.11 = 0.995$ ampere
Full-load voltage swing $\cong 0.896 \times 28 = 25.1$ volts
Full-load η of transistor $\cong 0.896 \times 78\% = 69.9\%$
Transformer η $\cong 80\%$

Therefore

>Overall full-load output
>circuit η $\cong 56\%$

On the basis of the preceding, we select the transistors whose characteristics are shown in Figs. 4.42 to 4.44. From the output characteristics,

>Full-load peak I_B $\cong 35$ ma
>Full-load peak V_{BE} $\cong 0.42$ volt
>Peak transistor input power $\cong 14.7$ mw
>Peak transistor output power $\cong 25$ watts

Therefore   Peak power gain $\cong 1700$
>$\cong 32.3$ db

The bias is set at say 0.15 volt (this should be checked experimentally). Referring to Fig. 4.45, a value of R_1 was chosen as 1 ohm so as to avoid excessive loss in the input circuit.

$$\text{Bias current} = (0.15/1) \text{ ampere} = 150 \text{ ma}$$

Arbitrarily selecting a bias battery voltage of 3 volts,

$$R_2 = 19 \text{ ohms}$$

$$\text{Bias battery power} \cong 3 \times 0.150 \cong 0.45 \text{ watt}$$

The peak input impedance in the common-base configuration is given by the ratio of the peak input voltage to the peak emitter current. For this transistor this is approximately

$$0.42/(1.11 + 0.035) \cong 0.37 \text{ ohm}$$

In order to drive the transistor to full output, the input signal should be increased by $(1 + 0.37)/0.37 \cong 5.7$ db. Then effective input loss is 5.7 db. Peak current amplification $\cong 1.11/0.035 \cong 32$. Then input impedance of the stage, inclusive of the bias resistor, is

$$(1 + 0.37)32 \cong 44 \text{ ohms}$$

Thus source impedance per transistor should be 44 ohms for best power transfer. The distortion should be checked for this source impedance by the method outlined in Sec. 4.4.4.3. It is important to note that the input curve to be used should include the bias resistance. The current-transfer characteristic is substantially unchanged.

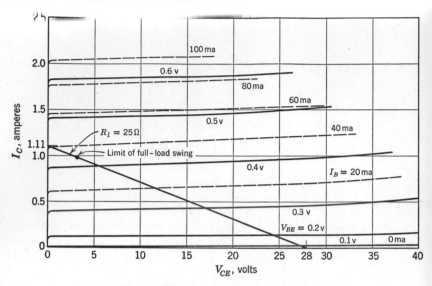

Fig. 4.42 Transistor output characteristics

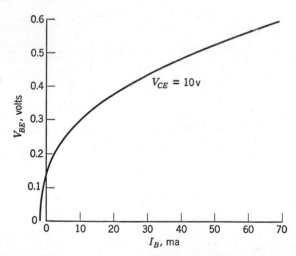

Fig. 4.43 Transistor input characteristics

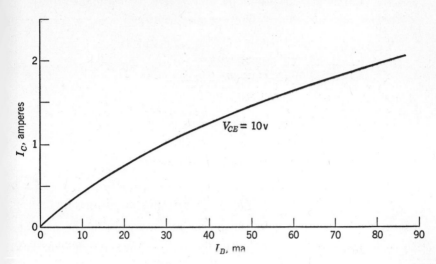

Fig. 4.44   Transistor transfer characteristics

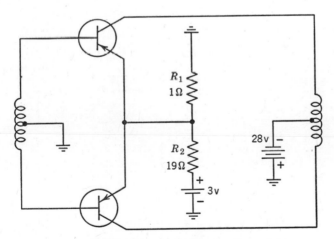

Fig. 4.45   Transformer-coupled class-B amplifier

4.4.4.5 Design of a Class-B Stage with Direct Coupling to the Load

Example Design for the following specifications:

$$
\begin{aligned}
\text{Load power} &= 12.5 \text{ watts} \\
\text{Overload capacity} &= 25\% \\
\text{Supply voltage} &= 28 \text{ volts}
\end{aligned}
$$

The design proceeds as follows:

$$
\begin{aligned}
\text{Power delivered to load} &= 12.5 \text{ watts} \\
\text{Overload capacity} &= 25\%
\end{aligned}
$$

Therefore the stage must be capable of delivering

$$
\begin{aligned}
12.5 \times 1.25 &= 15.6 \text{ watts} \\
&= 7.8 \text{ watts per transistor}
\end{aligned}
$$

Since this is identical with the power requirements of the previous design, the design remains unchanged, but the following differences may be noted.

$$
\text{Maximum inverse voltage} = 28 \text{ volts}
$$

Load resistance is a 50 ohms center-tapped resistance. If a center-tapped loudspeaker is used, the maximum inverse voltage will be slightly in excess of 28 volts.

$$
\text{Full-load } \eta \text{ of the transistor} = 69.9\%
$$

This is also the overall output circuit efficiency. The biasing network may be identical with that for the transformer-coupled stage, or it may take the form shown in Fig. 4.46. Note that the resistive load limits the

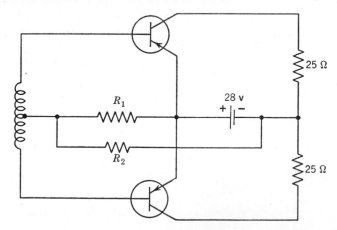

Fig. 4.46　Class-B amplifier with direct-coupling to the load

collector current under all conditions so that it is no longer mandatory to stabilize against thermal runaway. Biasing resistors in the input circuit may be used to eliminate cross-over distortion. An added feature of this bias connection is that a second battery becomes unnecessary.

The peak input impedance in the common-emitter configuration is V_{BE}/I_B = 12 ohms. Then a 30 ohm resistance may be chosen for R_1. If we set the bias voltage at 0.15 volt as before, the bias current is 0.15/30 ampere = 5 ma. Using the supply for the bias circuit, $R_1 + R_2$ = 5600 ohms, whence R_2 = 5570 ohms. Then effective input loss = 5.4 db. Input impedance per transistor, inclusive of the bias resistance, is approximately 42 ohms.

4.5   Driver Stages

Excluding the output stages, the driver operates at a higher level than the other transistor stages. The power that the driver is called upon to deliver to the output stage will often be of such a magnitude that the stage design will follow that of a high-level stage.

In addition to its relatively high power level, the driver is often required to perform the function of phase inversion when it is coupled to a push-pull stage.

A simple method of phase inversion consists in using a transformer with a center-tapped secondary winding. In certain applications the use of a transformer may be inadvisable; RC-coupled phase inverters may be used as an alternative.

Figures 4.47a and b show two forms of RC-coupled phase inverters. In the circuit of Fig. 4.47a, the voltage across R_1 and R_L is identical if R_1 and R_L are made equal. Then the powers delivered to the following stage will be identical if the source impedances are made equal. This may be done either by making R_1 and R_L very small so as to mask the effects of the transistor, or by adding a balancing resistance $R_2 \cong R_L$ as shown. The first method results in a low-impedance drive and the second in a relatively high-impedance drive.

The circuit of Fig. 4.47b consists of two identical stages, with an output taken from each stage. R_2 is used to balance the outputs from the stages, and its loading effect may be ignored. Whereas the source impedances for the two outputs are identical, it is important that there be 180° phase shift through the second transistor. If the power requirements of the phase inverter are severe, this circuit may be preferable since the driving power is shared by the two transistors.

The coupling of phase inverters to push-pull class-A stages may be done in a straightforward manner. With class-B amplifiers, the problem is complicated somewhat by the fact that each stage conducts during only one half of the cycle. It is consequently important that the input diode be part of a closed d-c circuit. This is the case when a transformer drive is used.

With an RC-coupled stage, the rectified component of the input signal builds up a voltage across the coupling capacitor, tending to drive the

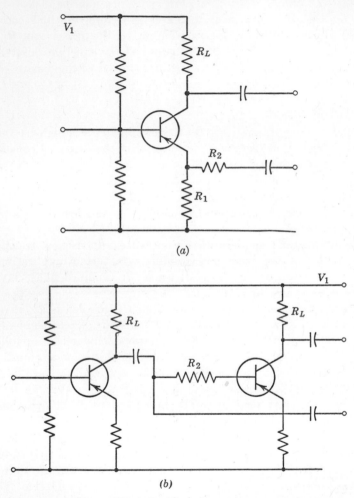

(a)

(b)

Fig. 4.47   Phase inverters

stage into extreme class-C operation. A closed d-c path may be provided for the input diode by the circuit of Fig. 4.48. In this circuit, the emitter diode conducts during one half of the cycle, and its shunt diode during the other half. As a result, the current through the capacitor is

sinusoidal, and the input signal does not cause a voltage build-up
across the capacitor.   Ideally, the forward characteristic of the diode
should be identical with the input characteristic of the transistor in the

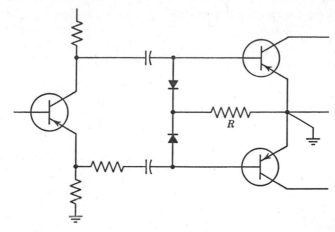

Fig. 4.48   *RC* coupling networks for class-B amplifiers

configuration used.   We may approximate this in practice by the addition of a suitable resistance in series with the diode.   This may take the
form of a common resistor *R*, as shown in Fig. 4.48.   The bias network

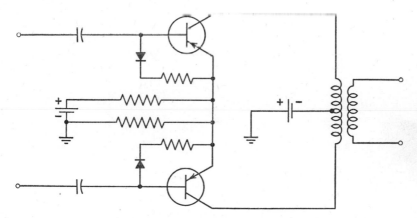

Fig. 4.49   *RC* coupling networks for class-B amplifiers

for the elimination of cross-over distortion may incorporate resistors R_1
and R_2, as in Fig. 4.41a, or may be inserted in the emitter lead, as shown
in Fig. 4.49.

It is important to note that one half of the input power is dissipated in the two shunting diodes, resulting in an effective input-circuit power loss of 3 db.

4.6　Direct-Coupled Circuits

It has been mentioned that transistors operate satisfactorily over a wide range of operating currents and voltages. This, coupled with the fact that both *n-p-n* and *p-n-p* transistors are available, results in the possibility of a large number of direct-coupled configurations.

Direct-coupled circuits allow signal amplification down to direct current. They result in a saving of circuit components and a reduction of both a-c and d-c losses. An additional feature which some of these circuits present is an improvement in the temperature stability due to the nonlinear compensation of one transistor by another.

While many such circuits have been designed,[4,5] a few are of outstanding interest. These are discussed in the following sections.

4.6.1　Complementary Symmetry

The use of *p-n-p* and *n-p-n* transistors in a complementary [4] connection (see Fig. 4.50) affords a simple method of eliminating the need for a separate phase inverter and for a push-pull output transformer. For

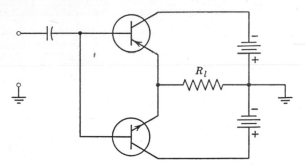

Fig. 4.50　Complementary-symmetry circuit using two transistors

class-B operation, each transistor conducts during only one half of the cycle, the *n-p-n* when the base is driven positive, and the *p-n-p* when the base is driven negative. In this manner, phase inversion is automatically accomplished. Since either one or the other of the transistors is conducting over the entire cycle, the stage may be capacitively coupled as shown, without the necessity for coupling diodes. Furthermore, all of the drive power is utilized, and the losses due to the shunt diodes are avoided.

The parallel connection of the outputs serves to recombine the positive and negative parts to form the whole signal, thus eliminating the need for a push-pull output transformer.

If the above circuit is to operate without transformers, and we impose the further condition that the batteries have one terminal at ground potential in order to supply power to the preceding stages, the transistors can only be operated in the common-collector configuration of Fig. 4.50. It has already been shown that this connection results in the least power gain of any configuration.

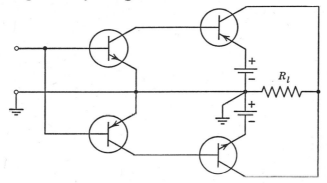

Fig. 4.51   Complementary-symmetry circuit using four transistors

Complementary symmetry circuits may be directly coupled in cascade as shown in Fig. 4.51. In this circuit each side of the push-pull stage is itself in a direct-coupled connection. This connection results in the realization of common-emitter gain in the driver stage.

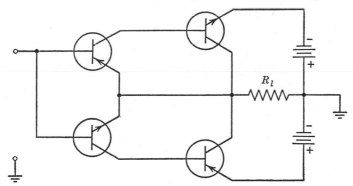

Fig. 4.52   Alternative version of Fig. 4.51

Another variation is shown in Fig. 4.52. In this connection the emitters of the driver stage are tied to the ungrounded end of the load, resulting in a large amount of degeneration.

If the circuits of Figs. 4.50 and 4.51 are used, *the transistors must be accurately matched with respect to their d-c as well as to their a-c parameters.* With the circuit of Fig. 4.52, this is not necessary, because of the large amount of negative feedback. It should be pointed out, however, that this advantage is obtained at the expense of power gain.

4.6.2   Compound Connections

Two transistors may be connected in the compound connection of Fig. 4.53 to obtain a single three-terminal unit. This form of connection was proposed by Darlington[5] for the purpose of obtaining a transistor having a value of α_b very close to unity. If α_{b1} and α_{b2} are the short-

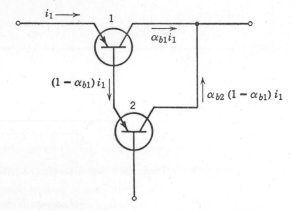

Fig. 4.53   Compound-connected transistors

circuit current-transfer ratios of the individual transistors, and α_b refers to the overall unit, it may be shown that

$$\alpha_b = \alpha_{b1} + \alpha b_2 - \alpha b_1 \alpha b_2 \qquad (4.90)$$

For our typical transistor,

$$h_{21b} = -\alpha_{b1} = -\alpha_{b2} = -0.98 \qquad (4.91)$$

Then $\qquad\qquad\qquad \alpha_b = 0.9996 \qquad\qquad\qquad (4.92)$

With reference to Fig. 4.53 it is seen that the current entering the second transistor is $(1 - \alpha_{b1})$ times the current entering the first transistor. As i_1 is increased, α_{b1} is reduced, and hence more current is diverted to the second transistor. The output current is the sum of the collector currents of the two transistors. The load-sharing properties of this device may be used to advantage in the design of power output stages with extremely low distortion requirements (on the order of $\frac{1}{2}\%$ for a single-ended class-A stage designed for 100% overload capacity).

Figure 4.54 shows the transfer characteristic for the compound connection compared with those for the individual transistors alone.

In general, the transistor that carries the majority of the load will have a higher rating than the other transistor. The function of this

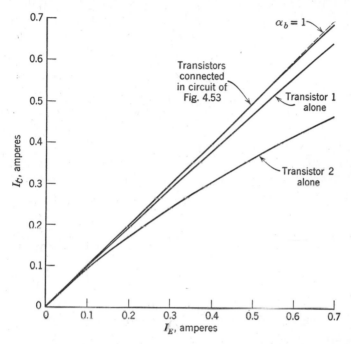

Fig. 4.54 Collector current versus emitter current for compound-connected transistors

other transistor is to supplement the performance of the first unit at high values of collector current.

Figure 4.55 shows a compound-connected amplifier stage in the common-emitter configuration. In this circuit T_2 is used to handle the majority of the load, and T_1 provides additional power during peak conditions. Since α_b for the entire unit is very close to unity, the input impedance of the stage is very high, as much as 100 times as large as that for T_2 alone. The stabilization of such a circuit is excellent, owing to the nonlinear compensation of one stage by the other. Furthermore as a consequence of the inherently large amounts of feedback involved, the circuit is relatively insensitive to changes in transistor parameters.

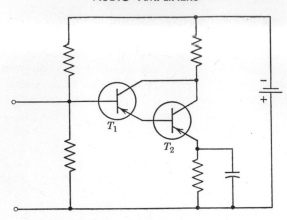

Fig. 4.55   Two-stage compound-connected amplifier

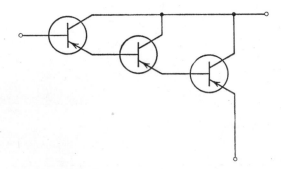

Fig. 4.56   Compound connection using three transistors

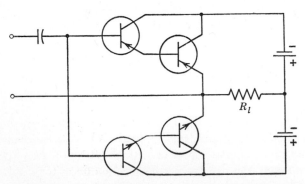

Fig. 4.57   Complementary-symmetry stage using compound-connected transistors

A logical extension of the above circuit is the use of three or more transistors, as in Fig. 4.56.   A further improvement of properties is obtained by the inclusion of this additional transistor.

As a consequence of the advantages of this connection, the stage is ideal for inclusion in a complementary symmetry connection.   Figure 4.57 shows a class-B amplifier stage of this kind.   With this circuit it is unnecessary to match transistors, or to provide for temperature stabilization.

4.6.3   Bridge Circuits

Direct-coupling methods ordinarily require the use of special loudspeakers.   For example, a speaker that is direct-coupled to a single-ended class-A output stage must pass the d-c collector bias current of the output transistor.   This causes the voice coil of a conventional

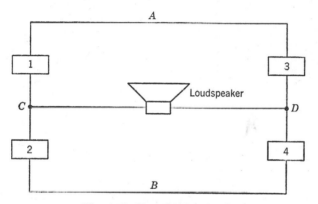

Fig. 4.58   Basic bridge circuit

speaker to be offset from its normal operating position, and distortion of the acoustical output may result.   On the other hand, a center-tapped speaker is used in the direct-coupled push-pull stage.   This type of modification, however, results in a reduction of the electrical-to-acoustical efficiency of the speaker because only one half of the winding is in use for each half-cycle.   These difficulties are largely overcome by the use of bridge circuits.   Figure 4.58 shows the basic bridge arrangement. The bridge is said to be balanced when the direct-voltage drops across the circuit elements 1, 2, 3, and 4 (which may be transistors, batteries or other elements), are such that the d-c potential across the speaker terminals CD is zero, regardless of the d-c supply voltage between A and B.   A change from the balanced condition brought about, for example, by an impedance change in one or more of the circuit elements will result in current flow in the speaker. Transistors may be used in the arms of the bridge to effect such changes, and hence power can be delivered to the loudspeaker load. Since no direct current flows in the load and no special voice-coil tapping arrangements are required, conventional speakers may be used.

Figure 4.59 shows an example of a bridge-connected direct-coupled output stage which employs two p-n-p transistors in the positions of circuit elements 1 and 2 of Fig. 4.58 and batteries in the positions of ele-

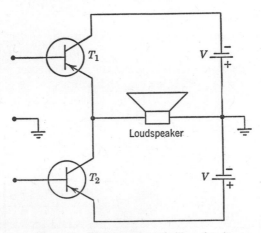

Fig. 4.59   Two-transistor bridge circuit

ments 3 and 4.   Transistor T_1 is operated in the common-collector configuration, whereas T_2 is operated in the common-emitter configuration. Because of the different operating configurations, the input drive signal at the base of T_1 must swing over a larger voltage range than that which drives T_2.   In addition, T_1 must be driven by a signal that is out of phase with that applied to T_2.   This type of input signal can be obtained from the collector and from the emitter of a conventional split-load phase inverter.   The complementary symmetry circuit of Fig. 4.50 is another example of a bridge circuit with two transistors.

Figure 4.60 shows various forms of the four-transistor bridge circuit. Transistors driven from the same phase are connected by dashed lines. It should be noted that the input and output circuits of Fig. 4.60b need not be referred to ground.   This may be of some advantage in certain applications.   The circuit of Fig. 4.60a uses 4 p-n-p transistors, whereas the circuits of Figs. 4.60b and c make use of both n-p-n and p-n-p units. To drive these stages, all that is necessary is that the transistor pair composed of 1 and 4 be driven out of phase with the remaining pair.

This is easily done with the circuits of Figs. 4.60b and c. On the other hand, the circuit of Fig. 4.60a is complicated by the different modes of operation of the transistors. For example, the pair composed of transistors 1 and 4 must be driven such that a large input voltage is fed to the common-collector transistor 1 and at the same time a low input

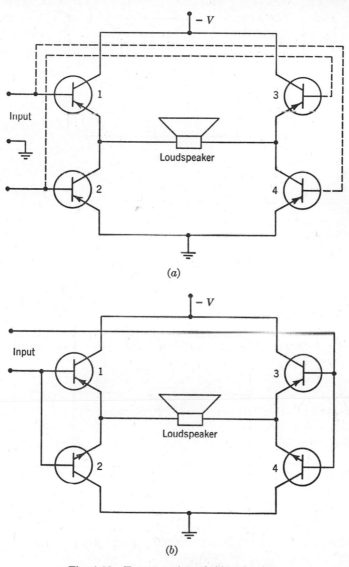

(a)

(b)

Fig. 4.60   Four-transistor bridge circuits

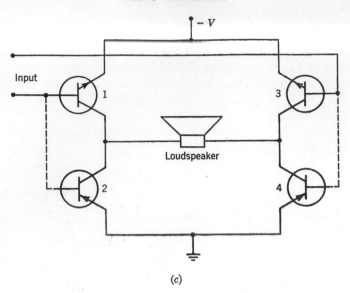

(c)

Fig. 4.60   (continued)

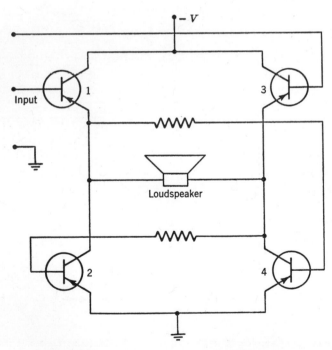

Fig. 4.61   Modified form of circuit of Fig. 4.60a

voltage be available for the common-emitter transistor 4. A multiple-winding transformer can be used to provide the necessary input signal. Figure 4.61 shows a method for simplifying the drive requirements of the circuit of Fig. 4.60a. In this circuit a portion of the output of one member of a transistor pair is used to drive its mate, thereby reducing both the number of inputs and the input power requirements.

Some of the more important characteristics of the circuits of Fig. 4.60 should be emphasized. The output is independent of power-supply ripple to the extent that the load-voltage excursions remain below the minimum instantaneous supply voltage. A single battery supply is used as opposed to a tapped supply or a tapped speaker in the two-transistor output stages. The peak-to-peak output voltage across the load can approach twice the supply voltage as in the transformer case. The maximum voltage the transistors experience, however, is just the supply voltage itself, compared with twice the supply voltage in the transformer case. The circuits are useful for those applications where very high power output is required, since each transistor contributes power to the load and shares the dissipation. Hence, twice the power output of a two-transistor output stage can be realized. It should be noted that the bridge output stages may be operated in class A or in class B. The theoretical efficiencies and transistor power dissipations correspond to those of conventional output stages operated in a similar class.

In the four-transistor bridge circuits it is possible, if desired, to operate only two of the transistors, say 1 and 3, as linear amplifiers and use transistors 2 and 4 as switches to interchange the connection of the power supply to the load. This allows the use of transistors with low dissipation ratings in two of the bridge positions. The circuit of Fig. 4.61 is easily arranged for this form of operation merely by adjusting the driving resistors which are connected to the bases of transistors 2 and 4 so that collector saturation occurs during their conduction periods.

Problems

1. Derive the expression for maximum gain given in eq. 4.13.

2. The chain of stages shown in Fig. 4.8 is terminated in a resistance of 4000 ohms. Compute the input impedance for each of the last three stages. Assume similar stages, no coupling networks, and the common-emitter configuration. Use the parameters given in Table 4.1.

3. Repeat problem 2 for the common-base and common-collector configurations.

4. Redesign the example of Sec. 4.2.2.4 for a temperature variation from 20 to 45° C. Use Fig. 3.1 to obtain the variation of I_{CO} with temperature. Compare

the performance of the two amplifiers. Is it now possible to use a 22-volt supply for the first stage?

5. Design a bass-boost tone control for the amplifier of problem 4. Turnover frequency should be 500 cycles, and 15 db boost is required.

6. Design a push-pull class-A stage with the following specifications:

$$\begin{aligned}
\text{Power output} &= 6 \text{ watts} \\
\text{Transformer } \eta &= 80\% \\
\text{Overload capacity} &= 20\% \\
\text{Supply voltage} &= 12 \text{ volts}
\end{aligned}$$

Use the characteristics of Fig. 4.34.

7. Design a push-pull class-B stage to the specifications of problem 6. A center-tapped loudspeaker is to be used as the load. What is the effect of a power-supply source impedance of one ohm?

Bibliography

1. R. F. Shea, *Transistor Audio Amplifiers*, Wiley, New York, 1955.

2. E. G. Nielsen, "Behavior of Noise Figure in Junction Transistors over Their Useful Frequency Spectrum," Paper presented at IRE–AIEE Transistor Circuit Conference, University of Pennsylvania, February 1956.

3. W. K. Volkers and N. E. Pedersen, "The Hushed Transistor Amplifier," *Proc. Natl. Electronics Conf.*, *11*, 83 (1955).

4. G. C. Sziklai, "Symmetrical Properties of Transistors and Their Applications," *Proc. IRE*, *41*, 717–724 (1953).

5. J. G. Linvill, "A New *RC* Filter Employing Active Elements," *Proc. Natl. Electronics Conf.*, *9*, 342–352 (1953).

Chapter 5

D-C Amplifiers
and Their
Applications

5.1 Introduction

Direct-coupled transistor amplifiers are commonly used for amplification of small d-c signals or signals of very low frequency. Signals of these types are encountered, for example, in instrumentation, digital and analog computers, biology, and medicine.

Direct coupling can also be used in conventional a-c amplifiers as a means of reducing the number of components required per stage and, in some cases, as a means of increasing the stability of bias with variation of temperature.

5.2 Problem of Drift

At the present state of the art, the use of transistors in d-c amplifiers is limited by the considerable drift of the output current. This effect occurs even when no signal is applied at the input of the amplifiers. Since the drift acts as if it were due to input signal variations, it cannot be distinguished from an actual signal.

The drift current in the output of a d-c amplifier stage is due to two sources: transistor parameter variation, which causes the current amplification of each stage to be a function of temperature (see Chapter 2), and the exponential increase in the collector saturation current I_{co}. At high temperatures the drift current is largely the result of changes in I_{co}, whereas at low temperatures the effect of changes in the transistor parameters predominates. However, in a properly designed d-c amplifier the effect of transistor parameter variation, other than I_{co}, may be practically eliminated if the operating point of each stage is adjusted so that it remains in the linear operation range of the transistor as temperature varies. Compensation of that part of the drift current which is due to changes of I_{co} is more difficult. Some nonlinear techniques to achieve this end will be given below.

5.3   Compensating Networks

5.3.1   Use of Temperature-Sensitive Resistors and Diodes

A temperature-sensitive resistance, for example a junction diode biased in the reverse direction, can be used as a means of compensation for the effect of I_{CO} variations and to some extent for the variation of other transistor parameters.[1] Such a diode has a relatively large negative temperature coefficient (approximately 7 to 8% per °C) and may be used as a temperature-sensitive element for the automatic adjustment of the bias of a transistor as shown in Fig. 5.1. By choice of a di-

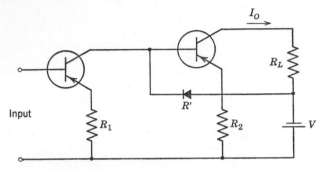

Fig. 5.1   Temperature-compensated amplifier

ode with an appropriate characteristic, the output current of the second stage can be kept constant as the ambient temperature varies.

For great accuracy, the desired compensating characteristic of the element should be determined experimentally for any pair of transistors used in the circuit. One convenient procedure is the following: in the circuit of Fig. 5.1, the reverse-biased diode resistance R' is replaced by a variable resistance. Then, for any given ambient temperature, the value of this resistance is adjusted so that the output current of the amplifier I_O remains constant. The plot of these values of resistance versus temperature will represent the desired characteristic of the temperature-sensitive element. After this curve has been obtained, a suitable diode biased in the reverse direction or some other type of temperature-sensitive resistance (for example a thermistor) can be found to replace the variable resistance. This resistance should have not only the required temperature characteristics but also the same thermal time constant as the transistors used in the circuit. If the last requirement is not satisfied, the chosen resistor will not respond to temperature changes simultaneously with the transistors, and therefore the amplifier will not be compensated during temperature transients.

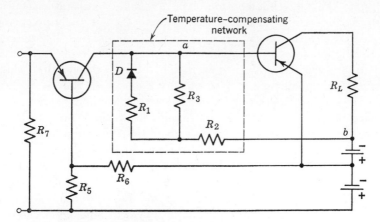

Fig. 5.2   D-c amplifier using temperature-compensation network

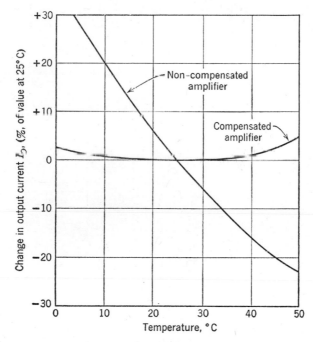

Fig. 5.3   Amplifier performance

Despite the fact that commercially available temperature-sensitive resistors offer a great variety of characteristics, it is usually not possible to select one with exactly the required characteristic. Therefore, in practice, it is necessary to "shape" the characteristic of the available temperature-sensitive elements to match them to the required characteristic. This shaping can be done by connecting the temperature-sensitive element in series or in parallel with other linear resistances or by using more complicated special shaping networks.[2] Such techniques require that the available temperature-sensitive resistor have a larger temperature coefficient than that of the required resistance.

Figure 5.2 shows a two-stage temperature-compensated d-c amplifier employing a junction diode D as a compensating element in conjunction with a shaping network (resistors R_1, R_2, and R_3). Figure 5.3 shows the temperature characteristic of a typical noncompensated amplifier and of a compensated amplifier utilizing the circuit of Fig. 5.2.

5.3.2   Use of an Auxiliary Transistor

In the compensation method described above, the junction diode may be replaced by an auxiliary transistor which acts as a temperature-

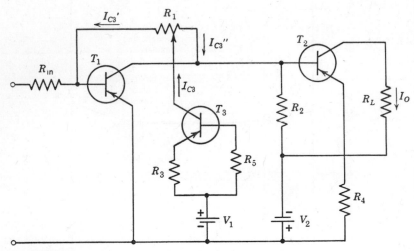

Fig. 5.4   Temperature compensation using an additional transistor

sensitive current generator.[3] This generator injects a cancellation current I_{C3} into the first stage to compensate for the combined effect of I_{CO1} and I_{CO2} of the first and second stages. Figure 5.4 shows the circuit diagram of this arrangement. Since practically all of the transistor parameters vary with temperature, it is desirable to choose values of the resistances external to the transistors to minimize this effect. The analysis of this circuit shows that this requirement can be approached by making

$$R_1 \ll (1/h_{22e})_1 \tag{5.1}$$

$$R_{in} \gg (h_{11e})_1 \tag{5.2}$$

$$R_4 \gg (h_{11b})_2 \tag{5.3}$$

$$R_L + R_4 \ll (1/h_{22e})_2 \tag{5.4}$$

$$R_2 \gg (1/h_{22e})_1 \tag{5.5}$$

In the above expressions the subscripts 1 and 2 refer to the first- and second-stage transistors T_1 and T_2, respectively. Using appropriate values, I_{CO} and the current-amplification factor h_{21e} become the principal temperature-sensitive parameters. To minimize the effect of the variation of the current-amplification factor $(h_{21e})_2$, the ratio R_1/R_4 should be chosen to be approximately one-half $(h_{21e})_2$ to $(h_{21e})_2$. If the ratio of R_1/R_4 is too high, the current amplification will be excessively temperature-sensitive; and, if it is too low, the current-transfer ratio will be too low. For the simplified equivalent circuit for which eqs. 5.1 to 5.5 hold, the current-amplification factor of the amplifier is

$$A_i \cong R_1(h_{21e})_1(h_{21e})_2/R_4\{1 + [(h_{21e})_1 + 1][(h_{21e})_2 + 1]\} \tag{5.6}$$

The choice of the resistors external to the compensation current generator T_3, should be based on the same considerations as for the amplifier stages (eqs. 5.1 to 5.5), in order to minimize the variation of all of the transistor parameters, except I_{CO} and h_{21e}, with temperature.

As can be seen from Fig. 5.4, the compensation current I_{C3} divides in R_1. Part of this current is fed into the input of the first stage as I_{C3}', and part I_{C3}'' goes into the junction of the output of the first stage and the input of the second stage. The division of I_{C3} into I_{C3}' and I_{C3}'' is determined by the position of the potentiometer R_1. If the value of I_{C3} is chosen to be two to four times the value of I_{CO3} of the compensating transistor T_3, then any deviation of I_{CO3} from the assumed average value, due to different transistors being used in that stage, can be easily corrected by adjusting R_1.

The value of I_{C3} is determined by the choice of resistors R_3 and R_5. This value is given by the following approximation:

$$I_{C3} = I_{CO3}(R_3 + R_5)/\{R_3 + R_5/[(h_{21e})_3 + 1]\} \tag{5.7}$$

If R_3 is large compared to $R_5/[(h_{21e})_3 + 1]$, eq. 5.7 may be rewritten as

$$I_{C3} \cong I_{CO3}(R_3 + R_5)/R_3 \tag{5.8}$$

The current I_{C3} is then essentially independent of $(h_{21e})_3$. From this equation it may also be seen that the condition $I_{C3} = 2I_{CO3}$ may be satisfied by making $R_3 = R_5$. The value of R_3 (hence of R_5) is normally chosen as 50 kilohms or higher to prevent the emitter-to-base voltage from becoming a factor which would prevent the use of eqs. 5.7 and 5.8. For the most satisfactory operation of the amplifier the

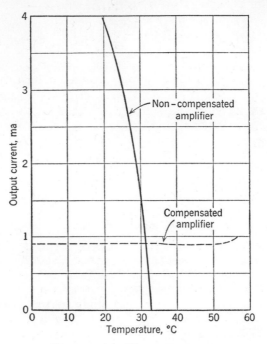

Fig. 5.5   Amplifier performance

saturation current I_{CO3} should be as low as possible, while the value of $(h_{21e})_3$ should be high.

A practical procedure for adjusting the compensating circuit is as follows: (1) measure the output current $(I_O)_1$ and the current-transfer ratio A_i of the overall amplifier without transistor T_3 in the circuit; (2) measure the saturation current I_{CO1} of the transistor used in the first stage; (3) plug in transistor T_3, and adjust potentiometer R_1 so that the output current $(I_O)_2$ satisfies the equation

$$(I_O)_2 = (I_O)_1 + A_i I_{CO1} \qquad (5.9)$$

The following are approximate values for such an amplifier: $R_{in} = 1$ megohm, $R_1 = 60$ kilohms, $R_2 = 20$ kilohms, $R_3 = R_5 = 50$ kilohms, $R_4 = 1$ kilohm, $V_1 = 10$ volts, and $V_2 = 20$ volts. If exact compensation is required at a specific temperature, the ambient temperature may be set to that value and R_1 readjusted to compensate for any change in output current. The drift may be reduced to about 1/20 of its original value by such an adjustment. Figure 5.5 shows the results of temperature compensation obtained from the circuit of Fig. 5.4. Using germanium transistors, a drift of under 1% may be obtained for the compensated amplifier in the temperature range 0 to 50° C. The long-time drift at room temperature will normally not exceed 0.05%, for an amplifier with a sensitivity better than 0.1 μa. It may be expected that the use of silicon transistors in such an amplifier will give better results.

For the operation of d-c amplifiers at higher temperatures, it is recommended that silicon transistors be used, since at these temperatures compensation becomes difficult with germanium transistors. High temperatures may also reduce the life and reliability of germanium transistors.

Transistors used in d-c amplifiers should be of high quality, with small I_{CO} (below 1 μa at 5 volts) and low noise figure (below 8 db at 1000 cps).

5.3.3   Chopping Techniques

For d-c amplifiers operating at very low levels, the problem of eliminating the output drift may be solved by employing a mechanical or electronic chopper. These choppers convert the d-c signal into an a-c signal, which is then amplified by an a-c amplifier giving an a-c output proportional to the input d-c signal. Figure 5.6 shows the circuit of

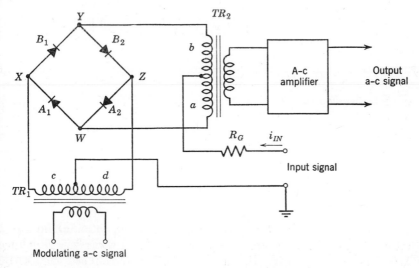

Fig. 5.6   Ring-bridge modulator

one such arrangement, commonly known as a "ring bridge modulator." [4]
This modulator utilizes four silicon diodes in a circuit balanced with respect to input and output. A modulating a-c signal ("reference signal")
is applied through a transformer to the terminals X and Z of the bridge.
Depending on the polarity of the modulating signal, the paths XYZ
and XWZ will alternately become conductive. Consequently a signal
current i_{IN} may accept only one of the paths a or b in transformer TR_2,
depending on the phase of the modulating signal. Whichever path is
open at that instant, the signal current i_{IN} will pass to the terminals
X, Z and windings c and d of transformer TR_1 as two equal components. In transformer TR_1 these components will be in inductive opposition; therefore the signal current i_{IN} will be commutated with respect
to the transformer TR_2, but not with respect to transformer TR_1. If
the diodes were perfect switches the commutation would be perfect,
with no residual voltages or currents being injected into the bridge.
Practical diodes, however, exhibit a small voltage drop when they are
conducting and a finite resistance when they are biased in the nonconducting direction. The net result of this imperfection introduces
an error in the bridge.

The magnitudes of the error current ΔI and the error voltage ΔV
present in the bridge are given approximately as

$$\Delta I = 0.5[(I_{B1} - I_{B2}) \pm (I_{A1} - I_{A2})] \qquad (5.10)$$

$$\Delta V = 0.25[(V_{B1} - V_{B2}) \pm (V_{A1} - V_{A2})] \qquad (5.11)$$

where the alternate signs apply when the diodes A_1 and A_2 (or B_1 and
B_2) are interchanged in position. Such a reversal can be used to minimize the error. The sensitivity of the bridge can be further improved
by applying the modulating signal from a high-impedance source and
tuning the primary winding of the output transformer to resonance at
the modulating frequency to reduce the harmonics. The sensitivity of
such a bridge can be made on the order of 10^{-8} ampere at temperatures
up to $80°$ C.

Figure 5.7 shows another low-level electronic chopper which consists
of two transistors A and B and a transformer, through which a square-
wave switches the transistors on and off. In this arrangement the output a-c signal is proportional to the magnitude of the d-c input. Owing
to the fact that the transistors are not perfect switches, there is a small
residual voltage across the load resistance R_L even when the input signal is zero. This imposes a practical limitation on the minimum signal
that can be amplified. A considerable reduction of this residual voltage
can be achieved by using transistors in inverted connections, i.e. by

using the emitter as collector and collector as emitter.[5,6] The circuit of Fig. 5.7 shows this type of connection.

By using fused junction transistors and a low-impedance signal source and operating with base currents on the order of several milliamperes, a sensitivity exceeding 10^{-6} ampere can be obtained over a relatively wide temperature range.

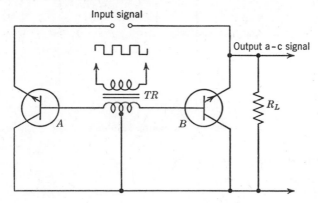

Fig. 5.7   Transistor chopper

5.4 Operational Amplifiers

One of the important applications of d-c amplifiers is in data-processing systems, such as analog computers, data-transmission links, and various automatic-control devices.

These circuits, which employ the d-c amplifier as a basic building block for analog-computing purposes, are generally known as "operational amplifiers." They can be used for summing, integrating, or differentiating analog voltages. The basic requirements in this type of amplifier are large current amplification, considerable feedback throughout the desired frequency band, and stability. Two examples, a summing and an integrating amplifier, are described below.

5.4.1 Summing Amplifiers

Figure 5.8 shows the principle of operation of a summing amplifier. It can be shown that, if R_G includes the input resistance of the amplifier A, then

$$(v_1 - v_G)/R_1 + (v_2 - v_G)/R_2 + \cdots + (v_N - v_G)/R_N$$
$$+ (v_O - v_G)/R_F = v_G/R_G \quad (5.12)$$

where v_1, v_2, $\cdots$, v_N are the signal voltages which are to be added.

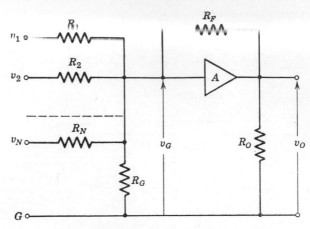

Fig. 5.8   Summing amplifier

From eq. 5.12 follows

$$v_1/R_1 + v_2/R_2 + \cdots + v_N/R_N$$

$$= v_G(1/R_1 + 1/R_2 + \cdots + 1/R_N + 1/R_G + 1/R_F) - v_O/R_F \quad (5.13)$$

If
$$R_1 = R_2 = \cdots = R_N = R_F = R$$

and
$$R_G \gg R$$

then
$$\frac{1}{R} \sum_N v_N \cong -\frac{1}{R}\left(\frac{N+1}{K} + 1\right) v_O \quad (5.14)$$

where K is the unilateral amplification of the amplifier without feedback.

For an amplifier with large K, eq. 5.14 reduces to

$$v_O \cong -\sum_N v_N \quad (5.15)$$

The large amount of negative feedback, commonly used in this type of amplifier, does not eliminate the problem of drift which is normally encountered in transistor d-c amplifier circuits. Consequently, the presence of drift in the output will modify eq. 5.15 as follows:

$$v_O \cong -\sum_N v_N + v_{\text{drift}} \quad (5.16)$$

In order to achieve higher accuracy from a summing amplifier, some compensation should be provided for the drift voltage v_{drift}. Suitable methods of temperature compensation have been described in Sec. 5.3.

An automatic zero-set (AZS) circuit can also be used as a means of drift compensation. Figure 5.9 shows such an arrangement,[7] consisting of a summing amplifier A and a relatively drift-free narrow-band d-c amplifier A'. The N input voltages and the output voltage v_O are ap-

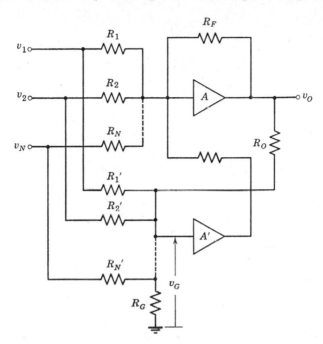

Fig. 5.9 Automatic zero-set arrangement

plied to a resistance summing network composed of resistors R_O, R_1', R_2', $\cdots$, R_N'.

If R_G is chosen such that

$$R_G \ll R_O, R_1', R_2', \cdots, R_N'$$

and $$R_O R_1, R_O R_2, \cdots, R_O R_N = R_F R_1', R_F R_2', \cdots, R_F R_N'$$

then the voltage across R_G will be

$$v_G \cong (R_G/R_O)v_{\text{drift}} \tag{5.17}$$

The voltage v_G is amplified by amplifier A' and is returned as a drift-corrective voltage to the input of the amplifier A. By proper choice of the gain of amplifier A', the drift voltage at the output of the summing amplifier A can be made negligible.

5.4.2 Integrating Amplifiers

Figure 5.10 shows a block diagram of an integrating amplifier. The relationship between the output and input voltages of the integrator can be expressed as

$$v_O = - (1/RC) \int_0^t v_I \, dt \qquad (5.18)$$

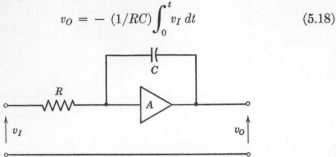

Fig. 5.10   Integrating amplifier

The basic requirements for an integrating amplifier are a large open-loop current amplification and a 180° phase reversal, which can be conveniently achieved by using an odd number of transistor amplifier stages in the common-emitter connection. In general, the number of stages, however, is restricted by the bandwidth and stability require-

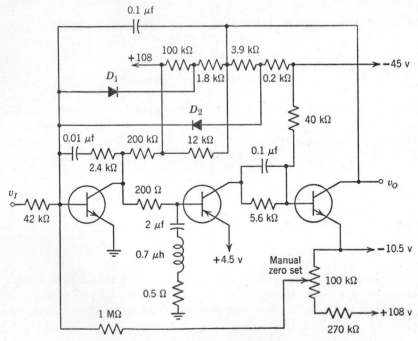

Fig. 5.11   Integrating amplifier

ments. Therefore, in each case, a compromise should be reached between gain, stability and bandwidth.

Figure 5.11 shows the circuit diagram of an integrating amplifier.[7] The silicon diodes D_1 and D_2 in this circuit prevent the integrator from overloading. Within a certain output voltage range, these diodes are biased in the reverse direction. If the output voltage does not fall within this range, one of the diodes starts conducting, and the integrator becomes a d-c amplifier with a voltage attenuation of approximately 10:1. The diodes should have very large reverse resistances and very small shunt capacitances.

Here again, as in the case of the summing amplifier, the problem of drift may be very serious. An automatic zero-set circuit can be used to compensate for this drift.

5.5 Some Other Applications of D-C Amplifiers

5.5.1 Difference Amplifiers

Figure 5.12 is a block diagram showing one possible difference amplifier arrangement. It can be shown that for this circuit

$$v_O \cong K(v_1 - v_2) \tag{5.19}$$

where v_1 and v_2 are two input signal voltages and K a constant which depends on the gain of the transistors used in the circuit.

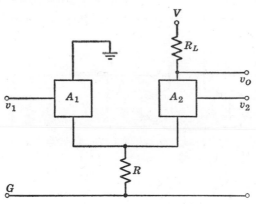

Fig. 5.12 Difference amplifier

Due to the common-mode effect,* there is a small voltage Δv present across R_L when $v_1 = v_2$. However, this voltage ordinarily introduces an error of only about 1% or less.

---

* The common-mode effect is usually defined as the ratio of the signal voltage Δv present across R_L when $v_1 = v_2$ to the voltage that appears across R_L when either v_1 or v_2 alone is zero.[9]

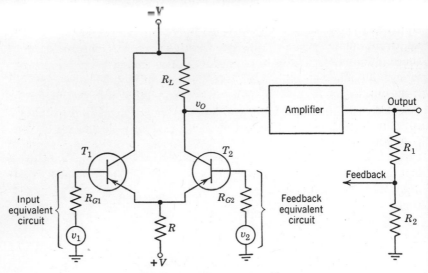

Fig. 5.13   Difference amplifier

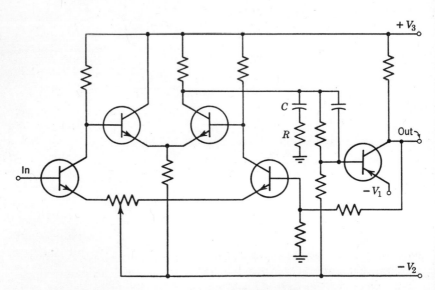

Fig. 5.14   Stabilized D-C amplifier

A difference amplifier can be used as a means of stabilizing the output and input impedances of a d-c amplifier, as well as for reducing the equivalent input drift. Figure 5.13 shows the basic principle of such an arrangement, where the difference amplifier is used as a first stage of the d-c amplifier. If the characteristics of both transistors of the difference amplifier are properly matched, the variations of their parameters due to temperature changes will practically cancel. Figure 5.14 shows a circuit using silicon transistors and employing difference circuits in the first and second stages of the d-c amplifier.[10]

A long-time stability of a few millivolts may be obtained with this type of amplifier. This stability is usually given in terms of "equivalent input drift," that is, that voltage which must be applied to the input of the amplifier to return the output to the "zero-signal" conditions.

5.5.2   Derivative Amplifiers

A d-c amplifier can be used in conjunction with an RC network to obtain a derivative amplifier. A block diagram of such an arrangement is shown in Fig. 5.15. Voltage v_I, which is to be differentiated, is ap-

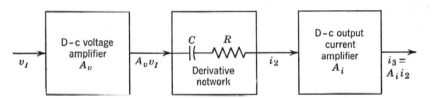

Fig. 5.15   Derivative amplifier

plied to an isolation amplifier which multiplies v_I by A_v, the voltage amplification of the isolation amplifier. The output of the isolation amplifier is then applied to an RC derivative network which supplies a current i_2 to the output d-c amplifier. The current i_2 is proportional to the derivative of the input voltage v_I over a limited but adequate range. If the value of R is made much larger than the terminating impedance of the d-c amplifier, the operation of the derivative network will be determined by the R and C of the derivative network. Thus a value of R on the order of 10 kilohms or higher will normally be sufficient for proper operation, since the input impedance of d-c amplifiers is usually 1 kilohm or less.

For some applications, a linear d-c output amplifier can be combined with a difference amplifier in order to facilitate calibration and allow zero adjustment for a constant input. In addition, the difference output stage normally provides greater stability and better linearity than an unbalanced output.

5.5.3 Logarithmic Amplifiers

A simple logarithmic circuit using a semiconductor diode is shown in Fig. 5.16 and its equivalent circuit in Fig. 5.17. The value of voltage v_J across the ideal diode is given by the equation

$$v_J = (kT/q) \ln [(i_D - I_S)/I_S] \tag{5.20}$$

where k is Boltzmann's constant, T is the absolute temperature, q is

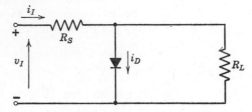

Fig. 5.16   Logarithmic network

the electronic charge, I_S is the diode saturation current, and i_D is the current flowing through the diode.

The actual voltage across the diode will be larger by the amount of the ohmic voltage drop $i_D R_D$. Equation 5.20 may be written to in-

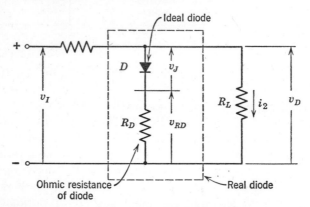

Fig. 5.17   Logarithmic network

clude the ohmic voltage drop and obtain an expression for the voltage v_D across the actual diode.

$$v_D = (kT/q) \ln [(i_D - I_S)/I_S] + i_D R_D \tag{5.21}$$

From this equation it may be seen that a logarithmic range may be obtained when i_D is much larger than I_S and when $i_D R_D$ is small compared to v_D. Furthermore, the value of the load resistance R_L must not be too small.

Figure 5.18 shows the block diagram of such a logarithmic amplifier, where a silicon diode could be used as the logarithmic element, followed

$$i_2 = k \log i_I + C$$

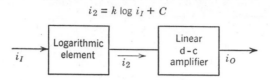

Fig. 5.18   Logarithmic amplifier

by a compensated linear d-c amplifier. The stability of the d-c amplifier must be very high. For example, the maximum output current of the logarithmic element may be only a few microamperes, and the minimum output current may be 0.1 μa. This requires a d-c amplifier

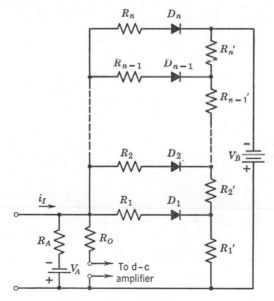

Fig. 5.19   Logarithmic network

with a long-term stability of at least one order of magnitude higher, i.e. an equivalent input drift current less than 0.01 μa.

The primary disadvantage of using semiconductor diodes as logarithmic elements is that nearly all of the diode properties are very tem-

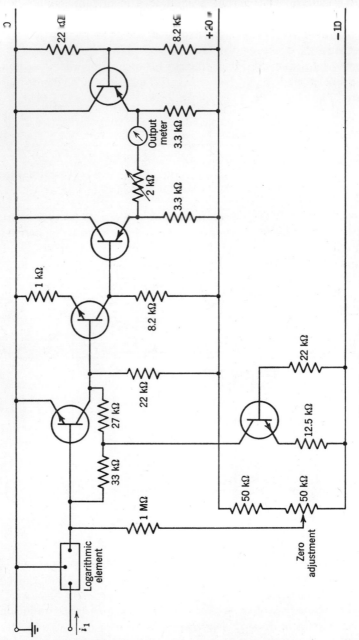

Fig. 5.20 Logarithmic meter amplifier

perature-sensitive. To obtain a true logarithmic characteristic, the ohmic voltage drop $i_D R_D$ must be canceled, and compensation is required for the effect of the variation of the saturation current I_S. This may be done by a compensating network; however, kT/q, the saturation current I_S, and the diode ohmic resistance R_D will change with temperature.

Figure 5.19 shows the schematic diagram of a circuit which may be used to obtain a more accurate logarithmic relationship. In this circuit the logarithmic characteristic is obtained by successive approximations. Initially all of the diodes, D_1 through D_n, are biased in the reverse direction, and therefore act as open switches. Since R_A is chosen to be much higher than R_O, the input resistance is simply R_O, and the input current i_I flows through R_O to the transistorized d-c amplifier. As the input current is increased, the diodes successively switch resistors R_1 through R_n into the circuit to shunt an increasingly larger portion of the current i_I. In this manner, a broken-line approximation is made to the desired logarithmic characteristic. The number of approximations used will depend upon the range and the accuracy desired; a detailed design procedure may be found in the literature.[11, 12]

Figure 5.20 shows a complete diagram of the logarithmic meter amplifier which includes the above-mentioned logarithmic circuit, a linear d-c amplifier, and a difference amplifier.

Though the stability of such a logarithmic amplifier with time is good, the temperature dependence will limit the ultimate sensitivity. For example, in the amplifier described above, the low range of input current is limited to approximately 10^{-0} ampere, when the ambient temperature range is 0 to 50° C.

5.5.4 Transistorized D-C Microammeter

Another useful application of d-c amplifiers is in the instrumentation field where they can be employed to increase the sensitivity of small d-c meters. The sensitivity of a standard 20 μa meter, which requires about 0.8 μw for full-scale deflection, can be easily increased by 20 db, using one transistor stage and a single miniature battery cell. The entire package can then be made small enough to be mounted behind or inside the meter case.[13]

Figure 5.21 shows the diagram of a balanced circuit which increases the sensitivity of the meter at least 40 times. In view of the large temperature coefficient of transistors, they should be matched carefully to minimize the residual zero drift over the desired temperature range. It should be pointed out, however, that it may be difficult to obtain a pair of completely identical transistors. Therefore, some residual zero

drift will always be present but can usually be made insignificant in a
well balanced circuit. The balance should be checked by short circuit
ing the input terminals (base-to-base). This should not cause any ap-

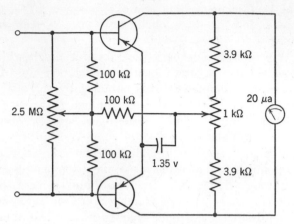

Fig. 5.21   Meter circuit

preciable zero shift. The circuit of Fig. 5.21 has an overall sensitivity
of 0.5 μa full scale compared to 20 μa for the meter itself.

Problems

1. In the circuit diagram shown in Fig. 5.2, assume that $R_7 = \infty$; $R_5 = R_6 = 0$;
$R_L = 100$ ohms, and the total external d-c resistance between points a and b, R',
is 6000 ohms at $T = 30°$ C. Assume also that both transistors are identical and
their collector currents are $I_{C1} = 0.5$ ma and $I_{C2} = 3$ ma, respectively. Using typical values of the transistor parameters (Table 4.1) and curves showing the variations of transistor parameters with temperature (Chapter 2), estimate approximately
what should be the value of R' at 40° and 50° C, in order to maintain the output
current of the second transistor unchanged. Consider the variations of I_{CO} with
temperature only.

2. Verify analytically the conditions 5.1, 5.2, 5.3, 5.4, and 5.5 under which variations of transistor parameters, with the exception of I_{CO} and h_{21e}, have minimum
effect on the stability of the amplifier shown in Fig. 5.4.

3. Derive the voltage amplification $v_O/v_2 = -v_O/v_1$ in terms of transistor parameters for the amplifier shown in Fig. 5.12. Assume $R_L \ll 1/h_{22e}$.

Bibliography

1. E. Keonjian, "Temperature-Compensated D-C Transistor Amplifier," *Proc.
IRE, 42,* 661–671 (1954).

2. E. Keonjian and J. S. Schaffner, "Shaping of the Characteristics of Temperature-Sensitive Elements, *Commun. & Electronics,* 14, 396–400 (Sept. 1954).

3. J. W. Stanton, "A Transistorized D-C Amplifier," *IRE Trans.*, *CT-3*, 65 (1956).

4. N. F. Moody, "A Silicon Junction Diode Modulator of 10^{-8} Ampere Sensitivity for Use in Junction Transistor Direct-Current Amplifiers," *Proc. Natl. Electronics Conf.*, *11*, 441–454 (1955).

5. R. L. Bright, "Junction Transistors Used as Switches," *Commun. & Electronics*, 17, 111–121 (March 1955).

6. A. P. Kruper, "Switching Transistors Used as a Substitute for Mechanical Low-Level Choppers," *Commun. & Electronics*, 17, 141–144 (March 1955).

7. F. H. Blecher, "Transistor Circuits for Analog and Digital Systems," *Bell System Tech. J.*, *35*, 295–332 (1956).

8. F. H. Blecher, "A Transistor Voltage Encoder," dissertation for D.E.E. degree, Polytechnic Institute of Brooklyn, 1955.

9. G. E. Valley and H. Wallman, *Vacuum Tube Amplifiers*, p. 443, McGraw-Hill, New York, 1948.

10. D. W. Slaughter, "Feedback-Stabilized Transistor Amplifier," *Electronics*, *28*, 174–175 (May 1955).

11. H. Goldberg and S. L. Fagen, "Notes on Logarithmic Network Design," *Natl. Conf. Proc. Aeronaut. Electronics*, Dayton, Ohio, 585–597 (1956).

12. T. P. Sylvan, "Logarithmic Attenuators Using Silicon Junction Diodes," *IRE Trans.*, *CT-3*, 69–70 (1956).

13. H. F. Starke, "The Transistor D-C Amplifier," *Radio & TV News*, *48*, 82–83 (December 1953).

Chapter 6

Tuned Amplifiers

6.1 Introduction

The function of tuned amplifiers is to amplify signals in a selected range of frequencies and to suppress signals whose frequency components fall outside the desired band. Frequency selection is achieved by appropriate *selective coupling networks*.

A tuned amplifier is characterized by its gain and by the nature of its gain-versus-frequency curve. In many cases the exact shape of the band-pass characteristic is not too important and the desired frequency response is specified by the *bandwidth*. In other instances the band-pass characteristic is specified more precisely by requiring prescribed relative responses at a larger number of frequencies. The number of amplifier stages that must be used and the required complexity of the interstage-coupling networks employed depend on the gain and selectivity specifications of the amplifier.

Most tuned amplifiers belong to the *narrow-band* type, the bandwidth being a small fraction of the center frequency. This chapter is concerned mainly with such amplifiers. The design of a *wide-band* amplifier often requires individual treatment and may involve more complications than narrow-band amplifiers.

6.2 Design of Narrow-Band Amplifier Stages

6.2.1 Approximations and Assumptions

In dealing with narrow-band amplifiers, design procedures can be simplified considerably by several convenient approximations.

The input and output impedances (or admittances) of transistor amplifiers are functions of the load and source impedances (or admittances), respectively. For tuned amplifiers, the impedances *reflected* by load and source to input and output, respectively, are rather involved functions of frequency. Taking these reflected impedances into account would complicate the design procedure considerably. Therefore, in this

160

section, their effect is neglected.   It will be assumed that input and output impedances of the transistor are independent of load and source impedances.   This approximation yields simple and in many instances reasonably accurate design methods, and is justified in dealing with neutralized circuits or amplifiers where internal transistor feedback is not excessive.   It should, however, be remembered that sometimes the effect of the reflected impedances may be important.   These effects will be described in Sec. 6.5.

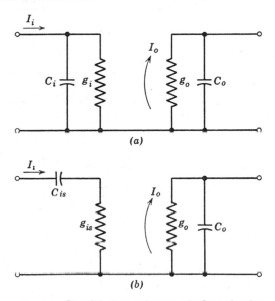

Fig. 6.1   Simplified transistor equivalent circuits

Furthermore, in discussing narrow-band amplifiers, we shall assume that both the input and the output impedances of a transistor can be approximated by parallel or series connections of frequency-independent resistances and capacitances.*   In reality, as has been shown in Chapter 2, the frequency response of these impedances is too complicated to be represented by such simple networks.   In fact, in the common-base stage, the input impedance is inductive.   However, for narrow-band amplifiers, the assumption of RC networks is admissible.   The inductive component of the common-base input impedance can, as a first approximation, be represented as a negative capacitance.

* The parallel representation is used generally.   In some instances, however, the series representation of the input impedance is more useful (see Sec. 6.2.3.3).   The parallel connection can be transformed to the equivalent series connection at the same frequency.   The transformation is valid within a narrow frequency range.

These assumptions allow a representation of the transistor by the approximate equivalent circuits of Fig. 6.1. The symbols used have the following significance: g_i is the input conductance, g_o is the output conductance, C_i is the input capacitance, C_o is the output capacitance, I_i is the input current, I_o is the short-circuit output current, and $I_o = h_{21}I_i$, where all quantities pertain to the particular transistor configuration being considered.

In computations dealing with networks containing both inductances and capacitances, one often encounters the expression $(f/f_0 - f_0/f)$,

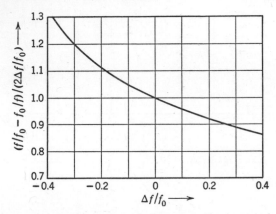

Fig. 6.2   Correction of error involved in approximation 6.1

where f_0 is the center frequency of the pass band. For the narrow-band case, the frequencies considered are close to f_0 and, designating $\Delta f = (f - f_0)$, we can write

$$f/f_0 - f_0/f \cong 2\Delta f/f_0 \qquad (6.1)$$

This approximation will be used throughout the following computations. The error involved is small as long as the fraction $2\Delta f/f_0$ is small as illustrated by Fig. 6.2.

6.2.2   Function of Interstage-Coupling Networks

The coupling network must perform the following basic functions: (a) provide the required band-pass characteristic, and (b) provide good power transfer from the driving stage to the driven stage.

Depending on the complexity of the coupling network to be used, certain conditions will be imposed upon the band-pass characteristic. For the present it will be assumed that we deal with symmetrical *

---

* The symmetry is usually geometrical symmetry; however, with approximation 6.1, the symmetry becomes arithmetical.

pass bands and that the required frequency-selective properties are specified principally by the bandwidth. The bandwidth B_n is defined as the interval between two frequencies at which the power response is $1/(n + 1)$ times the response at the center of the band. Thus, if $n = 1$, the bandwidth B_1 is the interval between frequencies at which the power transferred by the coupling network is one half of the power passed at the center frequency. In other instances the design problem may call for, say, $n = 3$. The choice of $n = 1$ corresponds to the 3-db bandwidth, while $n = 3$ corresponds to the 6-db bandwidth. The choice of n is dictated by the requirements of the particular application to be considered. The *fractional bandwidth* B_n' (normalized bandwidth) is defined as $B_n' = B_n/f_0$.

Good power transfer from driving stage to driven stage is an essential requirement in transistor amplifiers. This can be achieved by designing the coupling networks to have low ohmic losses and to provide proper impedance matching between successive stages.

In designing a tuned amplifier stage, the given quantities are usually the center frequency, the desired bandwidth (defined in terms of n) and the realizable values of Q for the various inductances to be used. The problem is to find the values of inductances and capacitances maximizing the power-transfer efficiency.

6.2.3 Amplifier Stages Using Single-Tuned Networks

6.2.3.1 Coupling-Network Configurations

If the coupling network consists of a single resonant circuit, there are four ways in which the driving and driven stages (T_1 and T_2, respectively) can be connected to the resonant circuit. The four arrange-

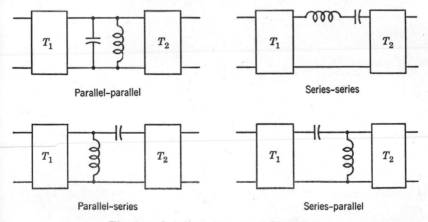

Parallel-parallel   Series-series

Parallel–series   Series-parallel

Fig. 6.3   Coupling-network configurations

ments are shown in Fig. 6.3. They are designated as the *parallel-parallel*, *series-series*, *parallel-series*, and *series-parallel* configurations For the moment we can assume that impedance matching is provided by "ideal transformers" inserted between the coupling network and one or the other of the associated transistor stages, as shown in Fig. 6.4.

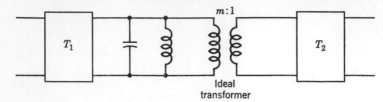

Fig. 6.4 Parallel-parallel coupling network with ideal transformer for impedance matching

With junction transistors the parallel-parallel and parallel-series arrangements are generally used. The series-series and series-parallel circuits lead to inconvenient inductance and capacitance values and to difficulties of impedance matching and are seldom used in junction transistor circuits.

6.2.3.2 Parallel-Parallel Coupling Networks [1]

The circuits of Fig. 6.5 are practical equivalents of the arrangement shown in Fig. 6.4. They differ from each other only by the fact that

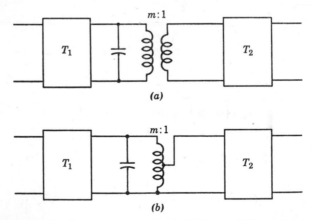

Fig. 6.5 Practical coupling networks of the parallel-parallel type

Fig. 6.5*a* makes use of a two-winding transformer, whereas Fig. 6.5*b* employs an autotransformer. In both cases the coupling coefficient between the windings must be close to unity.

Their equivalent circuits are shown in Fig. 6.6. Transistor T_1 is replaced by a current source I_{o1}, output conductance g_{o1} and output capacitance C_{o1}, while the input conductance g_{i2} and the input capacitance

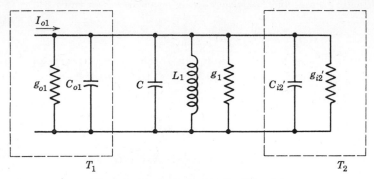

Fig. 6.6   Equivalent circuit of Fig. 6.5

C_{i2} of transistor T_2 are reduced to the admittance level of the transformer primary winding:

$$g_{i2}' = g_{i2}/m^2 \qquad (6.2)$$

$$C_{i2}' = C_{i2}/m^2 \qquad (6.3)$$

where m is the transformer turns ratio. g_1 is the equivalent parallel loss conductance of the primary inductance L_1, defined by

$$g_1 = 1/2\pi f_0 L_1 Q_0 \qquad (6.4)$$

where f_0 is the center frequency of the tuned amplifier and Q_0 is the "unloaded" Q of the transformer primary winding.

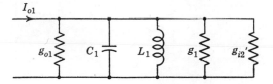

Fig. 6.7   Simplified equivalent circuit of Fig. 6.5

Lumping the capacitances together, we can define

$$C_1 = C_{o1} + C + C_{i2}' \qquad (6.5)$$

and the circuit of Fig. 6.6 can be reduced to that of Fig. 6.7.

The power available from T_1 is

$$P_1 = |I_{o1}|^2/4g_{o1} \qquad (6.6)$$

At f_0, the power delivered to T_2 is

$$P_2 = |I_{o1}|^2 y_{i2}'/(g_{o1} + g_{i2}' + g_1)^2 \tag{6.7}$$

We can now define the *power-transfer efficiency* as the ratio of P_2 to P_1:

$$\eta = P_2/P_1 = 4g_{o1}g_{i2}'/(g_{o1} + g_{i2}' + g_1)^2 \tag{6.8}$$

Equation 6.8 shows that, in order for η to be 1 (corresponding to 100% power transfer), g_{i2}' must be equal to g_{o1} (matched impedances), and the coil loss conductance g_1 must be zero.

Using the definition of the fractional bandwidth B_n' given under 6.2.2 and approximation 6.1, it can be shown that

$$B_n' = (g_{o1} + g_{i2}' + g_1)\sqrt{n}/Q_0 g_1 \tag{6.9}$$

Obtaining g_1 from eq. 6.9 and substituting into eq. 6.8, η is found as a function of g_{o1} and g_{i2}'. Equating $d\eta/dg_{i2}'$ to zero, we find the maximum power-transfer efficiency:

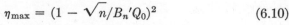

$$\eta_{max} = (1 - \sqrt{n}/B_n'Q_0)^2 \tag{6.10}$$

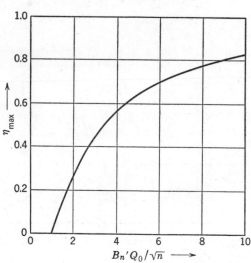

Fig. 6.8 η_{max} as a function of $B_n'Q_0/\sqrt{n}$

Equation 6.10 (and its graphical representation in Fig. 6.8) shows that, for a given n, the maximum realizable power-transfer efficiency is large if Q_0 and B_n' are large. B_n' is usually part of the amplifier specification and cannot be raised arbitrarily. Therefore, good power-transfer efficiency and narrow bandwidth are potentially conflicting requirements.   The power-transfer efficiency can be raised by increasing Q_0, but this is possible only to a certain extent, owing to evident physical limitations.

η_{max} is realized for $g_{o1} = g_{i2}'$, i.e. for

$$m^2 = g_{i2}/g_{o1} \qquad (6.11)$$

Equation 6.11 gives the desired transformer turns ratio.   The desired value of the primary inductance L_1 is

$$L_1 = 1/2\pi f_0 Q_0 g_1 = (B_n'Q_0 - \sqrt{n})/4\pi f_0 Q_0 g_{o1}\sqrt{n} \qquad (6.12)$$

The resulting value of L_1 is often too small to be realized with the desired high value of Q_0.   The effective Q_0 can be increased by using

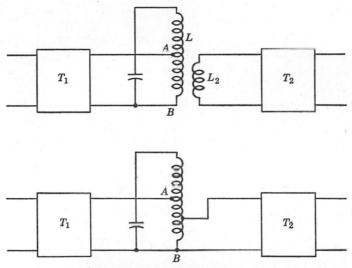

Fig. 6.9   Use of large tapped inductances to improve Q_0

the arrangements of Fig. 6.9.   The calculated value of L_1 then designates the portion of the primary inductance between points A and B. The total primary inductance can be many times L_1 and can usually be obtained with a satisfactory Q_0.

In certain gain-controlled amplifiers (see Chapter 11) which utilize variations of operating point, the conductive and susceptive components of transistor admittances are functions of the gain (i.e. functions of the d-c operating point).   This results in a shift of the center frequency of the amplifier and in a variation of the bandwidth as the gain changes.   These effects are undesirable and can be minimized by suitable mismatch. In such amplifiers g_{o1} and g_{i2}' are made unequal:

$$g_{i2}' - kg_{o1} \tag{6.13}$$

where $k \neq 1$ and its value is determined by imposing limits upon the permissible center frequency and bandwidth variations. Making $k \neq 1$ results in η being smaller than η_{max}:

$$\eta_{mismatched} = [4k/(1 + k)^2]\eta_{max} \tag{6.14}$$

It should be emphasized that the discussion of this section is based on the assumption that the coupling coefficient between the various portions of the transformer is close to 1. In many applications tight coupling as well as high Q_0 can be achieved by the use of ferrite cores or by embedding the transformer or inductance windings in ferrite cups.

The following example illustrates the design of a parallel-parallel coupling network:

Problem. Design a single-tuned parallel-parallel network to couple a common-emitter stage ($g_{i2} = 10^{-3}$ mho, $C_{i2} = 800$ $\mu\mu$f) to a preceding common-emitter stage ($g_{o1} = 10^{-4}$ mho, $C_{o1} = 10$ $\mu\mu$f). The center frequency is 260 kc, the required 6-db bandwidth is 10 kc. The loss in the coupling network must not exceed 3 db.

Solution. Since the bandwidth is specified at 6 db, we have $n = 3$. A loss not exceeding 3 db calls for $\eta_{max} \geq 0.5$.

From eq. 6.10 we have

$$Q_0 = \sqrt{n}/B_3'(1 - \sqrt{\eta}) = \sqrt{3}/0.039(1 - \sqrt{0.5}) \cong 150$$

The primary inductance can be obtained from eq. 6.12:

$$L_1 = (0.039 \times 150 - \sqrt{3})/(4\pi \times 2.6 \times 10^5 \times 150 \times 10^{-4}\sqrt{3}) \cong 48 \ \mu h$$

From eq. 6.11 we find the square of the turns ratio $m^2 = 10$, and consequently

$$L_2 = L_1/m^2 \cong 4.8 \ \mu h$$

The required total capacitance is

$$C_1 = 1/4\pi^2 f_0^2 L_1 \cong 7800 \ \mu\mu f$$

and $\quad C = C_1 - C_{o1} - C_{i2}/m^2 = 7800 - 10 - 80 \cong 7700 \ \mu\mu f$

This shows that the effect of transistor capacitances is negligible in this problem.

The required high value of Q_0 can be realized conveniently if we use larger inductance values, as shown in Fig. 6.9. Using such an arrangement, the total inductance L may be 480 μh, the portion between A and B being L_1. Then, the tuning capacitance is 770 $\mu\mu$f.

6.2.3.3 Parallel-Series Coupling Networks

Using parallel-parallel tuned circuits at high frequencies, especially in the case of cascaded common-base stages, the required number of

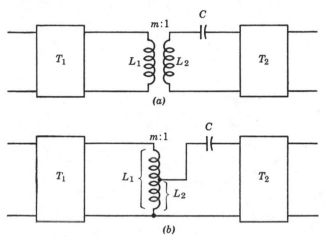

(a)

(b)

Fig. 6.10   Parallel-series coupled stages

secondary turns may be very small, and good coupling between primary and secondary windings is difficult to achieve. In such situations the parallel series arrangement is often preferable to the parallel-parallel configuration.

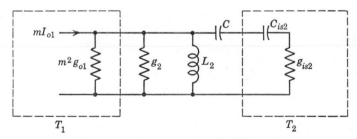

Fig. 6.11   Equivalent circuit of Fig. 6.10

Practical realizations of this configuration are shown in Fig. 6.10. Again, it is assumed that the coupling coefficient between transformer windings is close to unity. The circuits of Fig. 6.10 can be represented by the equivalent of Fig. 6.11, where all admittances are reduced to

the admittance level of the transformer secondary winding. To sim-
plify the calculations, the input admittance of T_2 is represented as a
conductance g_{is2} *in series* with a capacitance C_{is2} and the output capacitance C_{o1} of T_1 is neglected. This is permissible as long as the
bandwidth is sufficiently narrow and C_{o1} small. g_2 is the equivalent
parallel loss conductance of L_2.

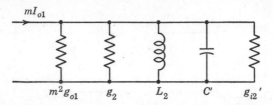

Fig. 6.12   Approximate equivalent circuit of Fig. 6.11

The series connection of C, C_{is2}, and g_{is2} can be replaced by an equivalent parallel connection of C' and g_{i2}' (see Fig. 6.12) with

$$C' \cong CC_{is2}/(C + C_{is2}) \tag{6.15}$$

$$g_{i2}' \cong 4\pi^2 f_0^2 C'^2/g_{is2} \cong 1/4\pi^2 f_0^2 L_2^2 g_{is2} \tag{6.16}$$

The fractional bandwidth B_n' is

$$B_n' = (m^2 g_{o1} + g_{i2}' + g_2)\sqrt{n}/Q_0 g_2 \tag{6.17}$$

The power-transfer efficiency is

$$\eta = 4m^2 g_{o1} g_{i2}'/(m^2 g_{o1} + g_{i2}' + g_2)^2 \tag{6.18}$$

Obtaining $m^2 g_{o1}$ from 6.17, substituting into eq. 6.18, and setting
$d\eta/dg_2 = 0$, we find that maximum power-transfer efficiency occurs for

$$g_2 = (B_n' Q_0 - \sqrt{n})g_{is2}/2\sqrt{n}\, Q_0^2 \tag{6.19}$$

This leads to the desired value of L_2

$$L_2 = (Q_0 \sqrt{n}/\pi f_0 g_{is2})/(B_n' Q_0 - \sqrt{n}) \tag{6.20}$$

The required transformer turns ratio is

$$m^2 = g_{is2}(B_n' Q_0 - \sqrt{n})^2/4nQ_0^2 g_{o1} \tag{6.21}$$

The maximum power-transfer efficiency $\eta_{\max}$ is the same as in the
parallel-parallel case, and is given by eq. 6.10. (It can, in fact, be
shown that eq. 6.10 applies to the single-tuned narrow-band case in

general.)   Consequently, the comments made there regarding the parallel-parallel case are applicable here as well.

Comparing the parallel-parallel and parallel-series configurations, one can state that both are equally useful in many narrow-band amplifiers having a fixed center frequency.   Their performance will, however, be different at frequencies remote from the center of the band, where the narrow-band approximation does not hold.   Also, as has been mentioned above, the parallel-series arrangement may be superior at high frequencies for cascaded common-base stages, where the parallel-parallel circuit requires very small secondary inductances.   Furthermore, in gain-controlled amplifiers,[2] where transistor admittances vary with the d-c operating point, the behavior of the parallel-series configuration differs from that of the parallel-parallel circuit considerably.   If the input conductance of T_2 increases in the circuits of Fig. 6.9, the bandwidth increases too.   On the other hand, an increase of the input conductance of T_2 in the circuits of Fig. 6.10 results in a decreased bandwidth.

The behavior of the parallel-series circuit also differs from that of the parallel-parallel circuit in amplifiers having a variable center frequency.

The following example illustrates the design of a parallel-series coupling network:

Problem.   A parallel-series-type single-tuned circuit is used as a coupling network between common-base stages having $g_{o1} = 10^{-4}$ mho, $g_{is2} = 2 \times 10^{-2}$ mho, and negligible C_{is2}.   The center frequency is 1.6 mc, and the required 3-db bandwidth is 50 kc.   Transformers with $Q_0 \cong 100$ are assumed to be available.   Design the network.

Solution: from eq. 6.10 we find η_{max}:

$$\eta_{max} = (1 - 1/3.1)^2 \cong 0.46$$

The secondary inductance is found from eq. 6.20:

$$L_2 = 100/[\pi \times 1.6 \times 10^6 \times 2 \times 10^{-2}(3.1 - 1)] \cong 480 \ \mu h$$

The square of the transformer turns ratio is found from eq. 6.21:

$$m^2 = [2 \times 10^{-2} \times (3.1 - 1)^2]/(4 \times 10^4 \times 10^{-4}) \cong 0.022$$

This gives the primary inductance L_1:

$$L_1 = m^2 L_2 \cong 10.6 \ \mu h$$

The tuning capacitance is

$$C \cong 1/4\pi^2 f_0^2 L_2 \cong 21 \ \mu\mu f$$

6.2.3.4 Mixed Coupling Networks

The coupling networks shown in Fig. 6.13 are among those used occasionally. In these networks the transistors are connected in series or in parallel with only a portion of the tuning capacitance.

The performance of these circuits within the pass band is similar to the previously treated cases. Outside the pass band, however, their behavior is different and may approximate the parallel-parallel or paral-

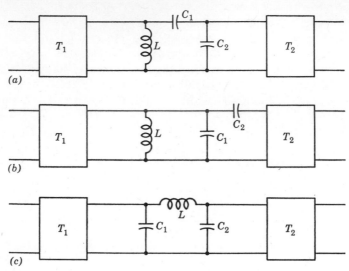

Fig. 6.13 "Mixed" coupling-network configurations

lel-series case, depending on the ratio C_1/C_2 and the transistor impedances. In gain-controlled amplifiers and in amplifiers having a variable center frequency, these configurations permit the realization of special bandwidth-versus-gain or bandwidth-versus-center-frequency characteristics.

These mixed configurations permit impedance matching and, consequently, optimum power transfer between successive stages without the use of transformers. This property is useful when transformers with the desirable turns ratios are not readily available.

6.2.3.5 Amplifier Stages with Variable Center Frequency

The center frequency of an amplifier stage can be made variable by making either the inductance or the capacitance of the coupling network variable. In such amplifiers it is often desirable to maintain the gain more or less constant as the center frequency varies. The gain has the tendency to change as the center frequency is varied for two reasons:

(*a*) The maximum available gain of transistors decreases with increasing frequency; (*b*) transistor input and output impedances are functions of frequency. In amplifiers with variable center frequency it is difficult to maintain optimum power transfer between successive stages throughout an extensive range of center frequencies using simple interstage-coupling networks and simple means of center-frequency variation.

The gain can often be equalized to a certain extent by matching impedances at the highest frequency. Then, the loss due to mismatch at lower frequencies is compensated by the larger power gain of the tran-

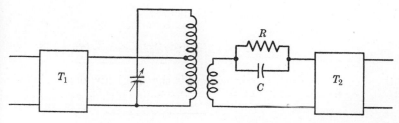

Fig. 6.14   Variable center-frequency amplifier with gain equalization

sistor at lower frequencies. If this method does not provide sufficient gain equalization, gain-correcting networks can be introduced. An example is shown in Fig. 6.14. At low center frequencies, R prevents part of the available power from reaching T_2. At higher frequencies, R is more effectively bypassed by C and a larger fraction of the available power reaches the input of T_2. Gain-correcting networks usually introduce considerable loss at all frequencies of interest, and, therefore, their use is to be avoided wherever possible.

Usually, as the center frequency is varied, the bandwidth varies also. For the parallel-parallel case (Fig. 6.5), the bandwidth B_n can be written

$$B_n^{PP} = (g_{o1} + g_{i2}/m^2 + g_1)f_0\sqrt{n}/Q_0g_1 \qquad (6.22)$$

If the capacitor is the variable tuning element, eq. 6.22 can be rewritten as

$$B_{n\text{var. }C}^{PP} = (g_{o1} + g_{i2}/m^2 + 1/2\pi f_0 L_1 Q_0)2\pi f_0^2 L_1\sqrt{n} \qquad (6.23)$$

Assuming that g_{o1}, g_{i2}, and Q_0 are independent of the center frequency, the bandwidth varies considerably with the center frequency. If, however, the inductance is the variable tuning element, the capacitance being constant, the bandwidth is

$$B_{n_{\text{var.}\ L}}^{PP} = (g_{o1} + g_{i2}/m^2 + 2\pi f_0 C/Q_0)\sqrt{n}/2\pi C \qquad (6.24)$$

In this case, if the losses due to $2\pi f_0 C/Q_0$ are negligible, the bandwidth remains constant as the center frequency changes.

Using the parallel-series arrangement of Fig. 6.10, eq. 6.17 gives the bandwidth:

$$B_n^{PS} = (m^2 g_{o1} + Q_0^2 g_2^2/g_{is2} + g_2)f_0\sqrt{n}/Q_0 g_2 \qquad (6.25)$$

With variable C and constant L, this leads to

$$B_{n_{\text{var.}\ C}}^{PS} = (m^2 g_{o1} + 1/4\pi^2 f_0^2 L_2^2 g_{is2} + 1/2\pi f_0 L_2 Q_0)2\pi f_0^2 L_2 \sqrt{n} \qquad (6.26)$$

If the second term in the parentheses is the dominant one (this term is due to the load represented by T_2), the bandwidth is constant as the center frequency changes.

Using the parallel-series arrangement with inductive tuning, we find

$$B_{n_{\text{var.}\ L}}^{PS} = (m^2 g_{o1} + 4\pi^2 f_0^2 C^2/g_{is2} + 2\pi f_0 C/Q_0)\sqrt{n}/2\pi C \qquad (6.27)$$

In this case, for constant bandwidth, the term $(m^2 g_{o1})$ must be made dominant. This can be done by using a large value of m.

If Q_0 is frequency-independent, the *fractional bandwidth* can be maintained constant in all cases by making the third term in all parentheses, i.e. the loss term, predominant. This implies considerably reduced power-transfer efficiency.

The discussion of this section neglected the frequency dependence of transistor input and output impedances. In reality, this frequency dependence is not negligible if the center frequency is varied throughout a wide range. Similarly, Q_0 is usually a function of the frequency. Therefore, the above analysis must be considered as being only qualitative.

6.2.4   Amplifier Stages Using Double-Tuned Networks

6.2.4.1   Coupling-Network Configurations

The performance of double-tuned coupling networks is superior to that of single-tuned networks; their frequency response within the pass band can be made flatter, they have a sharper cutoff at the edges of the band, and their attenuation at unwanted frequencies is higher.

Two tuned circuits can be coupled to each other in a number of ways to form a double-tuned arrangement. For example, circuits with inductive and capacitive coupling are shown in Fig. 6.15. Just as with single-tuned circuits, the terminations (i.e. source and load, or T_1 and T_2) can be connected to the coupling network in parallel or in series.

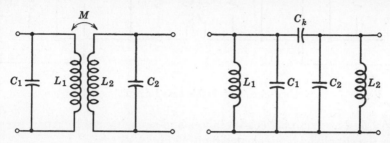

Fig. 6.15   Double-tuned circuits with inductive and capacitive coupling

Figure 6.16 shows, for example, a parallel-parallel circuit with inductive coupling and a parallel-series circuit with capacitive coupling.

The parallel-parallel circuit with inductive coupling is used most often,[1] and only this circuit will be discussed. The performance and design of other arrangements can be calculated in a similar manner.

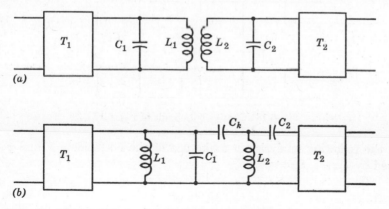

Fig. 6.16   Parallel-parallel circuit with inductive coupling and parallel-series circuit with capacitive coupling

6.2.4.2   Analysis of a Double-Tuned Circuit

Figure 6.17 shows the equivalent circuit of Fig. 6.16a. The inductances L_1 and L_2 are assumed to have equal unloaded Q's (Q_0), and the parallel loss conductances are $g_1(=1/2\pi f_0 L_1 Q_0)$ and $g_2(=1/2\pi f_0 L_2 Q_0)$,

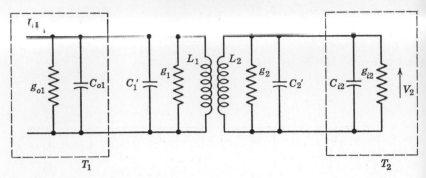

Fig. 6.17   Equivalent circuit of double-tuned parallel-parallel arrangement

respectively. Lumping conductances and capacitances together, we obtain the simplified equivalent circuit of Fig. 6.18 with

$$G_1 = g_{o1} + g_1 \qquad (6.28)$$

$$G_2 = g_{i2} + g_2 \qquad (6.29)$$

$$C_1 = C_{o1} + C_1' \qquad (6.30)$$

$$C_2 = C_{i2} + C_2' \qquad (6.31)$$

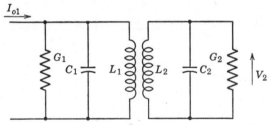

Fig. 6.18   Equivalent circuit of Fig. 6.17

In the following analysis we make use of the coefficients x and y defined by

$$G_1 = xg_1 \qquad (6.32)$$

$$G_2 = yg_2 \qquad (6.33)$$

Thus, the loaded primary and secondary Q's can be written, respectively:

$$Q_1 = Q_0/x \qquad (6.34)$$

$$Q_2 = Q_0/y \qquad (6.35)$$

The power available from the output of T_1 is

$$P_1 = |I_{o1}|^2/4g_{o1} \qquad (6.36)$$

The useful power fed to T_2 is

$$P_2 = |V_2|^2 g_{i2} \tag{6.37}$$

Consequently, the power-transfer efficiency is

$$\eta = P_2/P_1 = 4g_{o1}g_{i2}|V_2/I_{o1}|^2$$

$$= 4g_{o1}g_{i2}|z_{21}|^2 \tag{6.38}$$

where z_{21} is the open-circuit forward transfer impedance of the network shown in Fig. 6.18.

$|z_{21}|$ has been derived in the literature [3,4] and is

$$|z_{21}| \cong \frac{\mu}{(1 + \mu^2)(G_1 G_2)^{1/2}\{1 - [2(\mu^2 - b/2)/(1 + \mu^2)^2]\rho^2 + [1/(1 + \mu^2)^2]\rho^4\}^{1/2}} \tag{6.39}$$

where $\mu = k(Q_1 Q_2)^{1/2}$, k being the coefficient of coupling between L_1 and L_2

$b = Q_1/Q_2 + Q_2/Q_1$

$\rho = (Q_1 Q_2)^{1/2}(f/f_0 - f_0/f) \cong 2(\Delta f/f_0)(Q_1 Q_2)^{1/2}$

We define the *shape factor* θ:

$$\theta = 2(\mu^2 - b/2)/(1 + \mu^2) \tag{6.40}$$

The designation of θ as shape factor is justified by the fact that arrangements having the same θ have similar normalized frequency responses if $[\rho/(1 + \mu^2)^{1/2}]$ is used as the normalized frequency variable. This is clear if we rewrite eq. 6.39 as

$$|z_{21}| \cong \frac{\mu}{(1 + \mu^2)(G_1 G_2)^{1/2}\{1 - [\theta/(1 + \mu^2)]\rho^2 + [1/(1 + \mu^2)^2]\rho^4\}^{1/2}} \tag{6.41}$$

$\theta = 0$ corresponds to the case of *transitional coupling* (maximum flat response). The overcoupled case is associated with $\theta > 0$, whereas $\theta < 0$ pertains to the undercoupled case.

The value of $|z_{21}|$ at the center frequency is

$$|z_{21}|_{f=f_0} = \mu/(1 + \mu^2)(G_1 G_2)^{1/2} \tag{6.42}$$

Substituting eq. 6.42 into eq. 6.38, we find the midband power-transfer efficiency

$$\eta = 4g_{o1}g_{i2}\mu^2/(1 + \mu^2)^2 G_1 G_2 \tag{6.43}$$

The fractional bandwidth B_n' is determined from eq. 6.41 by setting

$$1 - [\theta/(1 + \mu^2)]\rho_n^2 + [1/(1 + \mu^2)^2]\rho_n^4 = n + 1 \qquad (6.44)$$

where ρ_n is the value of ρ at the cutoff frequencies. Using the approximation

$$\rho_n \cong B_n'(Q_1Q_2)^{\frac{1}{2}} \qquad (6.45)$$

eq. 6.44 can be written as

$$Q_1^2Q_2^2(B_n')^4/(1 + \mu^2)^2 - \theta Q_1Q_2(B_n')^2/(1 + \mu^2) - n = 0 \quad (6.46)$$

Using eqs. 6.32 to 6.35 and 6.40, eqs. 6.43 and 6.46 can be written in terms of the known constants Q_0, B_n', and θ:

$$\eta = 4(2 - \theta)(x^2 + y^2 + \theta xy)(x - 1)(y - 1)/(x + y)^4 \qquad (6.47)$$

$$Q_0^4(B_n')^4 - [\theta/(2 - \theta)]Q_0^2(B_n')^2(x + y)^2 - [n/(2 - \theta)^2](x + y)^4$$
$$= F(x, y) = 0 \qquad (6.48)$$

The maximum power-transfer efficiency realizable for given Q_0, B_n', and θ is obtained by maximizing eq. 6.47 with condition 6.48, i.e. by setting

$$\partial\eta/\partial x + \lambda\partial F/\partial x = 0 \qquad (6.49)$$

$$\partial\eta/\partial y + \lambda\partial F/\partial y = 0 \qquad (6.50)$$

This results in the following simple condition for obtaining the maximum value of η:

$$x = y \qquad (6.51)$$

6.2.4.3 Circuit Elements and Power Transfer

Substituting eq. 6.51 into eq. 6.48, we find

$$x = y = [Q_0B_n'(2 - \theta)^{\frac{1}{2}}/2n^{\frac{1}{4}}][(1 + \theta^2/4n)^{\frac{1}{2}} - \theta/2n^{\frac{1}{2}}]^{\frac{1}{2}} \qquad (6.52)$$

We can now determine the required circuit elements and the maximum power-transfer efficiency. We have

$$g_1 = g_{o1}/(x - 1) \qquad (6.53)$$

$$g_2 = g_{i2}/(x - 1) \qquad (6.54)$$

and, consequently, the required inductance values are

$$L_1 = (x - 1)/2\pi f_0Q_0g_{o1} \qquad (6.55)$$

$$L_2 = (x - 1)/2\pi f_0Q_0g_{i2} \qquad (6.56)$$

The required coefficient of coupling is

$$k = (x/Q_0)[(2 + \theta)/(2 - \theta)]^{\frac{1}{2}} \qquad (6.57)$$

If we designate the coefficient of transitional coupling (or critical coupling, since $x = y$ implies $Q_1 = Q_2$) by k_T, k_T being equal to $1/Q_1 = 1/Q_2$, then we can write

$$k/k_T = [(2 + \theta)/(2 - \theta)]^{1/2} \qquad (6.58)$$

Substituting eq. 6.52 into eq. 6.47, the maximum power-transfer efficiency is found to be

$$\eta_{\max} = (1 - \theta^2/4)(1 - 1/x)^2$$

$$= (1 - \theta^2/4)\{1 - [2\sqrt[4]{n}/Q_0 B_n'(2 - \theta)^{1/2}]/[(1 + \theta^2/4n)^{1/2}$$

$$- \theta/2\sqrt{n}]^{1/2}\}^2 \qquad (6.59)$$

For a given shape factor θ and given value of n, $\eta_{\max}$ is large if $Q_0 B_n'$ is large. This is qualitatively similar to the results obtained in the single-tuned case.

It is interesting to analyze the influence of the shape factor θ on $\eta_{\max}$. In many applications, the shape of the frequency response curve

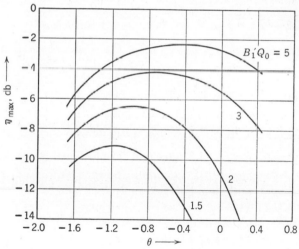

Fig. 6.19 $\eta_{\max}$ as a function of θ for different values of $B_1'Q_0$

is not of major importance, provided the requirements regarding B_n' and the skirt selectivity (which does not depend strongly on θ) are met. Consequently, we are interested in the value of θ, which maximizes $\eta_{\max}$ for given n, B_n', and Q_0. Unfortunately this computation is rather involved. Therefore, the dependence of $\eta_{\max}$ on θ, with $B_1'Q_0$ as parameter, is represented graphically in Fig. 6.19.

We see that transitional coupling ($\theta = 0$) does not, in general, lead to maximum midband power transfer. The maximum value of $\eta_{\max}$ is realized with less than critical coupling ($\theta < 0$). This maximum is not very pronounced for large values of $B_1'Q_0$, and, therefore, in such cases, transitional coupling may be employed without serious disadvantage. The situation is, however, quite different for small values of $B_1'Q_0$: although in such cases the power-transfer efficiency is always rather low, the transfer loss in the undercoupled case is considerably smaller than in the case of transitional coupling. Therefore, for low values of $B_1'Q_0$, undercoupled circuits should be used, wherever possible.

6.2.4.4   Circuit Elements and Power Transfer; Transitional Coupling

In the case of transitional coupling, $\theta = 0$ and eq. 6.52 becomes simply

$$x_T = Q_0 B_n'/\sqrt{2}\,\sqrt[4]{n} \tag{6.60}$$

The required inductance values are

$$L_1 = (Q_0 B_n'/\sqrt{2}\,\sqrt[4]{n} - 1)/2\pi f_0 Q_0 g_{o1} \tag{6.61}$$

$$L_2 = (Q_0 B_n'/\sqrt{2}\,\sqrt[4]{n} - 1)/2\pi f_0 Q_0 g_{i2} \tag{6.62}$$

The coupling coefficient is

$$k = k_T = x/Q_0 = B_n'/\sqrt{2}\,\sqrt[4]{n} \tag{6.63}$$

The maximum power-transfer efficiency becomes

$$\eta_{\max} = (1 - \sqrt{2}\,\sqrt[4]{n}/Q_0 B_n')^2 \tag{6.64}$$

6.2.4.5   Power Transfer of Single- and Double-Tuned Networks

It is useful to compare the maximum power-transfer efficiencies realizable by single- and double-tuned amplifier stages for equal given values of $B_n'Q_0$. This comparison is, of course, only significant if the skirt selectivity is of no interest. Since eq. 6.59 is unwieldy, we may compare the single-tuned and transitionally coupled double-tuned cases. From eqs. 6.10 and 6.64 the power-transfer efficiencies are equal if

$$\sqrt{n}/B_n'Q_0 = \sqrt{2}\,\sqrt[4]{n}/B_n'Q_0 \tag{6.65}$$

whence $n = 4$ (6.66)

This corresponds to a 7-db bandwidth. Whenever the bandwidth is defined for $n < 4$, the power transfer of the single-tuned coupling network is superior. If, on the other hand, one is interested in the bandwidth for $n > 4$, the transitionally coupled double-tuned network has better power transfer. It should be mentioned that, using under-coupled double-tuned circuits, it is often possible to obtain a power transfer superior to that of single-tuned circuits even if $n < 4$.

6.2.4.6   Practical Double-Tuned Circuits

The discussion of single-tuned and double-tuned coupling circuits has shown that a narrow bandwidth and good power transfer can be realized only if high values of Q_0 are used. Since high values of Q_0 are difficult

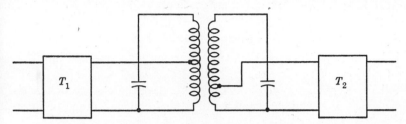

Fig. 6.20   Use of large tapped inductances to increase Q_0

to achieve with small inductances, it is advantageous to use properly tapped large inductances instead of the required small inductances. A practical parallel-parallel circuit using this method of obtaining higher effective Q_0 is shown in Fig. 6.20.

6.2.4.7   Design Example

Problem. Design a double-tuned circuit to be used as a coupling network between successive common-emitter stages having $g_{o1} = 10^{-4}$ mho, $g_{i2} = 10^{-3}$ mho, and negligible capacitances. The center frequency is 2 mc; the required 6-db bandwidth is 40 kc. The coupling factor should be $k = k_T/2$. Transformers having $Q_0 = 100$ are assumed to be available.

Solution. From eq. 6.58 we find the shape factor θ corresponding to $k = k_T/2$:

$$\theta = -1.2$$

From eq. 6.52 we compute x:

$$x = [(100 \times 2 \times 10^{-2} \times \sqrt{3.2})/(2 \times \sqrt[4]{3})]\{[1 + 1.44/(4 \times 3)]^{\frac{1}{2}}$$
$$+ 1.2/(2 \times \sqrt{3})\}^{\frac{1}{2}}$$
$$= 1.6$$

η_{max} is given by eq. 6.59.

$$\eta_{max} = (1 - 1.44/4)(1 - 1/1.6)^2 = 0.09$$

The power-transfer efficiency is poor (approximately 11 db loss in the coupling network) owing to the relatively narrow bandwidth.

From eqs. 6.55 and 6.56 we find the inductances L_1 and L_2:

$$L_1 = (1.6 - 1)/(2\pi \times 2 \times 10^6 \times 10^2 \times 10^{-4}) \cong 4.8 \ \mu h \quad \text{and}$$

$$L_2 \cong 0.48 \ \mu h$$

In a practical arrangement, the circuit of Fig. 6.20 should be used, the tapped portions of the inductances representing L_1 and L_2, respectively.

6.3　Comments on Wide-Band Amplifier Stages

It has been pointed out that transistor conductances and impedances are functions of the frequency. The design methods for narrow-band amplifiers were based on the assumption that the change of transistor impedances is negligibly small within the frequency range of interest.

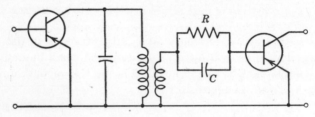

Fig. 6.21　Amplifier with frequency equalization

In wide-band amplifiers, the effect of transistor-parameter variation with frequency on gain and driving-point impedances of the transistor becomes important. In such cases it is necessary to use compensation techniques to obtain frequency responses eliminating the frequency dependence of transistor parameters. Whether a certain required frequency response necessitates frequency compensation techniques or not depends on the transistor type used, on the transistor configuration, and on the center frequency.

Techniques that may be used to compensate for transistor parameter variations are numerous. For example, Fig. 6.21 shows a single-tuned coupling circuit with an RC compensating network. Without compensation the attenuation at high frequencies would be greater than at the low-frequency end. The resistor R, unbypassed at low frequencies, introduces additional low-frequency attenuation, without greatly affecting the high-frequency response. The low-frequency attenuation could also be increased by using a trap tuned to a frequency below the pass band. A single trap can be used to compensate for the difference between low- and high-frequency attenuation of several cascaded stages.

It should be mentioned that while "bandshaping" techniques permit compensation of frequency-dependent transistor properties, they may also be used deliberately to make the band shape unsymmetrical, whenever this is desired.

For narrow-band amplifiers the approximation of eq. 6.1 was used. It should be remembered that this approximation is not valid for frequencies sufficiently distant from the center frequency (see Fig. 6.2).

6.4 Multistage Tuned Amplifiers

The preceding sections were concerned with the analysis and design of amplifier *stages*. In general, however, the specifications available to the design engineer require a certain *overall amplifier performance*, usually in terms of bandwidth, center frequency, and gain. It is then possible to determine systematically the requirements to be satisfied by individual stages in the following manner.

First, one selects the transistor type to be used. The approximate value of the maximum available gain of the transistor at the given center frequency can be estimated (see Sec. 6.6) or measured. Dividing the required overall gain (given in decibels) by the estimated stage gain determines the number of stages required.

Second, we consider the bandwidth. If the bandwidth B_N of the entire amplifier is given, this means that, at the two frequencies defining the limits of the pass band, the power gain of the entire amplifier must be $1/(N + 1)$ times the gain at the center frequency. If the number of tuned coupling networks used is M and all stages are to be identical, the individual stages will be characterized by

$$n = (N + 1)/M - 1 \qquad (6.67)$$

Once n is known, the individual stages can be designed.

The following *approximate formulas*, relating the 3-db bandwidth of a multistage amplifier using M tuned coupling networks to the 3-db bandwidth of an individual stage, are often very useful. For synchronous single-tuned stages we have

Individual bandwidth $\cong 1.2\sqrt{M} \times$ overall bandwidth

For synchronous transitionally coupled tuned stages we have

Individual bandwidth $\cong 1.1\sqrt[4]{M} \times$ overall bandwidth

Both formulas represent good approximations for $M \geq 2$.

In many cases, there are reasons for not using identical stages. For example, it may be difficult to realize the desired overall bandwidth using identical single-tuned stages with good power-transfer efficiency, whereas it would be wasteful to apply double-tuned circuits in all stages. It is then possible to design some stages with single-tuned circuits and others with double-tuned networks. The quantity $(N + 1)$ defining the bandwidth of the tuned amplifier can be distributed between amplifier stages in any desired manner.

In gain-controlled amplifiers and in limiting amplifiers, transistor conductances and capacitances vary as the gain is varied. This may result in undesirable variations of the center frequency and of the bandwidth. These effects can be avoided by designing the coupling networks adjacent to the gain-controlled stages as wide-band networks without appreciable selectivity and by obtaining the selectivity from coupling networks which are connected to stages with constant bias voltages and currents. In such cases we may have an amplifier with selectivity concentrated into one or two (often quite elaborate) coupling networks.

In many cases the exact shape of the frequency response of the amplifier is specified. It is difficult to give a design procedure generally applicable to such cases. The designer will analyze the required overall response and, remembering that it is the product of the frequency responses of individual coupling networks, will determine these individual required responses. For example, relatively flat response within the pass band can be obtained by using staggered-tuned stages or single-tuned stages in combination with overcoupled double-tuned stages.

6.5 Internal Feedback and Neutralization

6.5.1 Internal Feedback and Its Effects

Transistors are *non-unilateral* devices. In all three transistor configurations, if an excitation is applied to the output port, a response is obtained at the input port. In other words, the transistor has *internal feedback*. The non-unilateral nature of the transistor manifests itself in the fact that the matrix elements z_{12}, y_{12}, h_{12}, and g_{12} are not zero. These matrix elements represent different aspects of the internal feedback.

Internal feedback results in some undesirable phenomena in tuned transistor amplifiers.

(a) The input and output impedances (or admittances) of transistor amplifiers are functions of the load and source impedances (or admittances), respectively. Consequently, the design methods for tuned amplifiers outlined in the preceding sections must be considered as approxi-

mations, since these design methods assumed that transistor impedances are fixed quantities.

(b) With certain load (or source) impedances the input (or output)
impedance of a transistor amplifier may have a *negative real component*.
If a tuned circuit is connected to the input (or output), the circuit may
oscillate, even though no external positive feedback is applied. Similar behavior is common in high-frequency electron-tube circuits, where
internal feedback is provided by the grid-to-plate capacitance.

The following discussion is concerned with some possible undesirable
effects of internal feedback and their prevention.

6.5.2   Reflected Impedances (Admittances)

The circuit arrangement of Fig. 6.22 represents a transistor terminated in a source having an impedance Z_g and a load admittance Y_l.

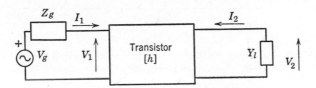

Fig. 6.22   Transistor with terminations

Using Table A.3 of the appendix, the input impedance Z_i and output
admittance Y_o can be written in the following form:

$$Z_i = h_{11} - h_{12}h_{21}/(h_{22} + Y_l) \qquad (6.68)$$

$$Y_o = h_{22} - h_{12}h_{21}/(h_{11} + Z_g) \qquad (6.69)$$

The second terms on the right-hand side of expressions 6.68 and 6.69
can be referred to as the "reflected" components of the input impedance
and output admittance, respectively. It is evident that, if h_{12} were
zero, the reflected components would vanish.

The problem of reflected impedances and admittances may become
quite involved in tuned high-frequency amplifier stages, owing to the
following facts:

(a) At higher frequencies transistor parameters are complex and frequency-dependent. Consequently, the reflected components are also
complex and frequency-dependent, and, therefore, it is difficult to take
their effect into account in analytical design procedures.

(b) The interstage-coupling network usually consists of one or more
resonant circuits. Consequently, the reflected impedance and admit-

tance components also display resonant effects (see Figs. 6.23 and 6.24, showing common-emitter input and output impedance components respectively for parallel-tuned terminations). In other words, in a multistage amplifier, internal feedback causes undesired coupling between tuned circuits at the input and at the output of an amplifier stage.

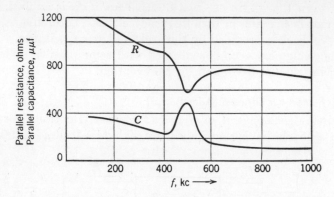

Fig. 6.23 Input impedance of common-emitter stage having parallel-tuned load impedance

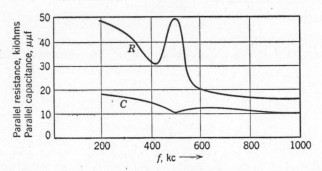

Fig. 6.24 Output impedance of common-emitter stage having parallel-tuned generator impedance

The practical effects of reflected impedance are: (a) the band pass characteristic of tuned amplifiers is distorted so that it becomes unsymmetrical; (b) the process of aligning multistage amplifiers may become a difficult problem, because the tuning of one stage has an effect on the tuning of others.

These difficulties of alignment can be minimized in synchronous single-tuned amplifiers by starting the tuning process at the last stage and proceeding to the preceding stages and then starting the process all over again. After about two complete tunings the amplifier can be considered aligned. However, in wide-band amplifiers with complicated frequency response (consisting often of staggered-tuned stages) the problem of alignment may become very serious.

The problem of reflected impedances can be reduced by careful design. Equations 6.68 and 6.69 show that the reflected component can be made small, if Y_l and Z_g are large. Thus a possible method of reducing the effect of reflected impedances is to apply a suitable impedance mismatch between stages. Furthermore, wherever consistent with other amplifier requirements, it is advantageous to make the reactances of the coupling network considerably smaller than the adjoining transistor reactances. The transistor reactances will then have practically no influence on the center frequency and on the band shape. These measures, however, result in reduced gain and reduced power efficiency.

Reflected impedances can be eliminated by neutralization. This method will be discussed in Sec. 6.5.4.

6.5.3 Stability of Tuned Amplifiers

A transistor amplifier may become unstable if the real component of its input or output impedance (or admittance) is negative. In order to determine the conditions under which instability may occur, we shall examine the behavior of these impedances as functions of the load and source impedances.[5]

The transistor input impedance is given by eq. 6.68. At high frequencies the quantities in this equation are complex and can be separated into real and imaginary components. We can write

$$h_{11} = h_{11R} + jh_{11I} \qquad (6.70)$$

$$h_{22} = h_{22R} + jh_{22I} \qquad (6.71)$$

$$h_{12}h_{21} = h_m = h_{mR} + jh_{mI} \qquad (6.72)$$

$$Y_l = G_l + jB_l \qquad (6.73)$$

$$Z_i = R_i + jX_i \qquad (6.74)$$

where the subscripts R and I denote real and imaginary components respectively. The real component R_i of the input impedance is

$$R_i = h_{11R} - [h_{mR}(h_{22R} + G_l) + h_{mI}(h_{22I} + B_l)]/$$
$$[(h_{22R} + G_l)^2 + (h_{22I} + B_l)^2] \qquad (6.75)$$

R_i vanishes if

$$h_{11R}(h_{22R} + G_l)^2 + h_{11R}(h_{22I} + B_l)^2 - h_{mR}(h_{22R} + G_l)$$
$$- h_{mI}(h_{22I} + B_l) = 0 \qquad (6.76)$$

We can now define a "load admittance plane," or in other words, a coordinate system in which G_l is measured along the horizontal axis and B_l along the vertical axis (see Fig. 6.25). Equation 6.76 represents a circle in the Y_l plane. The circle is the locus of those values of Y_l that make $R_i = 0$. It is easy to see that, h_{11R} being positive (which is usually true for transistor amplifiers), the region outside the circle represents the values of Y_l for which R_i is positive. For values of Y_l inside

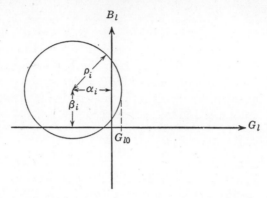

Fig. 6.25 Locus of pure imaginary input impedance in the load-admittance plane

the circle, R_i is negative, and, consequently, the inside of the circle is the region of potential instability.

We also see that, for the case shown in Fig. 6.25, the danger of instability exists only for positive values of B_l, i.e. capacitive load susceptances, provided that the load conductance is positive. Furthermore, if G_l exceeds the value G_{l0} (i.e. if the transistor is "loaded down" sufficiently), R_i cannot become negative for any value of B_l.

Using eq. 6.76, we can determine the coordinates α_i and β_i of the center of the circle and its radius ρ_i. We find

$$\alpha_i = h_{mR}/2h_{11R} - h_{22R} \tag{6.77}$$

$$\beta_i = h_{mI}/2h_{11R} - h_{22I} \tag{6.78}$$

$$\rho_i = |h_m|/2h_{11R} \tag{6.79}$$

A similar analysis can be made for the output admittance Y_o. We find that the real part of the output admittance, i.e. the output conductance G_o, vanishes on a circular locus in the "source impedance (or Z_g) plane." The radius of this circle and the coordinates of its center are

$$\alpha_o = h_{mR}/2h_{22R} - h_{11R} \qquad (6.80)$$

$$\beta_o = h_{mI}/2h_{22R} - h_{11I} \qquad (6.81)$$

$$\rho_o = |h_m|/2h_{22R} \qquad (6.82)$$

Here again, if h_{22R} is positive (as is usually true for transistors), the interior of the circle is the region of potential instability.

It must be emphasized that, even though $R_i < 0$ and $G_o < 0$ whenever Y_l and Z_g fall within the respective circles, this *does not imply*

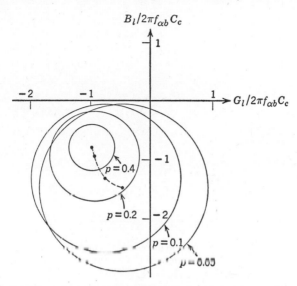

Fig. 6.26   Circles of imaginary input impedance in load-admittance plane for common-emitter transistor ($p = f/f_{\alpha b}$)

that the circuit is necessarily unstable; it only indicates *potential instability*. For example, if G_o is negative and the transistor is loaded at its output by a parallel tuned circuit having a resonant conductance G_l, for oscillation it is necessary that $G_l < |G_o|$.

Transistor parameters, source impedance, and load impedance are functions of frequency. Therefore, the location of the circles of purely reactive input and output impedances are different for different frequencies. Certain amplifier terminations may lead to potential instability at some frequencies, whereas they may fall within the stable region at other frequencies.

Figure 6.26 shows the circles of purely reactive input impedance for a transistor in the common-emitter configuration for the following set of transistor device parameters: $\alpha_{b0} = 0.99$, $r_b' = 75$ ohms, $r_\epsilon = 25$

ohms. The circles are plotted with the normalized frequency $p = (f/f_{\alpha b})$ as the parameter. The load-admittance plane is also normalized: the variables are $G_l/2\pi f_{\alpha b}C_c$ and $B_l/2\pi f_{\alpha b}C_c$, where $f_{\alpha b}$ is the α_b cutoff frequency and C_c is the collector capacitance.

This family of curves shows that, as the frequency increases, the circles gradually shift in the direction of the left half-plane. When f reaches a considerable fraction of $f_{\alpha b}$ (in Fig. 6.26 apparently around $f/f_{\alpha b} = 0.18$), the circle is entirely in the left half-plane. This implies that at higher frequencies there is no potential instability for positive load conductances. In other words, at higher frequencies the amplifier is unconditionally stable for any passive load. We also see that at lower frequencies, where portions of the circles are in the right half-plane (passive load admittances), potential instability occurs for negative values of B_l, i.e. for inductive load admittances.

Using either the set of eqs. 6.77 to 6.79 or the set 6.80 to 6.82, simple geometrical considerations show that the condition to be satisfied by the amplifier, in order that it be stable for all passive load and source admittances (impedances), is

$$|h_m| + h_{mR} < 2h_{11R}h_{22R} \qquad (6.83)$$

If this inequality is satisfied, the circles lie entirely in the left half-plane.

Using inequality 6.83 and the expressions for transistor h parameters derived in Chapter 2, we can determine, in terms of transistor device parameters, the approximate maximum frequency at which potential instability may occur for various transistor configurations. For the common-emitter configuration we find potential instability for

$$f/f_{\alpha b} \leq r_\epsilon/2r_b' \qquad (6.84)$$

If, for example, $r_\epsilon = 25$ ohms and $r_b' = 100$ ohms, the amplifier cannot be unstable at frequencies exceeding $(f_{\alpha b}/8)$.

The common-base and common-collector configurations exhibit a stronger tendency toward instability. We find they are potentially unstable up to frequencies exceeding $f_{\alpha b}$.

The above discussion enables us to draw several conclusions which should be considered in designing tuned amplifiers.

(a) Potential instability occurs only up to a fraction of $f_{\alpha b}$ if the common-emitter circuit is used. At higher frequencies this configuration is unconditionally stable. In the case of the common-base and common-collector circuits, instability may occur practically throughout the entire range of frequencies at which the transistor has useful amplification.

(b) In tuned amplifiers, where by a small shift of the frequency the imaginary components of source and load admittances may assume a large range of values, it is desirable to have $G_l > G_{l0}$ (see Fig. 6.25) and $R_g > R_{g0}$, so that, in changing the imaginary component of the termination (i.e. tuning), no danger of oscillation will exist. (This amounts to "mismatching" at input and output.)

(c) According to eq. 6.83, amplifiers can be stabilized by increasing h_{11R} or h_{22R}. This can be done, for example, by inserting stabilizing

Fig. 6.27   Stabilization with resistances

resistors at the input or output terminals, as shown in Fig. 6.27. This, of course, reduces the power gain, but may often be the simplest way to avoid instability.

(d) The transistor can also be stabilized by neutralization. This procedure is described in the following section.

6.5.4 Neutralized Amplifiers

Problems caused by reflected impedances and potential instability can be eliminated by *neutralizing* the internal feedback of transistors [6,7] Neutralization is a common technique often used in high frequency vacuum tube circuit design to eliminate the effect of the grid-to-plate capacitance. The procedure is to apply *external feedback* around an active device having internal feedback in such a fashion that the two feedback effects cancel. The composite neutralized arrangement will be without feedback, or, in other words, it will be unilateral.

A non-unilateral device can be neutralized in many different ways. The operation of various neutralized arrangements can be explained in terms of matrix algebra or by considering the neutralized circuits as balanced bridges.

Figure 6.28a shows an often-used neutralized common-base amplifier stage.[8] The high-frequency equivalent circuit of Fig. 6.28b explains the operation of the circuit. The transistor parameters C_c, r_b' and the external circuit elements R and C form a balanced bridge, provided that

$$R = kr_b' \qquad (6.85)$$

and
$$C = C_c/k \qquad (6.86)$$

where k is a constant. Any value of k can be used to neutralize the transistor, but the available power gain of the neutralized circuit will be a maximum if k is approximately equal to $(r_\epsilon/r_b')^{\frac{1}{4}}$.

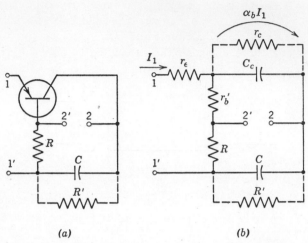

(a)   (b)

Fig. 6.28   Neutralized common-base amplifier and equivalent circuit

The operation of the circuit can also be explained by drawing the equivalent circuit as shown in Fig. 6.29. The circuit is represented as the series-parallel connection of the transistor and the neutralizing net-

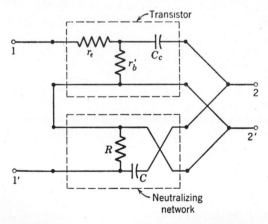

Fig. 6.29   Redrawn equivalent circuit of Fig. 6.28

work. It can be shown easily that in this case the h parameters h_{ij}'' of the composite circuit can be written in terms of the h parameters h_{ij} of the transistor and those of the neutralizing network (h_{ij}'):

$$h_{11}'' = h_{11} + h_{11}' \tag{6.87}$$

$$h_{12}'' = h_{12} + h_{12}' \tag{6.88}$$

$$h_{21}'' = h_{21} + h_{21}' \tag{6.89}$$

$$h_{22}'' = h_{22} + h_{22}' \tag{6.90}$$

The circuit will be unilateral if

$$h_{12}'' = h_{12} + h_{12}' = 0 \tag{6.91}$$

Consequently, we must have

$$h_{12} = -h_{12}' \tag{6.92}$$

and this explains the preceding requirements for C and R.

It must be mentioned that the circuit of Fig. 6.28 is neutralized only at high frequencies. The range of neutralization can be extended to low frequencies by paralleling C with a resistor R', with

$$R' = k/g_c \tag{6.93}$$

where g_c is the collector conductance of the transistor. The circuit is neutralized only for a given d-c bias because a change of the collector

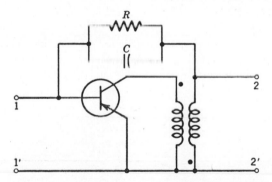

Fig. 6.30   Neutralized common-emitter amplifier

voltage or emitter current causes a change of C_c and results in unbalancing the bridge.

The circuit of Fig. 6.30 shows a neutralized common-emitter amplifier. The operation of this circuit can be explained by considering the equivalent circuit of Fig. 6.31. The transistor, followed by a phase-inverting transformer, and the neutralizing network are connected in parallel at both input and output terminal pairs. In such an arrangement the y parameters of the composite network are the sums of the y parameters of the two networks connected in parallel. Consequently the feedback admittance of the composite network is

$$y_{12}'' = -y_{12} + y_{12}' \qquad (6.94)$$

The minus sign before y_{12} is due to the phase-inverting transformer following the transistor. The circuit is unilateral if $y_{12}'' = 0$, i.e. if

$$y_{12}' = y_{12} \qquad (6.95)$$

At high frequencies y_{12e} is capacitive and can be represented (within

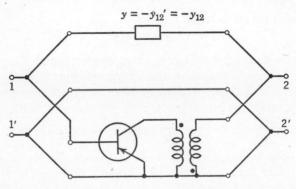

Fig. 6.31   Explanation of the operation of the circuit of Fig. 6.30

a narrow frequency band) as the parallel connection of a resistance R and a capacitance C. This leads to the arrangement of Fig. 6.30. In the vicinity of a given frequency, the parallel connection of R and C can be replaced by a resistance R' in series with a capacitance C'.

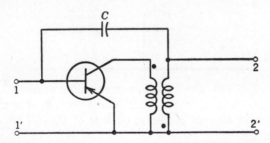

Fig. 6.32   Simplified version of the circuit of Fig. 6.30

This arrangement is often used, since it provides d-c isolation between input and output terminals. Experience shows that the effect of reflected impedances and the danger of instability are often sufficiently reduced, even if we omit resistance as shown in Fig. 6.32. The neutralizing capacitance C is approximately equal to the collector capacitance

C_c of the transistor, if the turns ratio of the phase-inverting transformer is unity.[9]

Many other neutralized arrangements can be designed and are sometimes used. Some additional circuits are shown in Fig. 6.33.

All neutralized arrangements are sensitive to changes of the d-c bias. They are valid only within a limited range of frequencies, since the de-

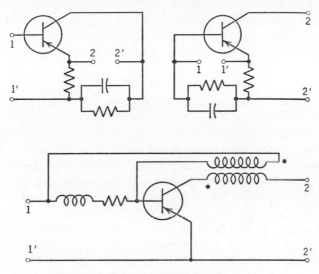

Fig. 6.33 Other neutralized arrangements

sign of neutralizing networks is usually based on relatively crude approximations of transistor feedback parameters.

6.6 Power Gain of Tuned Amplifiers

Figure 6.22 showed a transistor amplifier fed by a generator with generator impedance Z_g ($Z_g = R_g + jX_g$) and feeding a load admittance Y_l ($Y_l = G_l + jB_l$). The transducer gain is defined as the power delivered to the load divided by the available power of the generator. The transducer gain G_t is found to be

$$G_t = 4|h_{21}|^2 R_g G_l / |(h_{11} + Z_g)(h_{22} + Y_l) - h_{12}h_{21}|^2 \qquad (6.96)$$

At low frequencies, transistor parameters and terminating impedances can usually be considered as having no phase shift and the maximum value G_{tm} of G_t (G_{tm} = the maximum available power gain), as well as the values of $R_g = Z_g$ and $G_l = Y_l$ associated with this gain can be determined.

With tuned amplifiers the situation is different. It has been pointed out that, if suitably terminated, transistor amplifiers can oscillate without external feedback. Since oscillation corresponds to infinite power gain, we must conclude that, in regions of potential instability, arbitrarily high values of power gain can be obtained. Consequently, the concept of maximum power gain is not very useful in dealing with potentially unstable configurations.

It is, however, possible to calculate the maximum available power gain for frequencies where the transistor configuration is unconditionally stable. Thus, for the common-emitter stage, we have [10]

$$G_{tm} \cong (0.035/f^2)(f_{\alpha b}/r_b'C_c) \tag{6.97}$$

This expression is approximately valid for junction transistors with constant base-spreading resistance r_b' (alloy junction transistors) in the frequency range $0.05f_{\alpha b} < f < 2f_{\alpha b}$. Equation 6.97 is also a good approximation of the maximum power gain of a neutralized common-emitter amplifier in the frequency range of potential instability.

We see that the common-emitter gain decreases with the square of the operating frequency, is proportional to $f_{\alpha b}$, and is inversely proportional to the product $(r_b'C_c)$. The expression $(f_{\alpha b}/r_b'C_c)$ is, therefore, often referred to as the *figure of merit* of the transistor.

Expression 6.97 is not valid for grown junction transistors, where z_b' is complex and a function of the frequency. (See Chapter 2.) For such transistors in the common-emitter configuration [10]

$$G_{tm} \cong (0.03/f^{3/2})[f_{\alpha b}^{1/2}/C_c(r_b'r_\epsilon)^{1/2}] \tag{6.98}$$

where r_b' is the low-frequency value of z_b'. The gain decreases with $\sqrt{f^3}$, i.e. less rapidly than for alloy junction transistors.

The maximum available power gain of the neutralized common-base stage is (see Fig. 6.28a):

$$G_{tm} \cong 1/\{4r_b'(4\pi^2f^2C_c^2r_b' + g_c)[1 + (h_{11b0}/r_b')^{1/2}]^2\} \tag{6.99}$$

where h_{11b0} is the low-frequency value of h_{11b}. Equation 6.99 is approximately valid for $f < 0.5f_{\alpha b}$. It is, however, often difficult to realize this gain in practice because of the usually high output impedance involved.

Equations 6.97 to 6.99 can be used to compare the relative merits of different transistor types as high-frequency amplifiers.

Problems

1. (a) Design a single-tuned network to couple the output of a common-base stage to the input of another common-base stage. The parallel output resistance is 50 kilohms, the output capacitance 20 $\mu\mu f$, the input resistance 40 ohms with negligible reactive component, the center frequency 1 mc and the 6-db bandwidth 50 kc. A Q_0 of 100 can be realized for inductance values lying between 200 and 2000 μh. For larger or smaller inductance values Q_0 is less. Which is more practical: the parallel-parallel or the parallel-series arrangement?

(b) Assume that the amplifier uses common-emitter stages. The output resistance is 10 kilohms, the input resistance is 1 kilohm, and the parallel capacitances are negligible. Design a coupling network, and compare the parallel-parallel and parallel-series cases from the point of view of their practicality.

2. A single-tuned parallel-parallel circuit is used as coupling network between common-emitter stages. Assume $1/g_{o1} = 10$ kilohms. The second stage is gain-controlled, and its $(1/g_{i2})$ varies between 1 kilohm (at high gain) and 10 kilohms (at low gain). The reactive components are negligible. The operating frequency is 455 kc, the 6-db bandwidth is 9 kc, and $Q_0 = 150$. The bandwidth must not vary by more than 20% as the gain is varied. Design the network, and compute the maximum power-transfer efficiency η_{max}. How does this η_{max} compare with the one that could be obtained if the second stage were not gain-controlled?

3. A double-tuned circuit is used as the coupling network between common-emitter stages. The output resistance is 15 kilohms, the input resistance is 1.2 kilohms, and the capacitances are negligibly small. The center frequency is 455 kc, the required 13-db bandwidth is 10 kc, and $Q_0 = 160$. Design the network, and investigate the influence of the shape factor θ on the circuit parameters and on the shape of the band-pass characteristic.

4. Carry out an analysis similar to that of Sec. 6.2.4 for capacitively-coupled double-tuned networks.

5. An amplifier has the following specifications: power gain 100 db at 1 mc, and a 24-db bandwidth of 30 kc. The realizable Q_0 is 100. Transistors having input resistance of 1 kilohm, output resistance of 20 kilohms, negligible capacitances, and a power gain of 28 db at 1 mc are to be used. Design the amplifier, including coupling networks.

6. A transformer (primary inductance L_1, secondary inductance L_2, coupling coefficient $k = 1$) couples a common-base stage (input admittance: $Y_i = g_i + j2\pi fC_i$) to a preceding common-base stage (output admittance: $Y_o = g_o + j2\pi fC_o$). The amplifier operates at a high frequency, and the transformer together with C_o and C_i constitutes the tuning element *without* using additional lumped capacitances. Determine the required values of L_1 and L_2 for a given fractional bandwidth $B_n{}'$. What are the limitations on the power-transfer efficiency of such an arrangement?

7. A transistor has $f_{\alpha b} = 10$ mc, $r_b{}' = 75$ ohms, $C_c = 5$ $\mu\mu f$ and is operated at 2 mc in common-base configuration with parallel tuned circuits at its input and output. Determine, in the source admittance plane, the locus for which the conductive component of the output admittance vanishes. Determine the minimum value of source conductance for which the output conductance is positive, no matter what value the source susceptance has.

8. An alloy junction transistor and a grown junction transistor are both charac-

terized by $f_{ab} = 20$ mc, $C_c = 10$ $\mu\mu$f, and $r_b' = 150$ ohms. Which has higher gain as a common-emitter tuned amplifier? Plot the gain-versus-frequency curves between 400 kc and 10 mc. Assume a d-c emitter current of 1 ma.

Bibliography

1. R. R. Webster, "How to Design IF Transistor Transformers," *Electronics*, *28*, 156–160 (Aug. 1955).

2. W. F. Chow and A. P. Stern, "Automatic Gain Control of Transistor Amplifiers," *Proc. IRE*, *43*, 1119–1127 (1955).

3. G. E. Valley and H. Wallman, *Vacuum Tube Amplifiers*, McGraw-Hill, New York, 1948.

4. C. B. Aiken, "Two Mesh Tuned Coupled Circuit Filters," *Proc. IRE*, *25*, 230–272 (1937).

5. A. P. Stern, "Some Considerations on the Stability of Active Elements and Applications," *IRE Convention Record*, *4*, Part 2, 46–52 (1956).

6. A. P. Stern, C. A. Aldridge, and W. F. Chow, "Internal Feedback and Neutralization of Transistor Amplifiers," *Proc. IRE*, *43*, 838–847 (1955).

7. C. C. Cheng, "Neutralization and Unilateralization," *IRE Trans.*, *CT-2*, 138–145 (1955).

8. J. B. Angell and F. P. Keiper, "Circuit Applications of Surface Barrier Transistors," *Proc. IRE*, *41*, 1709–1712 (1953).

9. D. D. Holmes, T. O. Stanley, and L. A. Freedman, "A Developmental Pocket-Size Broadcast Receiver Employing Transistors," *Proc. IRE*, *43*, 662–670 (1955).

10. R. L. Pritchard, "High Frequency Power Gain of Junction Transistors," *Proc. IRE*, *43*, 1075–1085 (1955).

Chapter 7

Video Amplifiers

7.1 Introduction

An amplifier that provides gain throughout a wide band of frequencies, ranging from a few cycles per second up to several megacycles per second, such as is employed for example in television receivers, is known as a *video* amplifier. The general requirements of video amplifiers have been well established. The amplitude response characteristic must be reasonably uniform over the frequency range of interest, and at the same time the time delay of the amplifier must not vary appreciably throughout the required frequency range.

The bandwidth of a video amplifier is dependent on the specific requirement of the system. A television receiver has a video amplifier covering a band from 60 cps to about 4 mc. On the other hand, a radar set may need a video amplifier having a bandwidth of only about 2 mc. These amplifiers are all similar with respect to frequency response and phase-shift requirements. However, depending on the services they are designed to perform, they are different with respect to operating voltage and output power capabilities. Their design determines the faithfulness of reproduction of a picture in a television system, and of a pulse in a radar system. Consequently the video amplifier design is of paramount importance.

In using transistors as the active elements of a video amplifier, transistor properties must be studied thoroughly, not only for a single frequency or a relatively narrow frequency band, but over the entire bandwidth that the video amplifier is intended to cover. The variation of transistor parameters with operating point and with frequency has been discussed in Chapter 2.

7.2 Circuit Configurations

It has been shown in the preceding chapters that the transistor is a power-amplifying device. This is different from an electron-tube amplifier in that a transistor amplifier needs a finite amount of input signal power in order to obtain the amplified output. This requirement is due to the magnitudes of the impedances on the input side and on the output side of the amplifier. Because of difference in impedances it is frequently desirable to use matching transformers in IF and RF amplifier design, in order to maximize stage gain.

Usually a video amplifier must cover such a wide frequency band that it is impractical to use transformer coupling. The wide bandwidth is commonly obtained by using RC coupling together with appropriate compensation networks. The impedance mismatch results in a sacrifice of gain per stage in exchange for increased bandwidth.

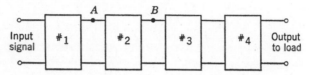

Fig. 7.1　Cascaded video amplifier stages

Figure 7.1 shows a block diagram of a video amplifier. Each box represents one transistor amplifier stage. The signal fed into stage 1 is amplified and fed into stage 2. Stages 2, 3, and 4 amplify the signal again, and finally the amplified signal is fed to the load by stage 4. As far as each individual stage is concerned, stages 1, 2, and 3 have the corresponding following stage as load. Stage number 4's load is the actual load of the whole amplifier. This actual load may be of high impedance, such as the control grid of a cathode-ray tube, or it can be of low impedance, such as the characteristic impedance of a coaxial cable. As a result the circuit design of the output stage of a transistor video amplifier is usually different from the preceding stages and deserves special consideration.

The circuit design of each of the low-level stages 1, 2, and 3 in Fig. 7.1 is normally identical, the preamplifier thus consisting of similar stages in cascade. The impedances at points A and B are approximately the same, and therefore the power gain of each stage is proportional to the square of the current amplification. On the other hand, the output stage may have a high impedance as the load, and in this case this stage must be designed to produce voltage amplification. The voltage amplification of this stage is a function of its input impedance and the load impedance. Conversely, if the load impedance is low, the last stage will be designed as a current amplifier.

It was shown in Chapters 1 and 2 that a junction transistor in the common-base configuration has a short-circuit current-amplification factor less than unity; therefore the common-base configuration cannot be used for iterative preamplifier stages. The common-collector configuration normally has an input impedance that is larger than the output impedance. There is no voltage amplification, and consequently it cannot be used for iterative preamplifier stages either. The remaining transistor configuration is the common-emitter circuit. The current-amplification factor of the common-emitter circuit is larger than unity for frequencies below the α_b cutoff frequency. The input impedance of the common-emitter circuit is normally lower than its output impedance. These properties make the common-emitter configuration suitable for the video-preamplifier applications. Either the common-base or the common-emitter configurations can be used in the output stage when the load impedance is large. If the load impedance is small, the common-collector configuration can be used.

7.3   Intermediate Stages

There are distinct problems in using transistors as the active elements of a video amplifier. If the transistor used in the intermediate stages has an α_b cutoff frequency much higher than the highest frequency of the video amplifier, the problems encountered in the circuit design are similar to those involved in the design of a video amplifier using electron tubes. However, if the α_b cutoff frequency occurs relatively close to the high-frequency end of the video band, the high-frequency transistor properties of the transistors themselves present the major problems of circuit design. In Chapter 2 the variation of transistor parameters with frequency was shown. These variations will result in frequency-dependent gain and phase-shift variation as the signal passes from stage to stage. These gain and phase-shift variations due to the transistor must be compensated for by proper circuit design.

7.3.1   Design of Intermediate Stages

It was shown above that the video preamplifier consists of similar stages in cascade. Since the design of all of the stages is usually the same, a study of one stage will suffice. This stage will have the preceding stage as the signal source, and the following stage as the load.

Owing to the properties of the transistor, the input impedance is smaller than the output impedance. The preamplifier stage is designed to amplify the input signal current. In this respect the function of a transistor video-amplifier stage is different from that of an electron-tube video stage which is designed to amplify the input signal voltage. This difference will be more apparent from the discussion of the input impedance of a video amplifier in Sec. 7.5.

In Sec. 7.2 it was seen that only the common-emitter configuration was found to be suitable for the cascaded video-preamplifier stage. Figure 7.2 shows a common-emitter transistor together with its associated circuits enclosed in a box. The output side of the preceding stage acts as the signal source. A signal current i is amplified by the factor

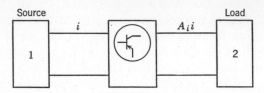

Fig. 7.2   Design principle of an intermediate stage

A_i. The circuit design requirement is to keep this amplification A_i constant over the video frequency band.

7.3.2   Low-Frequency Compensation

Since it is necessary to use a resistance-capacitance network as the interstage coupling circuit in order to obtain the wide frequency band, a blocking capacitor C, as shown in Fig. 7.3, is necessary to isolate the d-c bias currents and voltages for each stage. The transistors themselves present no special problems at low frequencies. Their parameters

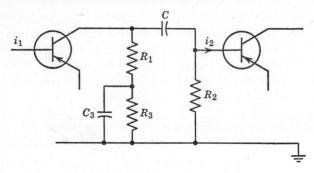

Fig. 7.3   Low-frequency compensation

are real and constant at audio frequencies. Input and the output resistances can be easily calculated by using formulas given in Chapter 4. However the low-frequency response is limited by the blocking capacitor C. The method of compensation is well known from the design of video amplifiers using electron tubes, and is shown in Fig. 7.3 as the parallel combination of C_3 and R_3. Let the input resistance and the output resistance be R_i and R_o, respectively. An equivalent circuit can be drawn as shown in Fig. 7.4. The signal current i_1 is amplified by the preceding transistor and appears as $\alpha_{e0}i_1$, where α_{e0} is the common-emitter short-circuit current-amplification factor at low frequencies. The condition for low-frequency compensation is

$$\left|\frac{\left(\dfrac{j\omega C}{j\omega C + 1/R_2 + 1/R_1}\right)\dfrac{1}{R_i}}{\dfrac{1}{R_o} + \dfrac{1/R_1(1/R_3 + j\omega C_3)}{1/R_1 + 1/R_3 + j\omega C_3} + \dfrac{j\omega C(1/R_2 + 1/R_i)}{j\omega C + 1/R_2 + 1/R_i}}\right|$$

$$= \frac{\dfrac{1}{R_i}}{\dfrac{1}{R_o} + \dfrac{1}{R_1} + \dfrac{1}{R_2} + \dfrac{1}{R_i}} \quad (7.1)$$

where $\omega = 2\pi f$ and f is the low frequency at which compensation is

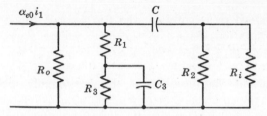

Fig. 7.4   Equivalent circuit for low-frequency compensation

desired. If R_o and R_2 are large in comparison with the other resistances, eq. 7.1 can be simplified, and the condition for compensation can be expressed as shown in eq. 7.2:

$$\left|1/\{1 + [(R_i/R_1)(1/R_3 + j\omega C_3)(1/R_i + j\omega C)/\right.$$

$$\left. j\omega C(1/R_1 + 1/R_3 + j\omega C_3)]\}\right| = 1/(1 + R_i/R_1) \quad (7.2)$$

The exact equations for R_i and R_o are given in the appendix, Table A.3, and may be written as

$$R_i = (\Delta^h_e + h_{11e}Y_l)/(h_{22e} + Y_l) \quad (7.3)$$

and
$$R_o = (h_{11e} + Z_g)/(\Delta^h_e + h_{22e}Z_g) \quad (7.4)$$

where $\Delta^h_e = h_{11e}h_{22e} - h_{21e}h_{12e}$, the determinant of the common-emitter h parameters. Since these expressions involve Y_l and Z_g, R_i and R_o depend on the low-frequency compensating networks of the preceding and the following stage. Equations 7.3 and 7.4 are rather complicated for practical purposes; however the following approximations can be used:

$$R_i \cong h_{11e} - r_{b}' + r_e/(1 - \alpha_b) \tag{7.5}$$

$$R_o \cong 1/h_{22e} = r_e + r_c(1 - \alpha_b) \tag{7.6}$$

Since the input impedance of a common-emitter transistor amplifier is much smaller than that of a tube amplifier, the coupling capacitance C is normally several orders of magnitude larger than the corresponding capacitance in the tube circuit. Fortunately transistors need only a low bias voltage, thus permitting a lower voltage rating and hence smaller physical size for the coupling capacitors.

7.3.3 High-Frequency Compensation

At the high-frequency end of the video band, the design problems are caused mostly by the transistors themselves. As mentioned before, if the transistor has an α_b cutoff frequency very much higher than the highest frequency of the video band, the circuit design is similar to that for tubes. The upper limit of frequency response of a transistor amplifier is determined principally by the transistors. Since the common-emitter configuration is used in the intermediate stage, the high-frequency response of a video amplifier will be greatly dependent on the common-emitter short-circuit current-amplification factor α_e.

It was shown in Chapter 2 that α_e, the short-circuit current-amplification factor of the common-emitter configuration, is related to the short-circuit current-amplification factor of the common-base configuration α_b by the equation

$$\alpha_e = \alpha_b/(1 - \alpha_b) \tag{7.7}$$

Letting $f_{\alpha b}$ be the α_b cutoff frequency of a transistor, it has been shown that the common-emitter cutoff frequency $f_{\alpha e}$ is approximately equal to $(1 - \alpha_{b0})f_{\alpha b}$, where α_{b0} is the low-frequency value of α_b. Since α_{b0} is very close to unity, the α_e cutoff frequency $f_{\alpha e}$ is normally one or two orders of magnitude lower than $f_{\alpha b}$.

Using eqs. 2.22 and 2.23, discussed in Chapter 2, we obtain the variation of α_b with frequency:

$$\alpha_b = \alpha_{b0} \cosh p/\cosh p\sqrt{1 + j2.5\omega/\omega_{\alpha b}p^2} \tag{7.8}$$

The variation of α_e with frequency can be calculated from eqs. 7.7 and 7.8. This has been done and the results are plotted in Fig. 7.5. Figure 7.5 gives the variation of the magnitude and the phase shift of α_e as a function of the normalized frequency $f/f_{\alpha b}$ for different values of α_{b0}. If the load impedance of a common-emitter amplifier is low, the gain per stage is approximately proportional to the short-circuit current-amplification factor squared. The curves in Fig. 7.5 indicate that, if the upper frequency approaches f_{ab}, a transistor with a small α_{b0} is about as good as a transistor having a high α_{b0} and the same f_{ab}. The curves of Fig. 7.5 also may be used to indicate approximately the quality

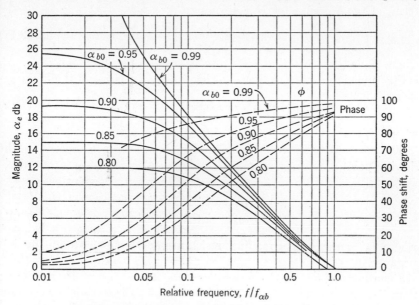

Fig. 7.5   The variation of α_e with normalized frequency

of transistor required in the video amplifier, as determined by the gain per stage desired in the amplifier.

If the frequencies concerned are all considerably lower than f_{ab}, an approximate expression for the variation of α_b with frequency is (see Chapter 2)

$$\alpha_b \cong \alpha_{b0}/(1 + jf/f_{ab}) \tag{7.9}$$

Using the relation of eq. 7.7,

$$\alpha_e \cong \alpha_{b0}/(1 - \alpha_{b0} + jf/f_{ab}) \tag{7.10}$$

Without high-frequency compensation the coupling circuit of Fig. 7.4 becomes, at high frequencies, that shown in Fig. 7.6. C_1 is the stray

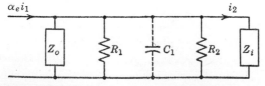

Fig. 7.6   The high-frequency equivalent circuit of an RC-coupled transistor amplifier without high-frequency compensation

capacitance of the circuit. The reactances of C and C_3 of Fig. 7.4 are negligible. The current-amplification factor α_e is given approximately by eq. 7.10. Z_o is the output impedance of the preceding stage. In terms of the h parameters,

$$Z_o = (h_{11e} + Z_g)/(\Delta^h_e + h_{22e}Z_g) \tag{7.11}$$

where Z_g is the source impedance seen by the preceding transistor. Z_i is the input impedance of the following stage. In terms of the h parameters Z_i is

$$Z_i = (\Delta^h_e + h_{11}Y_l)/(h_{22e} + Y_l) \tag{7.12}$$

where Y_l is the load admittance of the following stage.

The common-emitter h parameters are discussed in Chapter 2. The driving-point parameters are:

$$h_{11e} = r_b' + z_\epsilon/(1 - \alpha_b) \tag{7.13a}$$

$$h_{22e} = (g_c + j\omega C_c)/(1 - \alpha_b) \tag{7.13b}$$

where r_b' = the base-spreading resistance, z_ϵ = emitter diffusion impedance, g_c = collector conductance, C_c = collector capacitance.

Since normally Z_i is much smaller than Z_o, if R_1 and R_2 are larger than Z_i and the reactance of C_1 is high, the gain per stage is the current-amplification factor α_e squared. The curves in Fig. 7.5 show the gain per stage decreasing very rapidly with frequency. A compensating circuit is evidently needed in order to obtain a flat frequency response.

7.3.4　Interstage Peaking

Figure 7.7 shows the equivalent of a circuit containing both series and shunt peaking elements. Z_o is the output impedance of the pre-

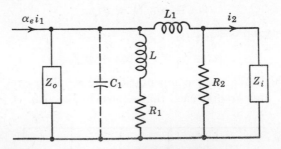

Fig. 7.7　Series-shunt peaking

ceding stage. Z_i is the input impedance of the following stage. C_1 is the stray capacitance. Inductances L and L_1 serve as the shunt and series peaking elements, respectively. The current amplification is

$$A_i = \frac{i_2}{i_1}$$

$$= \frac{\alpha_e R_2/[R_2 Z_i + j\omega L_1(R_2 + Z_i)]}{1/Z_o + j\omega C_1 + 1/(R_1 + j\omega L) + (R_2 + Z_i)/[R_2 Z_i + j\omega L_1(R_2 + Z_i)]}$$

$$(7.14)$$

If, as is usually the case, $R_2 \gg Z_i$, then eq. 7.14 can be simplified to

$$A_i \cong \frac{\alpha_e/(Z_i + j\omega L_1)}{1/Z_o + j\omega C_1 + 1/(R_1 + j\omega L) + 1/(Z_i + j\omega L_1)} \qquad (7.15)$$

Using eq. 7.13a for Z_i and eq. 7.13b for $1/Z_o$ as the approximations, the current amplification as given by eq. 7.14 or 7.15 can be calculated.

Let f_1 be the low-end cutoff frequency and f_3 be the high-end cutoff frequency of the video band. A medium frequency can be represented by f_2. Then $f_1 \ll f_2 \ll f_3$. In order to make a general study, let eq. 7.15 be normalized at f_3 by using the following relations:

$$k_1 = R_1/R_i \qquad (7.16)$$

$$k_2 = 2\pi f_3 L/R_i \qquad (7.17)$$

$$k_3 = 2\pi f_3 L_1/R_i \qquad (7.18)$$

$$k_4 = 2\pi f_0 C_1 R_i \qquad (7.19)$$

where R_i is the low-frequency value of Z_i. We have approximately

$$R_i \cong r_b' + r_e(1 - \alpha_{b0}) \qquad (7.20)$$

Using eq. 7.9 for α_b, eq. 7.10 for α_e, and eq. 7.13b for $1/Z_o$, we have

$$1/Z_o = (g_c + j\omega C_c)(1 + jf/f_{\alpha b})/(1 - \alpha_{b0} + jf/f_{\alpha b}) \qquad (7.21)$$

At frequency f_3, eq. 7.15 becomes

$$(A_i)_{f3} \cong \frac{\alpha_{b0}/(1 - \alpha_{b0} + jf_3/f_{\alpha b})}{1 + (Z_i/R_i + jk_3)[R_i/Z_o + jk_4 + 1/(k_1 + jk_2)]} \qquad (7.22)$$

If L and L_1 are zero, the effect of the stray capacitance C_1 and of the output impedance Z_o may be neglected, and eq. 7.22 reduces to

$$(A_i)_{f3} \cong [\alpha_{b0}/(1 - \alpha_{b0} + jf_3/f_{\alpha b})]k_1/(k_1 + Z_i/R_i) \qquad (7.23)$$

Using eq. 7.13a for Z_i,

$$Z_i/R_i = r_b'/R_i + z_e/R_i(1 - \alpha_b) \qquad (7.24)$$

where z_ϵ can be approximated by the expression [4]

$$z_\epsilon = r_\epsilon/(1 + jf/f_{ab}) \tag{7.25}$$

As an example, the fraction $k_1/(k_1 + Z_i/R_i)$ in eq. 7.23 is plotted in Fig. 7.8 for typical values of $r_b' = 100$ ohms, $\alpha_{b0} = 0.95$, $r_\epsilon = 25$ ohms, and values of $k_1 = 2, 1, \frac{1}{2}, \frac{1}{4}$. Since the input impedance Z_i decreases with frequency, a very simple high-frequency compensation scheme can be obtained by using a small value of R_1. Figure 7.8 shows that for a frequency range from $0.01 f_{ab}$ to f_{ab} a compensation corresponding to

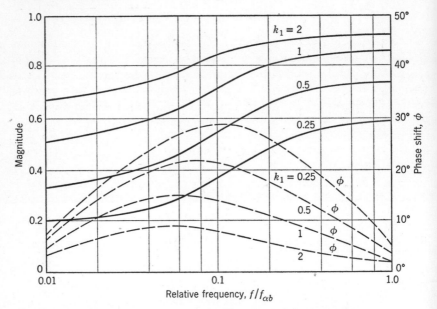

Fig. 7.8   Shunt peaking—the response of $k_1/(k_1 + Z_i/R_i)$

2.7 db can be obtained for $k_1 = 2$, 4.4 db for $k_1 = 1$, 6.8 db for $k_1 = \frac{1}{2}$, and 9.2 db for $k_1 = \frac{1}{4}$. However, since resistance R_1 also determines the gain per stage at low and medium frequencies, a low value of R_1 means low gain. The value of R_1 is therefore dictated by the required gain per stage at medium frequencies.

If L_1 is zero and L is not zero, a simple two-terminal high-frequency compensation circuit is obtained as shown in Fig. 7.9. Equation 7.22 is reduced to

$$(A_i)_{f3} \cong \frac{\alpha_{b0}/(1 - \alpha_{b0} + jf_3/f_{ab})}{1 + (Z_i/R_i)[(R_i/Z_o + jk_4 + 1/(k_1 + jk_2)]} \tag{7.26}$$

At an intermediate frequency f_2, $|Z_o| \gg R_i$ and the current amplification is approximately

$$(A_i)_{f2} \cong [\alpha_{b0}/(1 - \alpha_{b0})]k_1/(1 + k_1) \qquad (7.27)$$

Equating the magnitude of $(A_i)_{f3}$ in eq. 7.26 to the magnitude of $(A_i)_{f2}$ of eq. 7.27, the relation between k_1 and k_2 can be calculated.

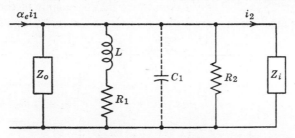

Fig. 7.9   Equivalent circuit for shunt peaking

If L is zero and L_1 is not zero, a simple series-peaking circuit is obtained. The equivalent circuit is shown in Fig. 7.10. Since the input impedance Z_i is normally small, any stray capacitance in parallel with it may be neglected. C_1 represents the stray capacitance at the output

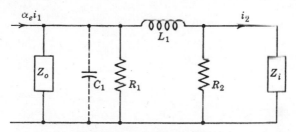

Fig. 7.10   Series peaking

terminal of the preceding stage. Equation 7.22 is now reduced to

$$(A_i)_{f3} \cong \frac{\alpha_{b0}/(1 - \alpha_{b0} + jf_3/f_{ab})}{1 + (Z_i/R_i + jk_3)(R_i/Z_o + jk_4 + 1/k_1)} \qquad (7.28)$$

By equating the magnitude of eq. 7.27 to the magnitude of eq. 7.28, the relation between k_1 and k_3 can be calculated.

7.3.5   High-Frequency Peaking by Impedance Transformation

It has been observed that the short-circuit current amplification of a common-emitter stage gradually decreases to unity as the frequency increases although there is still several decibels gain available. This gain can be utilized at the high-frequency end of a video amplifier. If some sort of impedance transformation is used. Consequently, the bandwidth can be extended, or the gain per stage can be increased to a higher value than otherwise possible.

Figure 7.11 shows the equivalent of a circuit employing the principle of impedance transformation. Z_o is the output impedance of the preceding stage; C_1 is the stray capacitance at the output of the preceding stage. The stray capacitance at the input of the following stage is neg-

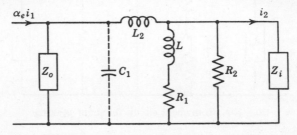

Fig. 7.11   High-frequency peaking by impedance transformation

lected because the input impedance is normally small. Inductances L_2 and L are designed to perform the impedance transformation.

Let the signal current fed into the second stage be i_2; then, neglecting R_2, the current amplification is

$$A_i = i_2/i_1 = [\alpha_e Y_1/(1/Z_o + j\omega C_1 + Y_1)]$$
$$\times \{(1/Z_i)/[(1/Z_o) + 1/(R_1 + j\omega L)]\} \quad (7.29)$$

where $Y_1 = 1/\{j\omega L_2 + [Z_i(R_1 + j\omega L)/(Z_i + R_1 + j\omega L)]\}$

The design problem becomes similar to that of an RF amplifier with a very low-Q single-tuned circuit.

7.3.6   High-Frequency Peaking by Feedback

The high-frequency peaking circuits described above are designed such that the amplitude of the signal current going into the next stage is constant with respect to frequency over the required frequency band. The medium-frequency response is reduced by using a relatively small resistance R_1 in the collector circuit. However, for transistors having a low-frequency alpha, α_{b0}, of 0.99 or larger, the common-emitter short-circuit current-amplification factor α_{e0} is very large, and at the same time the α_e cutoff frequency $f_{\alpha e} = f_{\alpha b}(1 - \alpha_{b0})$ is low. A reduction of R_1 to a very small value will decrease the gain at medium frequencies, and it is necessary to use a large shunt-peaking inductance at the high end.

Since the required value of R_1 is directly proportional to the medium-frequency input impedance of the following stage, it follows that, if the input impedance can be changed by a feedback circuit, the requirement on R_1 will also change. Figure 7.12 shows a feedback circuit consisting

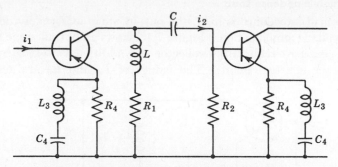

Fig. 7.12   High-frequency peaking by feedback

of R_4, L_3, and C_4 in the emitter circuit. With this feedback network, the short-circuit input impedance h_{11} is given by

$$h_{11} \cong h_{11e} + Z_3(1 + h_{21b}) \tag{7.30}$$

also
$$h_{21} \cong h_{21e} \tag{7.31}$$

where $Z_3 = jR_4(\omega L_3 - 1/\omega C_4)/[R_4 + j(\omega L_3 - 1/\omega C_4)]$

The exact output impedance of such a stage can be calculated by using eq. 7.11. However the open-circuit output impedance $1/h_{22}$ can be used as an approximation:

$$1/h_{22} = 1/h_{22e} + Z_3 \cong 1/h_{22e} \tag{7.32}$$

The equivalent circuit shown in Fig. 7.9 can now be used to calculate the gain per stage by using eq. 7.30 for Z_i and eq. 7.32 for Z_o. Thus

$$A_i = \alpha_e \frac{1/[h_{11e} + Z_3(1 + h_{21e})]}{h_{22e} + 1/(R_1 + j\omega L) + j\omega C_1 + 1/[h_{11e} + Z_3(1 + h_{21e})]} \tag{7.33}$$

At the resonant frequency of L_3 and C_4 (Fig. 7.12) the feedback impedance Z_3 becomes zero, and the gain has a peak at that frequency. The sharpness of this peak can be designed to meet the requirement by using the appropriate L_3/C_4 ratio and Q of the inductance L_3.

7.4   Output Stages

The output stage is treated separately from the intermediate stages, since the load impedance of the output stage is the actual load of the

system. This load may be of high impedance when the video amplifier
is used to drive a cathode ray tube, or small when the output stage is
used to deliver the amplified signal into a transmission line.

7.4.1 High-Impedance Load

If the load impedance is high, the output stage is normally designed
to give voltage amplification. Figure 7.13 shows an output stage having
a shunt-peaking circuit in the collector and additional peaking by feedback in the emitter circuit. The values of L_4 and R_5 are generally

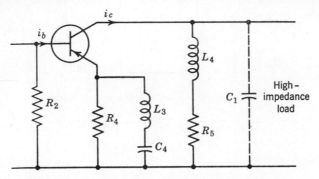

Fig. 7.13   Output stage with high-impedance load

larger than L and R_1 of the cascaded stage in Fig. 7.12. The values of
R_4, L_3, and C_4 will also usually be different from those in Fig. 7.12.

The values of R_5 and L_4 are chosen to obtain maximum possible impedance without limiting the bandwidth. Since the impedance on the
output side is larger than the input impedance, the output stage may
have voltage amplification even if the short-circuit current-amplification
factor h_{21b} is close to unity.

7.4.2 Low-Impedance Load

When the output stage of a video amplifier is used to deliver the signal
into a transmission line, the load impedance is usually low, on the order
of 50 to 300 ohms. In electron-tube circuits, the cathode follower stage
is often used. In the transistor video amplifier, the common-collector
configuration has more or less a similar property: its input impedance
is higher than the output impedance. This is especially true when the
frequency is low. As the frequency increases, the input impedance
becomes capacitive and decreases in magnitude. Since the input impedance of this last stage is part of the load of the video stage preceding
it, the design of the preceding stage must take the properties of this
input impedance into account.

Figure 7.14a shows a common-collector output stage feeding a low-impedance load R_l. The equivalent circuit of the output side can be drawn as shown in Fig. 7.14b, where Z_o represents the output impedance of the common-collector stage. The values of L_5 and R_6 are usually much smaller than L_4 and R_5 in Fig. 7.13. The output impedance Z_o

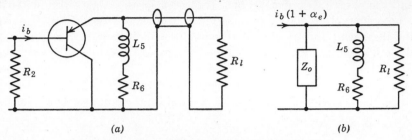

(a)   (b)

Fig. 7.14   Output stage with low-impedance load

can be calculated from eq. 7.11, using the common-collector h parameters.

7.4.3   The Output Power Capability

The output voltage is an additional requirement that is usually specified for a video amplifier. The problems encountered in transistor video-amplifier design are very similar to those for electron-tube video amplifiers. The available output voltage of an electron-tube video amplifier is determined by the product of the amplification of the stage and the grid cutoff voltage of the last tube. Therefore, for a given bandwidth, the output capability is limited only by the properties of the tube used. This is also true for the transistor video amplifier. For a given bandwidth, the output capability is limited by the properties of the transistor used. The properties involved are: (a) the ability to maintain stable operation when biased with large emitter current and high collector voltage, (b) linear V_{CB}, I_C characteristics with I_B as parameter, (c) good high-frequency properties maintained at the high bias point. In short, the above requirements specify a good high-frequency power transistor. The accompanying table will give an idea of the required power-handling capability of the output transistor.

Bandwidth, MC	Output Voltage, V_{pp}	Minimum D-C Standby Power-Handling Capability
4	100	1 watt
4	50	250 mw
2	100	500 mw
2	50	150 mw

High-frequency small-signal transistors are generally measured and specified at a low power bias point, such as $I_E = 1$ ma, $V_{CB} = 5$ volts. This bias point is typical for small-signal operation. However, in a video amplifier, if the input signal is large, the emitter bias current and the collector bias voltage must be much higher than 1 ma and 5 volts, and the electrical properties of a transistor at this high bias point will be considerably different from those at the small bias values. One of the important factors that determines the high-frequency response of the amplifier, the α_b cutoff frequency $f_{\alpha b}$, deteriorates with increase of I_E, and an increase in V_{CB} only improves it slightly. Since the design of a video-amplifier stage is based on the current amplification of each stage, the behavior of $f_{\alpha b}$ has a direct effect on the bandwidth obtainable from a given transistor.

7.5   Input Impedance of a Video Amplifier

The principles of design of intermediate and output stages have been discussed with the assumption that a signal current i_1 (or i_b) is given. The peaking circuits are so designed that this signal current is amplified, but its relative amplitude is kept constant over the required frequency band. In practice, the signal fed into a video amplifier is either obtained from the detector following a video IF amplifier, from the transmission pick-up devices, or from a transmission cable. For the first two cases, the signal sources usually have a high internal impedance.

If the input stage of the video amplifier is a common-emitter amplifier with negative feedback, the input impedance is given approximately by eq. 7.30. If a common-collector stage is used as the input stage, then the input impedance is approximately

$$Z_i \cong Z_l(1 + \alpha_e) \qquad (7.34)$$

The impedance Z_l includes the input impedance of the following stage and of the peaking circuit preceding it. The input impedance given by eq. 7.30 or by eq. 7.34 decreases as the frequency increases. However, since the signal source has a high internal impedance, it acts like a constant-current generator. If the input stage discussed above is connected directly to this signal source, then the signal current will be practically constant with respect to frequency as long as the signal voltage is constant.

If the input signal is small compared with the bias current I_E of the first stage, the first peaking network will normally be connected between the first and second stages. However, when the input signal is relatively large, the amplified signal can drive the first transistor amplifier either to emitter current cutoff or to collector voltage cutoff. This

phenomenon is especially evident at low signal frequencies when the
current amplification is high.   To prevent such clipping, a frequency-
compensating circuit is sometimes necessary at the input side of the
first stage.   This circuit is used to attenuate part of the signal current
at low frequencies when the gain of the transistor amplifier is high.
This circuit can be either a simple shunt-peaking circuit as shown in

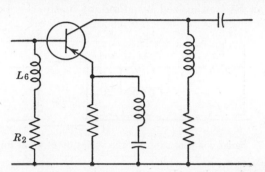

Fig. 7.15   Shunt peaking in the base circuit of the first video-amplifier stage

Fig. 7.15 or a network connected between the signal source and the
first video amplifier stage.

If the signal is obtained from a transmission line, the signal source is
normally of low impedance.   Owing to the variation of the input impedance with frequency, the signal current fed into the video amplifier
will be frequency-dependent.   Although this effect is not desirable, it
can be easily compensated for in the video amplifier.   However, the

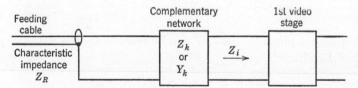

Fig. 7.16   Compensation for the variation of input impedance

effect of the variation of input impedance with frequency on the transmission line is often objectionable.   It is usually necessary to terminate
the transmission line with its characteristic impedance Z_R which is, for a
low-loss line, a resistance R.   Proper termination of the transmission
line is necessary to avoid undesirable reflections and standing waves.

For the purpose of supplying the proper termination, a network should
be inserted between the line and the first video stage to compensate for
the variation of input impedance as shown in Fig. 7.16.   Let the input

impedance of the transistor be Z_i. If the characteristic impedance R is greater than or equal to the real component of Z_i, then series compensation can be used as in Fig. 7.17. Thus, setting

$$Z_i + Z_k = R \tag{7.35}$$

and given Z_i as a function of frequency, the series complementary impedance Z_k can be synthesized by standard methods. For instance, if

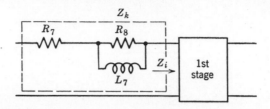

Fig. 7.17 Series compensation for the variation of input impedance

the short-circuit input impedance h_{11e} of the common-emitter configuration is used as the input impedance Z_i,

$$Z_i \cong h_{11e} = r_{b}' + z_{\epsilon}/(1 - \alpha_b)$$

The complementary impedance Z_k is

$$Z_k = R - r_{b}' - z_{\epsilon}/(1 - \alpha_b) \tag{7.36}$$

Using the approximations 7.9 and 7.25, we find

$$Z_k = \{[(R - r_{b}')(1 - \alpha_{b0}) - r_\epsilon] + j(R - r_{b}')f/f_{\alpha b}\}/(1 - \alpha_{b0} + jf/f_{\alpha b}) \tag{7.37}$$

The impedance given by eq. 7.37 can be realized by the network shown in Fig. 7.17 where

$$R_7 = R - r_{b}' - r_\epsilon/(1 - \alpha_{b0})$$

$$R_8 = r_\epsilon/(1 - \alpha_{b0})$$

$$L_7 = r_\epsilon/2\pi f_{\alpha 0}(1 - \alpha_{b0})^2$$

If the characteristic impedance R is smaller than the real component of Z_i, shunt compensation can be used. Thus:

$$1/Z_i + 1/Z_k = 1/R \tag{7.38}$$

or $$1/Z_k = (Z_i - R)/RZ_i$$

This leads to the network shown in Fig. 7.18.

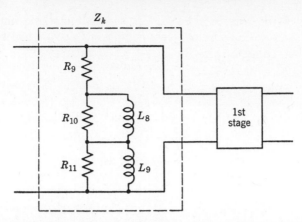

Fig. 7.18   Shunt compensation for the variation of input impedance

When the first stage is operated in a common-base configuration for the purpose of better impedance matching at low impedance level, the same type of series or shunt compensation principles can be used.

7.6   Example of Video-Amplifier Design

In order to illustrate the principles of designing a transistor video amplifier, a numerical example is given below. The properties of the transistor used in this example are assumed to be as follows: $r_e = 25$ ohms, $r_b' = 100$ ohms, $\alpha_{no} = 0.95$, $f_{ab} = 16$ mc, $C_c = 4$ $\mu\mu$f, and $g_c = 10^{-6}$ mho. The desired bandwidth is 4 mc. The low-frequency cutoff must be $f_1 = 30$ cps.

Since $f_3/f_{ab} = 0.25$, from Fig. 7.5 the gain that can be obtained from each stage is about 10 db (corresponding to $A_i = 3.16$). Using eq. 7.27, at a medium frequency f_2,

$$3.16 = [0.95/(1 - 0.95)]k_1/(1 + k_1) = 19k_1/(1 + k_1)$$

whence $k_1 \cong 0.2$

Equation 7.16 gives $R_1 = 0.2R_i$, where R_i can be computed by eq. 7.20 when there is no feedback.

$$R_i = 100 + 25/(1 - 0.95) = 600 \text{ ohms}$$

When there is feedback in the emitter circuit, R_i is given by eq. 7.30:

$$R_i = 600 + R_4/(1 - 0.95)$$

Using eq. 7.13a for Z_i,

$$\lambda_i = r_v' + r_e/(1 - \alpha_{b0} + jf/f_{ab})$$

at f_3, $(Z_i)_{f3} = 118 - j94$ ohms

Using eq. 7.21 for $1/Z_o$ at f_3,

$$(1/Z_o)_{f3} = (3.6 + j1.7)10^{-4} \text{ mho}$$

The estimated stray circuit capacitance $C_1 = 10 \ \mu\mu\text{f}$; therefore

$$k_4 = 2\pi f_3 C_1 R_i = 25 \times 10^{-5} \times R_i$$

With no feedback $R_i = 600$, and we have $k_4 = 0.15$; and

$$(Z_i/R_i)_{f3} = (118 - j94)/600 = 0.206 - j0.16$$

$$(R_i/Z_o)_{f3} = 0.22 + j0.10$$

and $\alpha_{b0}/(1 - \alpha_{b0} + jf_3/f_{ab}) = 0.95/(0.05 + j0.25)$

$$= 3.73 \lfloor -78.7°$$

Equation 7.22 gives

$$(A_i)_{f3} = 3.73 \lfloor -78.7°/\{1 + (0.20 - j0.16 + jk_3)[0.22 + j0.10$$

$$+ jk_4 + 1/(0.2 + jk_2)]\}$$

$$= 3.73 \lfloor -78.7°/\{1 + [0.20 + j(k_3 - 0.16)][0.22 + 0.2/(0.04$$

$$+ k_2{}^2) + j(0.10 + k_4 - k_2/(0.04 + k_2{}^2)]\}$$

In order to obtain constant amplitude, let the magnitude of $(A_i)_{f3}$ be equal to 3.16, or

$$\left| 1 + [0.20 + j(k_3 - 0.16)]\left[0.22 + \frac{0.2}{0.04 + k_2{}^2} \right.\right.$$

$$\left.\left. + j\left(0.10 + k_4 - \frac{k_2}{0.04 + k_2{}^2} \right) \right] \right| = \frac{3.73}{3.16} = 1.18$$

By inspection, if $k_3 = 0.16$, the above equation reduces to

$$|1 + 0.20[0.22 + 0.2/(0.04 + k_2{}^2)] + j0.20[0.25 - k_2/(0.04 + k_2{}^2)]|$$

$$= 1.18 \quad \text{or} \quad k_2 = 0.59$$

The low-frequency response depends on the value of the blocking condenser C. Since the bias voltage of a transistor is relatively low, the physical size of a 10-μf, 10-volt condenser is not so large that it will produce appreciable additional stray capacitance. Let $C = 10 \ \mu$f. At

$f_1 = 30$ cps, with no low-frequency compensation, the amplification is

$$(A_i)_{f1} = [0.95/(1 - 0.95)][R_1/(R_1 + R_i) + 1/j2\pi f_1 C]$$
$$= 2.55 \,\underline{|36.4°}$$

or 1.9 db down from the medium-frequency gain. Using eq. 7.2 for the low-frequency compensation,

$$|1/[1 + 5(1/R_3 + j\omega C_3)(0.00167 + j0.0019)/(j0.0019)(0.00835$$
$$+ 1/R_3 + j\omega C_3)]| = 1/6$$

or $\quad |[1 + 5(1/R_3 + j\omega C_3)(1 - j0.88)/(0.00835 + 1/R_3 + j\omega C_3)]| = 6$

Let $R_3 = 1500$ ohms; then $C_3 = 50\ \mu f$.

Summarizing the above results, we have

$$R_1 = k_1 R_i = 120 \text{ ohms}$$
$$L = k_2 R_i/2\pi f_3 = 14.1\ \mu h$$
$$L_1 = k_3 R_i/2\pi f_3 = 3.8\ \mu h$$
$$R_3 = 1500 \text{ ohms}$$
$$C_3 = 50\ \mu f$$

The complete circuit is shown in Fig. 7.19.

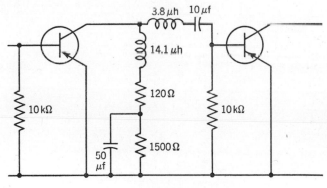

Fig. 7.19   Design example

Problems

1. Using h_{11e} and $1/h_{22e}$ for the low-frequency input and output resistances, respectively, derive a simple expression for low-frequency compensation.

2. In the simple two-terminal shunt-peaking circuit shown in Fig. 7.9, if the effect of the stray capacitance C_1 is negligible, derive an expression for the value of the

peaking inductance L in terms of other circuit parameters and the transistor parameters.

3. If the stray capacitance C_1 in the series-peaking circuit shown in Fig. 7.10 is combined with the output impedance Z_o, derive an expression for the peaking inductance L_1 in terms of other circuit parameters and the transistor parameters. Compare this result with the answer of problem 2.

4. Derive an expression for the current amplification A_i if the peaking-by-feedback circuit is used together with the series-peaking circuit.

5. Given a transistor having the following properties: $r_\epsilon = 25$ ohms, $r_b' = 100$ ohms, $\alpha_{b0} = 0.95$, $f_{ab} = 16$ mc, $C_c = 4$ $\mu\mu$f, and $g_c = 10^{-6}$ mho, plot the common-emitter short-circuit input impedance h_{11e} for frequencies from 60 cps to 4 mc.

6. Find the complementary impedance Z_k for the transistor of problem 5.

Bibliography

1. R. B. Dome, *Television Principles*, McGraw-Hill, 1951.

2. S. Helt, *Practical Television Engineering*, Rinehart, 1950.

3. F. R. Stansel, "The Common-Collector Transistor Amplifier at Carrier Frequencies," *Proc. IRE*, *41*, 1096, (1953).

4. R. L. Pritchard, "Frequency Variations of Junction Transistor Parameters," *Proc. IRE*, *42*, 786 (1954).

5. W. M. Webster, "On the Variation of Junction-Transistor Current-Amplification Factor with Emitter Current," *Proc. IRE*, *42*, 914 (1954).

Chapter 8

Oscillators

8.1 Introduction

The basic requirements of an oscillator circuit are a nonlinear power-gain device, a path for external or internal regenerative feedback, and an external energy source. The use of transistors as nonlinear power-gain elements in oscillators, therefore, does not render obsolete the theory of oscillators which has been developed for electron tubes. On the contrary, as will be shown in the next section, many of the classical electron-tube oscillator configurations may be adapted to transistors by direct analogy.

Nevertheless, since basic differences between transistors and vacuum tubes do exist, the design of transistor oscillators by analogy or duality must not be carried too far. For example, the fact that transistors are less unilateral than electron tubes and that they have a considerable internal phase shift within the frequency range of usable power gain makes the design of high-frequency stable transistor oscillators a good deal more complicated than the design of equivalent electron-tube oscillators. On the other hand, the fact that the static characteristics of transistors are linear over a wider operating range than the corresponding characteristics of electron tubes makes it possible to design transistor oscillators that are considerably more efficient than their electron-tube counterparts.

Oscillators may be divided into two general categories—harmonic and relaxation.[1] In a harmonic oscillator the *instantaneous* excursion of the operating point is essentially restricted to a range of values over which the circuit exhibits a negative resistance, or an impedance with a negative real part. In a relaxation oscillator, the instantaneous excursions of the operating point are not restricted to this region. A characteristic of the harmonic oscillator is that the active element is continually supplying power to the passive elements associated with it. In a relaxation oscillator there is an interchange of power between the active element and the passive elements. One or more of these passive elements must be capable of energy storage, and this interchange of energy usually occurs in a discontinuous or switched manner. The harmonic oscillator generally derives its regenerating action through a feedback circuit which has the required amplitude and phase characteristic to cause oscillation. Thus, the frequency of oscillation is largely determined by the characteristics of this feedback network. The frequency of relaxation oscillators is usually controlled by the charge and discharge times associated with the interchange of energy between the active and the passive elements.

8.2   Harmonic Oscillators

Harmonic oscillators may be considered to be composed of an element of power amplification, a feedback path which returns a part or all of the output power to the input in the proper phase, and a nonlinear element which limits the amplitude of oscillation. The role of the power-amplification element in the harmonic oscillator can be looked upon as supplying energy to replace that which is dissipated in the external circuit elements.

A number of transistor oscillators may be devised, modeled after familiar electron-tube oscillators.[2-4] The frequency of oscillation and oscillator starting conditions can be calculated in a number of ways. One method involves setting down the oscillator equivalent circuit and solving the appropriate mesh or nodal equations. A slight variation of this method results if the oscillator is considered to be composed of a current amplifier and a current-feedback network. It should be emphasized that the oscillator calculations that follow are based on linear-circuit analysis, and hence the starting frequency as determined from this type of analysis in general does not necessarily correspond to the operating frequency. Therefore, the frequency relations that result are in this sense approximations to the actual oscillator frequency.

8.2.1   Phase-Shift Oscillator

Figure 8.1 illustrates a junction-transistor phase-shift oscillator. A feedback path is provided by the network composed of the load resistor R_L, three resistors, and three capacitors. Resistors R_1, R_2, R_3, and R_L serve to bias the transistor so that it operates in the linear range of its characteristics. The starting conditions and operating frequency of this oscillator can be calculated in the following manner. Figure 8.2 shows the general network for a common-emitter feedback oscillator. The transistor equivalent circuit based on the h parameters is incorporated. The oscillator can be considered to be composed of a current amplifier

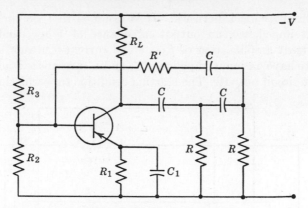

Fig. 8.1   Phase-shift oscillator

$$R_2,\ R_3 \gg h_{11e}\ R' = R - h_{11e}$$

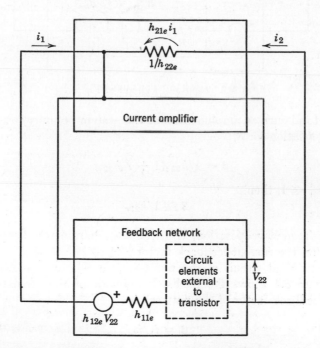

Fig. 8.2   Transistor feedback oscillator

and a current-feedback network. It is assumed that the amplifier has
zero input impedance, an output impedance of $1/h_{22e}$, and a short-
circuit current amplification of h_{21e}. The current-feedback network is
assumed to have an input impedance Z_i and a current-feedback factor β
for a short-circuit output. The starting condition for oscillation, namely

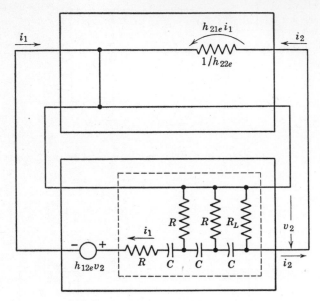

Fig. 8.3   Equivalent circuit of Fig. 8.1

that the total current amplification of the system be unity, leads to the
following relation for β,

$$\beta = 1/h_{21e}(1 + Z_i h_{22e}) \tag{8.1}$$

If $|Z_i h_{22e}| \ll 1$, then

$$\beta \cong 1/h_{21e} \tag{8.2}$$

For high-frequency operation, the transistor parameters become complex; hence, the current-feedback factor β must be complex.

The equivalent circuit of the phase-shift oscillator is shown in Fig.
8.3. Figure 8.4 shows the feedback network of the oscillator. The
current-feedback factor of the network is

$$\beta = i_1/i_2 \tag{8.3}$$

This can be calculated by considering the circuit loop equations. If

$v_2 h_{12e}$ is negligible, then β becomes

$$\beta = R_L R^2 / [(5R + R_L)/\omega^2 C^2 - R^3 - 3R^2 R_L - (6R^2 + 4RR_L$$
$$- 1/\omega^2 C^2)/j\omega C] \quad (8.4)$$

The condition for oscillation is given by eq. 8.2. The real and imaginary parts of eq. 8.4, when equated to the feedback factor β of eq. 8.2, yield

$$h_{21e} R_L R^2 = -R^3 - 3R^2 R_L + (5R + R_L)/\omega^2 C^2 \quad (8.5)$$

and $\qquad (1/j\omega C)[(1/\omega^2 C^2) - 6R^2 - 4RR_L] = 0 \qquad (8.6)$

Hence the angular frequency of oscillation becomes

$$\omega^2 \cong 1/(6R^2 + 4RR_L)C^2 \quad (8.7)$$

and the required current amplification for sustained oscillation is

$$h_{21e} \cong 23 + 29R/R_L + 4R_L/R \quad (8.8)$$

Sustained oscillations will occur if the transistor current transfer ratio is at least the value given by eq. 8.8. If the transistor current transfer

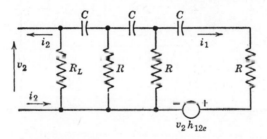

Fig. 8.4   Phase-shift feedback network

ratio is in excess of this value, the output will be limited by the transistor nonlinearities, and a distorted waveform will result.

It is interesting to calculate the minimum transistor current-transfer ratio required to sustain oscillation. Let $R_L = kR$; then eq. 8.8 becomes

$$h_{21e} \cong 23 + 29/k + 4k \quad (8.9)$$

This is a minimum for a value of k equal to approximately 2.7. Hence,

$$R_L \cong 2.7R \quad (8.10)$$

and $\qquad\qquad\qquad h_{21e} \cong 45 \qquad\qquad\qquad (8.11)$

Therefore a transistor with a current transfer ratio of at least 45 is necessary, and R_L should be about 2.7 times the value of R.

The phase-shift oscillator can be modified for power applications by utilizing power transistors as amplifiers in each of the legs of the RC phase-shift network. With three transistors it is possible to obtain three-phase output voltage across the collector load impedances. A discussion of this type of feedback oscillator is presented in Chapter 12.

8.2.2   Colpitts Oscillator

The junction-transistor version of the Colpitts oscillator is illustrated in Fig. 8.5. Capacitors C_1 and C_2 in combination with the inductor L form a resonant tank circuit. A fraction of the current flowing in the

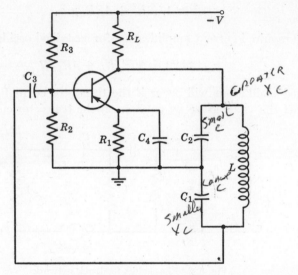

Fig. 8.5   Colpitts-type oscillator

tank circuit is fed back regeneratively to the base circuit of the transistor by way of a low-impedance path furnished by capacitor C_3. The transistor operating point is established by the resistors R_1, R_2, R_3, and R_L. These circuit elements are of sufficient impedance so that the a-c operation of the circuit is not affected.

The oscillator can be analyzed according to the procedure outlined in Sec. 8.2.1. Alternatively, the frequency of oscillation and oscillator starting condition can be determined by writing the loop equations of the equivalent circuit and setting the determinant equal to zero. Figure 8.6 shows an equivalent circuit of the Colpitts oscillator. By the above technique, we obtain

$$(j\omega L + 1/j\omega C_1 + 1/j\omega C_2)[(h_{11b} + 1/j\omega C_1)(-j\omega L - 1/h_{22b})$$

$$+ j\omega L h_{12b} h_{21b}/h_{22b}] + (1/j\omega C_1)[(j\omega L h_{12b} + 1/j\omega C_1)(j\omega L + 1/h_{22b})$$

$$- (j\omega L h_{12b})j\omega L] - (j\omega L)[(j\omega L h_{12b} + 1/j\omega C_1)(h_{21b}/h_{22b})$$

$$- j\omega L(h_{11b} + 1/j\omega C_1)] = 0 \quad (8.12)$$

The oscillator starting conditions and frequency of oscillation are found by setting the real and imaginary components of eq. 8.12 to zero. As- *These Eq.*

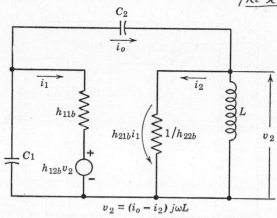

$$v_2 = (i_o - i_2) j\omega L$$

Fig. 8.6   Equivalent circuit of the Colpitts oscillator

suming that the transistor h parameters are real quantities, equating the imaginary portion of eq. 8.12 to zero gives

$$(\omega^2 L - 1/C_1 - 1/C_2)(-L/C_1 - h_{11b}/h_{22b}) + \omega^2 L^2/C_1 - L/C_1{}^2 = 0$$

$$(8.13)$$

from which the angular frequency is given by

$$\omega^2 = 1/LC_T + h_{22b}/C_1C_2h_{11b} \quad (8.14)$$

where

$$C_T = C_1C_2/(C_1 + C_2) \quad (8.15)$$

The starting condition for oscillation, on the other hand, is determined by setting the real component of eq. 8.12 to zero. This leads to the following expression for h_{21e} assuming that ω^2 is very nearly given by $1/LC_T$ and that h_{11b} and h_{12b} can be neglected:

$$h_{21e} = C_1/C_2 \quad (8.16)$$

The frequency of the oscillator of Fig. 8.5 is, therefore, largely determined by a resonant circuit composed of the capacitors C_1 and C_2 in series with the inductance L. Sustained oscillations can occur if C_1 is h_{21e} times the capacitance of C_2.

An interesting variation of the Colpitts oscillator has been described by J. K. Clapp and by other investigators.[5,6] Figure 8.7 illustrates the transistor version of this modification. The principal feature of this

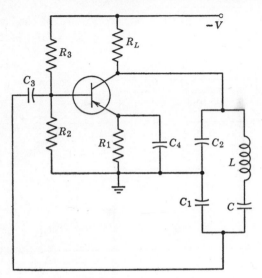

Fig. 8.7   Modified Colpitts oscillator

circuit is that a resonant element composed of an inductance L in series with a capacitor C is substituted for the tuning inductance of the Colpitts oscillator. This arrangement results in substantial improvement in the frequency stability of the oscillator with respect to variations of the transistor parameters with temperature and supply voltage.

If the capacitance represented by the series combination of C_1 and C_2 is large compared with that of capacitor C, the frequency of oscillation is very nearly given by

$$\omega^2 \cong 1/CL \qquad (8.17)$$

and the condition for sustained oscillation is given by eq. 8.16. A further discussion of this oscillator is given in Sec. 8.2.7 of this chapter.

8.2.3   Hartley Oscillator

A junction-transistor version of the Hartley feedback oscillator is illustrated in Fig. 8.8. Feedback in the base circuit of the common-emitter transistor stage is accomplished by capacitor C_2 and by the transformer winding represented by inductance L_2. The mutual inductance M completes the feedback network to the collector circuit. Capacitor C_1, in conjunction with the transformer inductances, forms a resonant circuit which largely determines the frequency of oscillation. The d-c operating point is established by the base bias currents flowing in resistors R_1, R_2, and R_3, and by the oscillator supply voltage V.

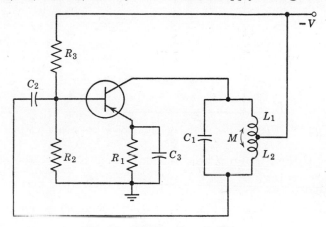

Fig. 8.8   Hartley-type oscillator

An analysis of the oscillator following the method outlined in Sec. 8.2.2 leads to the following expression for the angular frequency:

$$\omega^2 = 1/[C_1(L_1 + L_2 + 2M) - (L_1L_2 - M^2)\, h_{22b}/h_{11b}] \quad (8.18)$$

Oscillations will occur if

$$h_{21e} \cong (L_1 + M)/(L_2 + M) \quad (8.19)$$

For a coupling coefficient of unity, the frequency of oscillation is determined by a resonant circuit consisting of capacitor C_1 in parallel with the combined transformer inductance $(L_1 + L_2 + 2M)$. Oscillations will occur if the inductance $(L_1 + M)$ is approximately equal to the inductance $(L_2 + M)$ times the current-amplification factor h_{21e}.

The tapped inductance of Fig. 8.8 can be a transformer with separate primary and feedback windings such as that of the Hartley-type oscillator illustrated in Fig. 8.9. This arrangement allows an additional degree of flexibility to enter the oscillator design in that it is possible to obtain the d-c base bias current from the collector bias supply or from a separate d-c source. In Fig. 8.9, R_1, R_2, and R_3 constitute the bias network, and

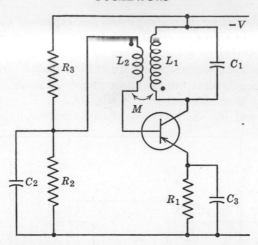

Fig. 8.9   Hartley-type oscillator with separate feedback winding

capacitors C_2 and C_3 provide a low-impedance path for the oscillator feedback current.

The Hartley circuit can be readily modified for push-pull operation by providing center-tapped primary and feedback windings on the trans-

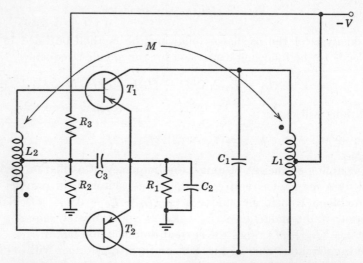

Fig. 8.10   Push-pull Hartley oscillator using coupled coils L_1, L_2

former. Figure 8.10 shows a push-pull version of this oscillator. Oscilla-tory currents flow in the tank circuit formed by the winding L_1 and capacitor C_1. Winding L_2 serves to energize the base circuits of the transistors in the proper phase to sustain oscillation. The d-c operating point is determined by the current flowing in the resistors R_1, R_2 and R_3, and by the oscillator supply voltage V. By operating the transistors in class B or class C, substantially greater power output can be obtained over that realized from the single-ended version.

8.2.4 Tuned-Base Tuned-Emitter Oscillator

Figure 8.11 shows the circuit of an oscillator which employs series-resonant LC tuning elements in the transistor base and emitter circuits.

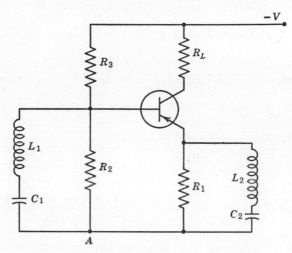

Fig. 8.11   Tuned-base, tuned-emitter oscillator

Capacitor C_1 and inductor L_1 form the base resonant element, and L_2 and C_2 form the emitter resonant element. Resistor R_L connected in the transistor collector circuit is the oscillator load. The resistors R_1, R_2, and R_3 provide d-c bias paths and are usually of large impedance compared with the a-c component values.

The frequency of oscillation and starting condition may be calculated by the previous methods or by considering the simplified equivalent circuit shown in Fig. 8.12. In this circuit R_2 is neglected, and Z_i is the input impedance appearing between the base of the transistor and the point A, neglecting the effect of R_1. If the load resistance R_L is sufficiently small, less than

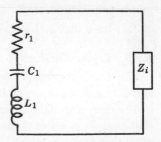

Fig. 8.12 Simplified equivalent circuit of the oscillator of Fig. 8.11

1000 ohms for typical small-signal transistors, and $\omega/\omega_{ab} \gg 1 - \alpha_{b0}$, then the input impedance is approximately

$$Z_i \cong (\omega_{ab}/\omega)[(\omega L_2 - 1/\omega C_2) + (r_b' + r_2)(\omega/\omega_{ab})]$$

$$+ j[(\omega L_2 - 1/\omega C_2) - (\omega_{ab}/\omega)(r_\epsilon + r_2)] \quad (8.20)$$

where r_2 represents the loss resistance of L_2. The loop impedance Z of Fig. 8.12 is then

$$Z \cong r_1 + (\omega_{ab}/\omega)[(\omega L_2 - 1/\omega C_2) + (r_b' + r_2)(\omega/\omega_{ab})]$$

$$+ j\{(\omega L_1 - 1/\omega C_1) + [(\omega L_2 - 1/\omega C_2) - (\omega_{ab}/\omega)(r_\epsilon + r_2)]\}$$

$$(8.21)$$

For series resonance the imaginary component is zero; hence

$$\omega L_1 \cong -\omega L_2 + 1/\omega C_1 + 1/\omega C_2 + (\omega_{ab}/\omega)(r_\epsilon + r_2) \quad (8.22)$$

and the frequency of oscillation is given by

$$\omega^2 \cong [\omega_{ab}(r_\epsilon + r_2) + 1/C_1 + 1/C_2]/(L_1 + L_2) \quad (8.23)$$

If $\omega_{ab}(r_\epsilon + r_2)$ is small, then

$$\omega^2 \cong 1/[(L_1 + L_2)C_1C_2/(C_1 + C_2)] \quad (8.24)$$

In order that the circuit may oscillate, the input impedance Z_i must exhibit a negative resistance, and this occurs when

$$1/\omega C_2 > \omega L_2 + (r_b' + r_2)(\omega/\omega_{ab}) \quad (8.25)$$

The frequency of oscillation is largely determined by a tank circuit composed of the inductances L_1 and L_2 in series with capacitors C_1 and C_2, and it is necessary that the reactance of C_2 be larger than the reactance of L_2 plus a factor that takes into account the loop resistances in Z.

8.2.5 Crystal Oscillators

For fixed-frequency oscillators, a much higher degree of frequency stability can be achieved by replacing the frequency-controlling element in the conventional transistor oscillator by a quartz crystal. This substitution is possible since the equivalent electric circuit of a quartz crystal approximates an LC circuit with an extremely high Q. If the crystal is made with a very small temperature coefficient (so-called GT cut) a high degree of stability can be achieved.

Figure 8.13 shows the circuit diagram of a crystal-controlled oscillator where the tank circuit is replaced by a crystal. For a high degree of stability, it is desirable to have the capacitances C_1 and C_2 as large as

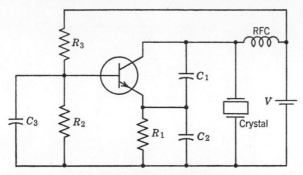

Fig. 8.13   Crystal oscillator

possible.[7] Typical values of these capacitances for many of the n-p-n and p-n-p junction transistors operating in the frequency range 0.1 to 1 mc are as follows: $C_1 = 40$ to 200 $\mu\mu$f, $C_2 = 1000$ to $10{,}000$ $\mu\mu$f.

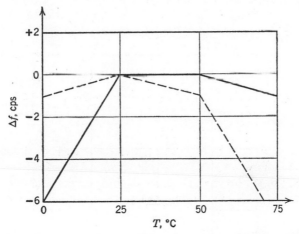

Fig. 8.14   Frequency characteristics of crystal-controlled oscillators

Figure 8.14 shows frequency deviation as a function of temperature, obtained from two typical 100-kc crystals used in the circuit of Fig. 8.13. The frequency-stability-versus-temperature characteristic of the oscillator is controlled primarily by the crystal since the change in the resonant frequency of crystals is similar to the change shown in the curves of Fig. 8.14.

Another 100-kc crystal oscillator of high stability [8] is shown in Fig 8.15. In this circuit a junction transistor and a high precision quartz crystal are used. The tank circuit is tuned to 100 kc. The frequency

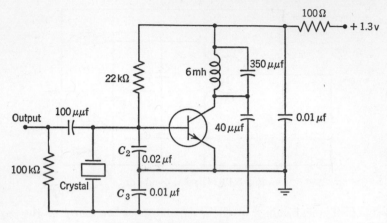

Fig. 8.15　Crystal oscillator circuit

stability of this oscillator is one part in 10^8 per degree centigrade or per 0.1 volt change of supply voltage. Such an oscillator can be used as a secondary frequency standard for calibration of laboratory instruments.

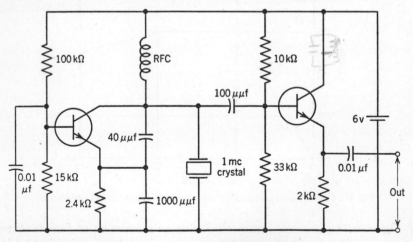

Fig. 8.16　Crystal-controlled oscillator

Figure 8.16 shows a two-stage, 1-mc crystal-controlled oscillator where the second stage serves as a buffer to minimize the effect of the load on the frequency of oscillation. With this arrangement the frequency does not change significantly for values of load resistance in excess of 10 kilohms.

For high-frequency crystal-controlled oscillators, the transistor triode can be replaced by a tetrode. The crystal should be used in the series-resonant mode in order to minimize the effect of the reactive components of the tetrode parameters on the frequency of oscillation. Figure 8.17 shows an experimental tetrode oscillator operating in the 50 mc to 100 mc range. The crystal is operated in the series-resonant mode; at the

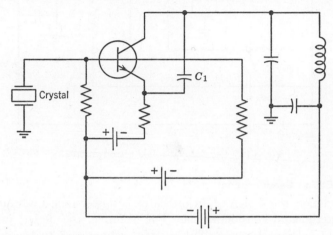

Fig. 8.17   Crystal-controlled tetrode oscillator

resonant frequency the base is therefore practically short-circuited to ground. The emitter-to-base capacitance of the emitter junction and the feedback capacitance C_1 form a voltage divider, and a proper amount of output signal across the tank circuit in the collector circuit is fed back to the emitter. At the resonant frequency of the crystal, this circuit functions in a manner similar to that of the Colpitts oscillator.

With some tetrodes, the internal feedback from collector to emitter may be sufficient to cause oscillation. Consequently, the external feedback capacitance C_1 is not always necessary.

The stability of the frequency depends largely on the amount of resistance in the base circuit at the resonant frequency. Thus, the effective Q of the crystal must be high and the base-spreading resistance r_b' must be small.

Figure 8.18 shows a modification where the crystal is inserted in the emitter lead. Feedback from collector to base is accomplished by inductive coupling. At the resonant frequency, the emitter is short-circuited to ground, and the circuit functions as a feedback oscillator.

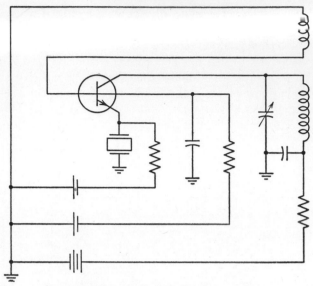

Fig. 8.18   Crystal-controlled tetrode oscillator

8.2.6   Design Considerations

In practice, the design of an oscillator is based upon both analytical and experimental considerations. For example, the design procedure for a typical low-power oscillator might correspond to the following outline: (1) a transistor is selected that has adequate power gain at the proposed oscillator frequency; (2) the type of oscillator circuit is selected; (3) a suitable bias point is decided upon, and d-c stabilization networks are incorporated if desired; (4) the values of the tank-circuit components are determined.

Once the transistor and basic circuit are selected, an appropriate operating point must be established, following the bias methods discussed in Chapter 3. If the oscillator incorporates a tank circuit, its component values are primarily dependent upon the desired operating frequency and the effective Q of the circuit. A value for the tank inductance can be obtained by considering the loaded Q of the tuned circuit. The parallel-resonant circuit may be considered to be shunted by the output impedance of the transistor, the transformed input impedance, and the oscillator load which may be inductively or capacitively coupled to the tank circuit. If R_L is the effective oscillator load resistance, r_o the resistive component of the transistor output impedance, and ω_0 the oscillator frequency, then a first approximation for the tuning inductance L is

$$L \cong (1/Q\omega_0)/(1/R_L + 1/r_o) \tag{8.26}$$

and the tank-circuit capacitance should be approximately

$$C \cong 1/\omega_0{}^2 L \tag{8.27}$$

In eq. 8.26, Q pertains to the loaded tank circuit, and must be high for good frequency stability. A trimming capacitor C' can be used to make final adjustments of the oscillator frequency to the desired value.

8.2.7 Frequency Stabilization Techniques

Frequency stability is an essential requirement for most oscillators, including transistor oscillators which usually suffer from changes in frequency due to variation either in the transistor or in the circuit parameters. For example, a change in collector or emitter potential will result in a change in the collector capacitance. A change in the coupled load causes a change in the equivalent shunt resistance of the tank circuit with a consequent change in frequency. Another cause of frequency instability is the effect of temperature on the transistor parameters.

The frequency stability can be defined as the ratio of the relative change in frequency to the relative change in the factor causing this frequency shift. Thus, for example the voltage-frequency stability is

$$D_{fv} = (\Delta f/f)/(\Delta V/V) \tag{8.28}$$

There are several measures that may be taken in order to improve the stability of the transistor oscillator. However, the frequency stability of an oscillator can never exceed that of its frequency-controlling element (e.g. the tank circuit), unless there is a special means of providing compensation for any frequency shift due to this controlling element. Therefore, in considering the merits of different oscillator circuits, it is convenient to assume that the frequency-controlling element by itself is stable, and to examine the extent to which the frequency is changed by the presence of the transistor.

Since the parameters of the transistor vary with the operating point, one technique of frequency stabilization is to maintain a constant supply voltage. A low-voltage silicon breakdown diode circuit is one example of such a constant-voltage supply (see Chapter 3). If the supply voltage of the transistor cannot be maintained constant, then some form of compensation network must be used which will minimize the influence of the transistor parameters on the frequency of oscillation.

It may be shown that the frequency of oscillation of a tube oscillator can be made almost independent of the parameters of the tube by inserting suitable reactances in series with the grid or with the plate. Similar techniques may be employed for transistors. In one such arrangement, a conventional Colpitts transistor oscillator employs a stabilizing inductance connected in series with the base and having a reactance

$$X_b = X_1(1 + X_1/X_2) \tag{8.29}$$

where X_1 and X_2 are the capacitive reactances in the tank circuit.

If a stabilizing inductance is used in series with the collector, its reactance should be

$$X_c = -X_2(1 + X_2/X_1) \tag{8.30}$$

For a Hartley oscillator, these reactances have the following values.

Base stabilization:

$$X_b = [(X_2 + X_m)/(X_1 + X_m)][2X_m - X_1(X_2 + X_m)/(X_1 + X_m)] - X_2 \tag{8.31}$$

Collector stabilization:

$$X_c = [(X_1 + X_m)/(X_2 + X_m)][2X_m - X_2(X_1 + X_m)/(X_2 + X_m)] - X_1 \tag{8.32}$$

Since these compensating reactances are frequency-dependent, this method is not suitable for variable-frequency oscillators.

Stability can be achieved with respect to changes of the internal capacitances of the transistor by connecting the transistor to points on the tuned circuit of as low impedance as possible.

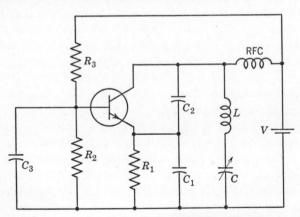

Fig. 8.19   Clapp oscillator

Stability against variation of tube parameters, due to changes in supply voltages, can be achieved by substituting a series LC circuit for the tuning inductance of the Colpitts' oscillator.[5]   A transistorized version of this type of oscillator is shown in Fig. 8.19.   Experimental results with this oscillator have shown that by using C_1 and C_2 on the order of a few hundred micromicrofarads, stability on the order of 200 to 400 parts per million can be easily obtained over a frequency range of 0.1 to 1.0 mc,[9] for a 10% change in supply voltage.

Another important problem is associated with operation in the linear portion of the transistor characteristic in order to keep the amplitude of the harmonics at a minimum. This will require some form of limiter

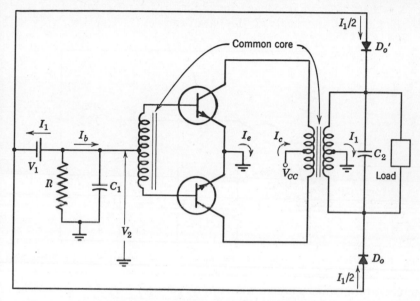

Fig. 8.20   Variable-frequency oscillator

external to the active element. Such a limiter is particularly important for variable-frequency oscillators since the amplitude of oscillation ordinarily varies with the tuning.

Figure 8.20 shows such a circuit arrangement.[10] This is a push-pull version of a transistor oscillator using two junction transistors in class A, B, or C operation (depending on output loading and the transformer turns ratio). The amplitude limitation and stabilization have been achieved in this circuit by comparing the output voltage swing with a fixed-reference voltage and feeding back the difference voltage so as to control the base current. Thus, whenever either end of the output winding attempts to swing negatively below the voltage $V_2 - V_1$, either diode D_o or D_o' conducts a pulse of current. If I_b is large enough to sustain an output swing larger than $V_2 - V_1$, these current pulses will flow periodically at twice the frequency of oscillation, giving rise to the average current I_1. This current subtracts from the base current I_{b_1} thereby reducing the amplitude of oscillation until it barely exceeds $V_2 - V_1$. The magnitude of I_1 is not critical and can be adjusted to any desired value by adjusting R.

Further refinement of this circuit can be achieved by obtaining the reference voltage from a source such as a breakdown diode instead of the battery V_1.

A serious cause of frequency instability is temperature. This is due to the fact that practically all the parameters of the transistor vary with

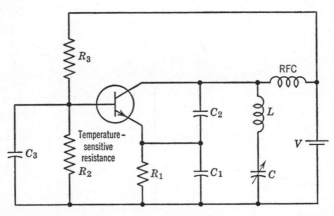

Fig. 8.21   Frequency stabilization by means of temperature-sensitive resistance

temperature, which, unlike the supply voltage, may be impractical or impossible to control. One of the transistor parameters that is affected considerably by temperature variation is the collector back current I_{CO}. A variation of I_{CO} produces a change in operating point and there-fore causes additional changes in the transistor characteristics.

Another property of the transistor that is temperature-sensitive is the input capacitance. For example, in the circuit of Fig. 8.19, the capacitance C_1 is one of the frequency-determining elements. This capacitance is also in parallel with the emitter diffusion capacitance of the transistor C_ϵ given by:

$$C_\epsilon \cong qI_E/kT\omega_{\alpha b} \tag{8.33}$$

This diffusion capacitance, which may have a value up to several thou-sand micromicrofarads, is therefore directly proportional to the emitter current of the transistor. By controlling the magnitude of this current one can control the capacitance C_ϵ and hence the frequency of oscillation. This may be accomplished as shown in Fig. 8.21. Resistors R_1, R_2, and

R_3 supply the bias for the transistor. R_2 is a temperature-sensitive resistance with negative temperature coefficient. By proper choice of the characteristic of this resistance, the effect of temperature on frequency can be minimized.

8.3   Relaxation Oscillators

Relaxation oscillators are characterized by regenerative circuits or devices in combination with RC or RL elements. Relaxation oscillations generally occur as a result of the switching action between an active device and the circuit elements. As a result, the output waveform is due to the charging and discharging of energy-storage elements in the circuit and may show sharp discontinuities. By varying the charge and discharge times, a wide variety of waveforms may be obtained, e.g. pulse, sawtooth, and square waves.

The frequency of oscillation depends upon the time constants associated with the charge and discharge of the inductive or capacitive energy-storage elements and the dynamic range over which the amplifying devices are active. This frequency may be easily varied over a wide range extending from zero to a value determined by the frequency limitations of the active device.

8.3.1   Negative Resistances

8.3.1.1   Negative-Resistance Characteristics

For design purposes, it is often convenient to represent the regenerative properties of relaxation-type circuits by negative resistances. The negative-resistance characteristics of semiconductor circuits may usually be measured and calculated by d-c techniques, and this makes it possible to design many types of relaxation oscillators by simple load-line analysis.

Negative-resistance circuits or devices are characterized by static driving-point resistance curves which, at least over a limited portion of the V,I plane, exhibit a falling voltage with increasing current. This behavior is due to a regeneration process, which may be attributed to external positive feedback, as in the case of junction-transistor multivibrator circuits, or to internal electron multiplication effects, as in the case of dynatron oscillators employing electron-tube tetrodes.

In electronic circuits and devices, two types of negative-resistance characteristics are encountered. These are illustrated in Fig. 8.22 and are referred to as N- and S-types. The basic difference between the two is the value of the derivatives at the turning points. For the N-type, dV/dI at points P and Q is equal to zero, and for the S-type dV/dI at P' and Q' is equal to infinity. In each case, the negative resistance is

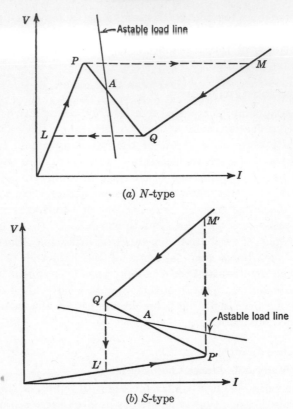

(a) N-type

(b) S-type

Fig. 8.22 Negative-resistance characteristics

bounded by two positive-resistance regions. Owing to the differences in the turning-point derivatives, the N-type curve is double-valued in current for a given voltage, whereas the S-type characteristic is double-valued in voltage for a given current.

In the design of relaxation oscillators, a condition that must be fulfilled is that the d-c operating point of the circuit shall fall within only the negative-resistance region of the N or S characteristic. The static load line, representing the resistance connected to the terminals at which the V,I characteristic is measured, is then of the form shown in Fig. 8.22, where the astable operating point is denoted by A. Theoretically, and in most practical circuits, it is possible to stabilize in the negative-resistance region; if it were not, the static curves could not be measured. An additional requirement for relaxation oscillators, therefore, is for energy-storage elements to be present in the circuit in order to utilize the double-valued properties of the V,I curves. For N-type characteristics of the type shown in Fig. 8.22a, the current must be permitted to increase along a constant-voltage line; this condition implies that capacitive elements are required to initiate oscillation. On the other hand, for S-type characteristics, the voltage must be allowed to increase along a constant-current path, which implies that inductive elements are required to initiate oscillation. Relaxation oscillators may therefore be built that utilize but a single storage-type circuit element, as is illustrated in Fig. 8.23.

The excursion path of the operating point in negative-resistance oscillators is indicative of the internal phase-shift characteristics of the

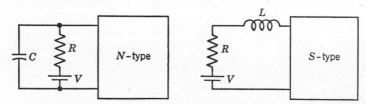

Fig. 8.23   Negative-resistance relaxation oscillators

device or circuit. For example, in N-type circuits, the operating point moves along the path designated as LP in Fig. 8.22 until the peak voltage is reached. The operating point then "snaps" to point M along a constant (or initially constant) voltage line. The voltage then decreases along path MQ until the valley coordinate is reached, at which time the circuit becomes unstable again and the operating point quickly shifts along path QL to the starting point of the cycle. Thus, in N-type oscillator circuits, the operating point excursion follows a clockwise rotation in the V,I plane. Clockwise rotation of this type is associated with an inductive impedance, since the voltage leads the current, and hence N-type driving-point impedances in the V,I plane are associated with inductive reactances. Conversely, in S-type oscillator circuits, the operating-point excursion in the V,I plane follows a counterclockwise rotation and corresponds to a voltage which lags the current. Consequently, an S-type characteristic of the type illustrated in Fig. 8.22 is indicative of a capacitive reactance which is related to the internal driving-point impedance of the circuit.

The effect of internal reactances in negative-resistance devices or circuits is generally twofold. First, increasing phase shift between the voltage and current occurs as the frequency of oscillation is increased. Second, the negative resistance tends to decrease in magnitude until it finally reaches zero and positive values as the frequency is increased. At this point, oscillation can no longer occur. These effects will be illustrated in the discussion of particular devices which exhibit internal regeneration and which are therefore referred to as negative-resistance devices.

8.3.1.2 Negative-Resistance Devices

Figure 8.24a illustrates a point-contact transistor circuit which is characterized by a negative resistance across the input terminals. The small-signal T-equivalent circuit for this configuration is shown in Fig. 8.24b; a T-equivalent is employed because it is illustrative of the re-

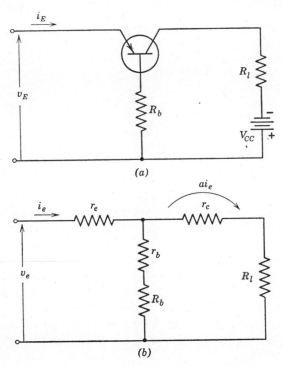

Fig. 8.24   Point-contact transistor negative-resistance circuit

generative effect which results in the negative resistance. Now, if it is assumed that

$$|R_l/r_c| \ll |1 - \alpha_{b0}| \quad \text{and that} \quad |(r_b + R_b + R_l)/r_c| \ll 1$$

the input resistance of the circuit of Fig. 8.24b at low frequencies is

$$r_i \cong r_e + (r_b + R_b)(1 - \alpha_{b0}) \tag{8.34}$$

Since point-contact transistors have a low-frequency short-circuit current amplification, α_{b0}, which is greater than unity, it is apparent that the input resistance given by eq. 8.34 is negative if

$$(r_b + R_b)(\alpha_{b0} - 1) > r_e \qquad (8.35)$$

Thus, it is seen that the negative resistance is due to positive current feedback from the collector to the base of a transistor which has current amplification in excess of unity. The same mechanism explains the negative-resistance characteristics of p-n-p-n transistors (see Chapter 1); as a matter of fact, considerable evidence indicates that the fabrication process of point-contact transistors results in p-n-p-n structures.

It is interesting to derive the frequency dependence of the input impedance due to the frequency variation of the current-amplification factor α_b. If, as a first-order approximation,

$$\alpha_b \cong \alpha_{b0}/(1 + j\omega/\omega_{ab}) \qquad (8.36)$$

eq. 8.34 becomes

$$z_i = r_e + (r_b + R_b)[1 - \alpha_{b0} + (\omega/\omega_{ab})^2]/[1 + (\omega/\omega_{ab})^2]$$
$$+ j\omega[(r_b + R_b)\alpha_{b0}/\omega_{ab}]/[1 + (\omega/\omega_{ab})^2] \qquad (8.37)$$

If we denote the maximum frequency at which a negative resistance occurs as ω_m, then

$$\omega_m = \omega_{ab}\{[\alpha_{b0} - 1 - r_e/(r_b + R_b)]/[1 + r_e/(r_b + R_b)]\}^{1/2} \qquad (8.38)$$

or, if $r_b + R_b \gg r_e$,

$$\omega_m \cong \omega_{ab}(\alpha_{b0} - 1)^{1/2} \qquad (8.39)$$

The frequency limit ω_m is that frequency at which the real part of eq. 8.37 vanishes, and represents the limiting fundamental frequency at which the device can oscillate. Thus, the frequency variation of α_b causes the resistive component of the input impedance to tend toward zero and positive values with increasing frequency. It is also clear from eq. 8.37 that the reactive part of the input impedance is inductive, and hence an N-type negative-resistance characteristic may be expected. A two-terminal equivalent of the circuit illustrated in Fig. 8.24, which is referred to the input (emitter-ground) terminals and which may be derived from eq. 8.37, is shown in Fig. 8.25. The parameter corre-

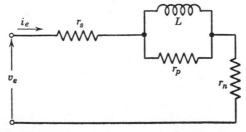

Fig. 8.25   Two-terminal a-c equivalent of point-contact transistor circuit

spondence between the circuits of Figs. 8.24 and 8.25 are as follows:

$$i_s = i_e \tag{8.40a}$$

$$r_p = \alpha_{b0}(r_b + R_b) \tag{8.40b}$$

$$r_n = (1 - \alpha_{b0})(r_b + R_b) \tag{8.40c}$$

$$L = \alpha_{b0}(r_b + R_b)/\omega_{ab} \tag{8.40d}$$

The two-terminal equivalent of Fig. 8.25 may be used to derive a stability criterion for the circuit of Fig. 8.24a. For example, if it is desired to stabilize the circuit within the negative-resistance region of operation, a situation that may arise for measurement purposes or for applications of the transistor to active filters (see Chapter 12), the input capacitance must be low enough to prevent the circuit from oscillating. If a capacitor C is placed between the input terminals of the equivalent of Fig. 8.25 and the resultant loop equation is solved for the condition that the damping term be zero or positive, the following criterion is obtained, for the assumption that $r_s \ll r_p$:

$$|L/r_p| > |r_nC| \tag{8.41}$$

Substituting eqs. 8.40b and 8.40c into eq. 8.41 results in

$$C \leq 1/[(\alpha_{b0} - 1)(r_b + R_b)\omega_{ab}] \tag{8.42}$$

Since, from eq. 8.34, $r_i \cong (r_b + R_b)(1 - \alpha_{b0})$, the stability criterion is

$$C \leq 1/(-r_i)(\omega_{ab}) \tag{8.43}$$

Hence, the greater the magnitude of the negative resistance, the smaller

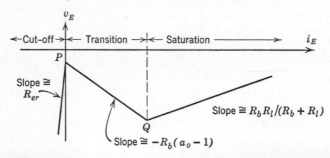

Fig. 8.26   Negative-resistance characteristic of point-contact transistor

will be the input capacitance for which the circuit is stable when the d-c operating point is within the negative-resistance region of operation. A result identical to eq. 8.43 may be derived for p-n-p-n transistors.[11]

In practical devices, the negative-resistance region is always bounded by positive-resistance regions. In the point-contact transistor circuit of Fig. 8.24a, a positive-resistance region will occur when the transistor is cut off and when the transistor is saturated. The idealized v_E, i_E characteristic will then appear as illustrated in Fig. 8.26. Although the three-region straight-line representation of the resistance characteristic is only an approximation to the experimental curve, it is generally accurate enough for engineering calculations.

The peak- and valley-point coordinates are given by [12]

$$(i_P, v_P) \cong \{0, [-(r_b + R_b)V_{CC}]/(r_b + R_b + r_c + R_l)\} \tag{8.44}$$

$$(i_Q, v_Q) \cong \{V_{CC}/[\alpha_{b0}(R_l + R_b + r_b) - (r_b + R_b)],$$

$$(r_b + R_b)(1 - \alpha_{b0})V_{CC}/[\alpha_{b0}(r_b + R_b + R_l) - (r_b + R_b)]\} \tag{8.45}$$

The double-base diode (see Sec. 1.6.5) exhibits a negative-resistance region due to field effects.[13] The common-base-1 configuration is illustrated in Fig. 8.27a. When minority carriers are injected into the bar from the junction, they drift to base 1 because of the electric-field gradient. However, owing to the high resistivity of the bar material, the carriers give rise to a resistance modulation effect which causes an additional current to flow from the battery supply V_{BB}. The net effect of this current regeneration is a negative resistance which may be measured between the junction and base 1. An equivalent circuit for the double-base diode, which is applicable only to the negative-resistance region, is illustrated in Fig. 8.27b. In the equivalent network, r_{b1} and r_{b2} represent the base-1 and base-2 region resistances, respectively, and r_j is the equivalent junction resistance. The input resistance of the equivalent circuit is

$$r_i \cong r_j + (1 - \gamma_0)r_{b1}r_{b2}/(r_{b1} + r_{b2}) \tag{8.46}$$

where γ_0 is the low-frequency internal current-amplification factor. For p-n-type double-base diodes γ_0 is related to the majority and minority carrier mobilities by

$$\gamma_0 = 1 + \mu_n/\mu_p \tag{8.47}$$

where the subscripts n and p refer to electrons and holes, respectively. In germanium, the mobility ratio μ_n/μ_p is approximately equal to 2.

A set of negative-resistance characteristics for the double-base diode is illustrated in Fig. 1.17 (Chapter 1). As with the point-contact transistor, the negative-resistance region is bounded by two positive-resist-

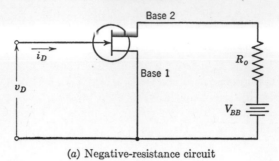

(a) Negative-resistance circuit

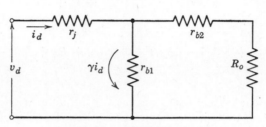

(b) Small-signal equivalent circuit

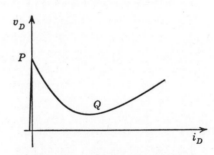

(c) Negative-resistance characteristic

Fig. 8.27   Negative-resistance properties of the double-base diode

ance regions, the latter corresponding to cut off and saturating states of the device.   The peak- and valley-point coordinates are given approximately by

$$i_P \cong 0 \tag{8.48a}$$

$$v_P \cong [r_{b1}/(r_{b1} + r_{b2})]V_{BB} \tag{8.48b}$$

$$i_Q \cong (\mu_p/\mu_n)(V_{BB}/r_{b2}) \tag{8.48c}$$

$$v_Q \cong \frac{kT}{q} \ln\left[\left(\frac{\mu_p}{\mu_n}\right)\left(\frac{V_{BB}}{r_{b2}I_s} + 1\right)\right] + \frac{\mu_p}{\mu_n}\left(\frac{r_{b1}'}{r_{b2}}\right)V_{BB} \tag{8.48d}$$

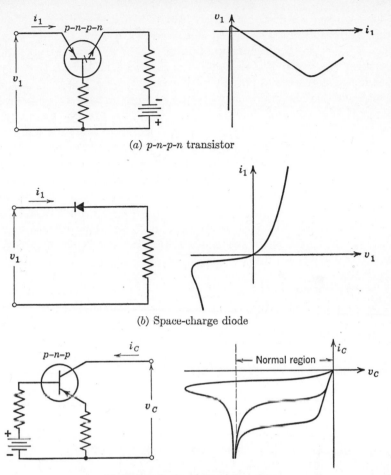

(a) *p-n-p-n* transistor

(b) Space-charge diode

(c) Avalanche breakdown transistor

Fig. 8.28   Negative-resistance devices

where I_s is the saturation current of the junction and r_{b1}' is the equivalent resistance of the base-1 region in the high junction-current region of operation.

The negative-resistance characteristics of point-contact transistors are due to diffusion-current regeneration effects, whereas the negative-resistance characteristics of double-base diodes are due to drift-current regeneration effects.   The conjugate-emitter, or hook-collector-type transistor, also exhibits diffusion-current regeneration and hence may be used in negative-resistance circuits.   A typical configuration and characteristic curve for the *p-n-p-n* transistor is illustrated in Fig. 8.28a.

Other semiconductor effects which lead to negative-resistance characteristics are attributed to avalanche breakdown and occur in certain types of junction diodes and junction transistors.[14] Diodes that utilize this effect are referred to as space-charge diodes and exhibit negative-resistance characteristics of the type illustrated in Fig. 8.28b. Avalanche breakdown also occurs in some junction transistors when the collector voltage is raised to a value that exceeds the normal breakdown potential. The effect is accompanied by an increase in the common-base current-amplification factor to a value greater than unity. The collector negative-resistance characteristic which results from avalanche breakdown effects in junction transistors is illustrated in Fig. 8.28c.

All negative-resistance devices may be used as relaxation oscillators if the d-c bias point is established in the negative-resistance region and if sufficient energy storage, as obtained from inductances and capacitances, is provided by the external circuit. Several types of relaxation oscillators are described below.

8.3.2 Multivibrators

The classical multivibrator is essentially a two-stage amplifier with regenerative feedback. It is a versatile circuit since it can be used in three different modes of operation: astable, monostable, or bistable. The monostable and bistable modes will be considered in applications to pulse circuits in Chapter 10. As an astable or free-running circuit, the multivibrator is widely used as a square-wave oscillator. Examples of both RC-coupled and RL-coupled multivibrators are given below.

8.3.2.1 RC-Coupled Multivibrators

A junction-transistor multivibrator circuit, which is analogous to the electron-tube Eccles-Jordan configuration, is illustrated in Fig. 8.29. The two transistors are cross-coupled from collector to base by C_k and R_k. Resistors R_e, which are in series with the emitter leads, are included for bias stability purposes (see Chapter 3). Base bias is provided for the transistors by the division of the voltage supply V through the network consisting of R_l, R_k, and R_b. An alternative method for providing base bias is achieved by returning the resistors R_k directly to the battery supply V. An advantage of the configuration illustrated in Fig. 8.29 is that the d-c path between V and ground, which is provided by $R_l + R_k + R_b$, causes a leakage current to flow through R_l even when the transistors are cut off, and this external leakage can be used to swamp the effects that are caused by changes in I_{CO}.

A useful technique for analyzing the circuit of Fig. 8.29 is to obtain its negative-resistance characteristic and then determine what criteria

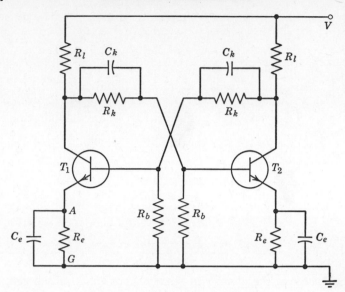

Fig. 8.29   *RC*-coupled multivibrator

must be used in order to make the circuit oscillate.[15]   For example, if R_e of transistor T_1 is removed and the terminals AG are used as a driving-point pair to obtain a static V_{E1}, I_{E1} characteristic, a curve of the type illustrated in Fig. 8.30 may be derived.   The negative-resistance region,

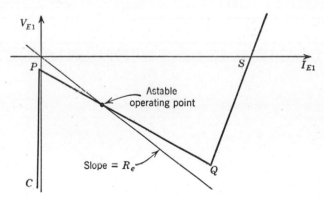

Fig. 8.30   Static driving-point characteristic seen between points A and G in the circuit of Fig. 8.29

bounded by points P and Q, occurs when transistors T_1 and T_2 are simultaneously active.   Region PC occurs when T_1 is cut off and region QS corresponds to the saturation state of T_1.   When R_e is connected between the terminals A and G, the d-c operating point of the circuit may be calculated by finding the point of intersection of R_e, when considered as a load line, with the driving-point resistance characteristic (curve $CPQS$). If this intersection occurs within the negative-resistance region only, the circuit is astable and hence potentially free-running.

In analyzing the negative-resistance characteristic of the symmetrical multivibrator of Fig. 8.29, it is convenient to define the following design parameters.

$$K = R_b/(R_b + R_k + R_l) \qquad (8.49)$$

$$X = R_l/R_e \qquad (8.50)$$

$$A = \Delta v_C/V \qquad (8.51)$$

$$\psi = (1/K)|v_{BE}/V| \qquad (8.52)$$

In eq. 8.51, Δv_C is the change in steady-state collector voltage which results when the transistors are driven from cutoff to conduction, or vice-versa, and is given approximately by $\Delta v_C \cong \alpha_b KXV(1 - \psi)$. In eq. 8.52, v_{BE} is the steady-state base-emitter voltage drop of the conducting transistor. Although v_{BE} is a function of emitter current, a working value may be assumed for a given emitter-current range. (For example, for emitter currents in the 1–10 ma range, v_{BE} may be assumed equal to approximately 0.1 to 0.2 volt for germanium transistors, and 0.6 volt for silicon transistors.)

It can then be shown that the peak- and valley-point coordinates, P and Q, respectively, in Fig. 8.30, are given approximately by

$$\text{Peak} \begin{cases} i_P \cong 0 & (8.53a) \\ v_P \cong KV[1 - \alpha_{b0}KX(1 - \psi)] & (8.53b) \end{cases}$$

$$\text{Valley} \begin{cases} i_Q \cong \dfrac{-V}{\alpha_{b0}R_l}\left[1 - K\dfrac{1 + \alpha_{b0}KX\psi}{1 + \alpha_{b0}K^2X}\right] & (8.54a) \\ v_Q \cong KV\left[\dfrac{1 + \alpha_{b0}KX\psi}{1 + \alpha_{b0}KXR_b/(R_b + R_k)} - \psi\right] & (8.54b) \end{cases}$$

From eqs. 8.53a–8.54b, it can be shown that, if $\psi \ll 1$, the symmetrical multivibrator will be unstable for the condition

$$KX < 1 \qquad (8.55)$$

If eq. 8.55 is satisfied, the frequency of oscillation of the multivibrator will be determined by the time required for the transistors to recover from their cutoff states. For example, in the circuit of Fig. 8.29, if T_1 is suddenly switched from a cutoff condition to a conducting state, a positive step is transmitted to the base of T_2 through the coupling capacitor C_k. This positive step causes T_2 to cut off but the positive transient decays as the coupling capacitor charges. When the potential at the base of T_2 becomes negative again, T_2 becomes active, and the circuit will regenerate such that T_2 is driven into saturation and T_1 is driven into cutoff. The frequency for a complete cycle is given by

$$f \cong -1 \Big/ \left\{ 2C_k R_k K \left(1 + \frac{X}{u}\right) \ln \left[\left(\frac{1-A}{A}\right) \left(\frac{K + KX/u}{1 - K - KX/u}\right) \right] \right\} \quad (8.56a)$$

where
$$u = R_b/R_e \quad (8.56b)$$

Equation 8.56a does not take into account the frequency variation of the transistor parameters, and hence only approximate design values should be expected at frequencies above $f_{\alpha e}$.

It can be shown that the maximum frequency of oscillation of the free-running multivibrator is approximately equal to the geometric mean of the α_b and α_e cutoff frequencies of the transistor.[15] Thus, since $f_{\alpha e} \cong f_{\alpha b}/\alpha_{e0}$,

$$f_{\max} \cong f_{\alpha b}/\sqrt{\alpha_{e0}} \quad (8.57)$$

where $f_{\max}$ is the maximum frequency of oscillation and α_{e0} is the low-frequency current-amplification factor for the common-emitter transistor. In general, eq. 8.57 is fairly representative for alloy-type transistors but is usually too optimistic for grown types where junction efficiency is important and where r_b' is associated with a considerable capacitive component. Furthermore, since the derivation of eq. 8.57 neglects saturation effects in the transistor, it represents a theoretical limit only for nonsaturating circuits (see Chapter 10).

The analytical results given above may be used to derive a synthesis procedure for designing free-running multivibrators. For example, the circuit specifications may require an oscillator to deliver a collector-voltage swing of Δv_C and a collector-current swing of Δi_C when working from a source voltage of V; in addition, the desired frequency of oscillation f is usually specified. The design problem is then to select the proper values of R_l, R_b, R_k, R_e, C_k, and C_e in order to meet the given requirements. A specific procedure for such a design technique is illustrated below.

Circuit Requirements. V, Δv_C, Δi_C, f specified.

Problem. Solve for R_l, R_b, R_k, R_e, C_k, C_e.

Procedure. 1. For design realizability, select K such that

$$(1 - A) \quad \text{and} \quad A > K \gg |v_{BE}/V|$$

2. Select u:

(*a*) Requirement for astable operation:

$$u > \frac{(1 - K)^2}{1 - K - A/\alpha_{b0}(1 - \psi)}$$

(*b*) For design realizability:

$$\alpha_{e0} \gg u > A/\alpha_{b0}(1 - \psi)(A - K)(1 + K - A)$$

(*c*) For insensitiveness to change in I_{CO}:

$$u \ll \Delta i_C/I_{CO\max}$$

3. Calculate (KX):

$$(KX) = u/2 - [(u/2)^2 - uA/\alpha_{b0}(1 - \psi)]^{\frac{1}{2}}$$

4. Calculate R_e: $R_e = (KV/\alpha_{b0}\,\Delta i_C)(1 - \psi)$

5. Calculate R_l: $R_l = XR_e$

6. Calculate R_b: $R_b = uR_e$

7. Calculate R_k: $R_k = (u/K - u - X)R_e$

8. Calculate C_k:

$$C_k = -1 \Big/ \left\{ 2fR_kK\left(1 + \frac{X}{u}\right) \ln\left[\left(\frac{1 - A}{A}\right)\left(\frac{K + KX/u}{1 - K - KX/u}\right)\right]\right\}$$

9. Select C_e: $1/2\pi fR_e > C_e \gg 1/R_e\omega_{\alpha b}$

Example. Suppose that it is desired to design a multivibrator which will oscillate at 10 kc and operate from a 12-volt source. The desired collector-voltage swing is 6 volts, and the collector-current swing is specified as 2 ma. Germanium transistors are available, and the parameters of interest are: $v_{BE} = 0.2$ volt, $\omega_{\alpha b} = 10^7$ radians per second, and $\alpha_{e0} = 20$. The circuit will be operated in an environment where the maximum temperature may cause I_{CO} to increase to a value in the neighborhood of 50 μa. The design procedure, as outlined above, is as follows:

1. Select K. $0.5 > K \gg 0.016$

Thus, select, for example, $K = 0.2$. Hence, $\psi = 0.08$.

   2. Select u.

   (a) Criterion for astable operation: $u > 2.9$

   (b) Design realizability: $20 \gg u > 2.7$

   (c) I_{CO} insensitiveness: $u \ll 40$

Hence, select, for example, $u = 7$.

   3. Calculate $KX = 0.62$. Thus, $X = 3.1$.

   4. Calculate $R_e = 1.1$ kilohms.

   5. Calculate $R_l = 3.4$ kilohms.

   6. Calculate $R_b = 7.7$ kilohms.

   7. Calculate $R_k = 27.4$ kilohms.

   8. Calculate $C_k = 0.007$ μf.

   9. Select, for example, $C_e = 0.001$ μf.

The circuit configuration designed above is illustrated in Fig. 8.29, and the waveforms obtained at various points in the circuit are illustrated in Figs. 8.31 and 8.32.

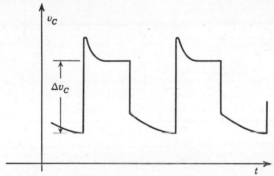

Fig. 8.31   Collector voltage waveform of multivibrator

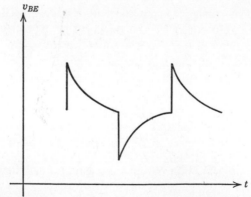

Fig. 8.32   Base-emitter voltage waveform of multivibrator

8.3.2.2 RL Coupled Multivibrator

Figure 8.33 illustrates a form of an RL multivibrator which utilizes to good advantage the square-loop hysteresis characteristics of a high-remanence magnetic core.[16] In this circuit the two transistors alternately switch from a cutoff state to a conducting state and thus cause the battery supply V_{CC} to be switched across windings N_1 and N_2 in alternate succession. When T_1 conducts, a positive potential is induced

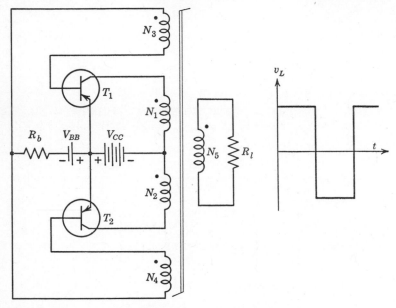

Fig. 8.33 RL-type multivibrator

in all the windings. Thus, the conduction of T_1 is regenerated, owing to the build-up of a negative potential at its base, while T_2 is simultaneously driven into cutoff by the build-up of a positive potential at its base. The number of turns on the control windings N_3 and N_4 determine the magnitude of the regeneration signals and cutoff potentials applied to the bases of the transistors. During the time that T_1 conducts, the magnetic core is driven to positive flux saturation, as illustrated in the hysteresis curve of Fig. 8.34. Upon saturation, the induced voltages in the windings collapse, and there is a consequent loss of base drive by T_1. As the current in N_1 decreases, the saturation flux level decreases slightly, but this change in flux is enough to induce a negative potential in the windings and to cause T_2 to become conducting. When T_2 begins its conduction cycle, the negative potential induced in N_3 and

N_4 (negative at the dots in Fig. 8.33) causes T_1 to cut off and T_2 to regenerate. The magnetic core is now driven to a state of negative flux saturation by the current in N_2, and hence a complete cycle of the hysteresis loop is traversed.

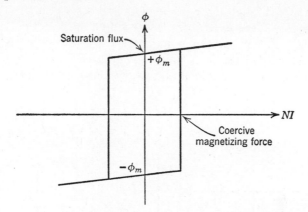

Fig. 8.34　Square-loop magnetic hysteresis curve

In the multivibrator circuit of Fig. 8.33, the flux build-up across N_1, due to the conduction cycle of T_1, is given by

$$d\phi/dt = V_{CC}/N_1 \qquad (8.58)$$

Thus

$$\int_0^{t_1} \left(\frac{V_{CC}}{N_1}\right) dt = \int_{-\phi_m}^{+\phi_m} d\phi \qquad (8.59)$$

and the first half-cycle period is

$$t_1 = 2\phi_m N_1 / V_{CC} \qquad (8.60)$$

In eq. 8.60, the dimension of t_1 is in seconds, ϕ_m is in webers, and V_{CC} in volts. If $N_1 = N_2$, the frequency of oscillation of the magnetic-core multivibrator is

$$f = 1/2t_1 = V_{CC}/4\phi_m N_1 \qquad (8.61)$$

From eq. 8.61 it is apparent that the oscillation frequency is directly proportional to the supply voltage V_{CC}. The RL multivibrator is a very efficient circuit for high-power requirements and will be described in further detail in Chapters 11 and 12 in relation to sweep circuit and converter applications.

8.3.2.3 Double-Base Diode Multivibrator

A multivibrator that utilizes the negative-resistance characteristics of the double-base diode is illustrated in Fig. 8.35.[17] Operation of the circuit may be described as follows: capacitor C is charged from the battery supply through the resistance R_2 and the diode D. During the charging cycle of the capacitor, D is conducting, but the double-base diode is cut off. When the potential across C becomes equal to or slightly greater than the peak-point potential of the double-base diode, the latter becomes unstable and switches into the conducting state.

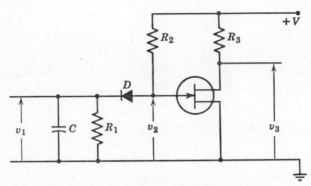

Fig. 8.35 Double-base diode multivibrator

The junction potential v_2 is then clamped to a low value, causing the diode D to become biased in the reverse (nonconducting) direction. The capacitor will then discharge through the resistance R_1, until the potential v_1 is approximately equal to the junction potential v_2 of the double-base diode. At this instant the diode becomes conducting again and the current through the junction of the double-base diode reverses, causing the latter to be driven into its cutoff state. Capacitor C will then recharge, and the cycle becomes repetitive.

The waveforms generated by the astable circuit of Fig. 8.35 are illustrated in Fig. 8.36. The frequency of oscillation is determined by the charging and discharging action of the capacitor. If the peak-point potential, corresponding to the negative-resistance characteristic of the double-base diode, is denoted by v_P and the valley-point potential by v_Q, the time it takes the capacitor to charge from v_Q to v_P is

$$t_c = \frac{R_1 R_2 C}{R_1 + R_2} \ln \left[\frac{R_1 V/(R_1 + R_2) - v_Q}{R_1 V/(R_1 + R_2) - v_P} \right] \qquad (8.62)$$

The time it takes C to discharge from v_P to v_Q is

$$t_n = R_1 C \ln (v_P/v_Q) \tag{8.63}$$

In eqs. 8.62 and 8.63, v_Q is the voltage at which the junction potential of the double-base diode is clamped when the diode D is nonconducting. However, for maximum output voltage, v_Q should be approximately equal to the valley-point potential. It should be noted that the cur-

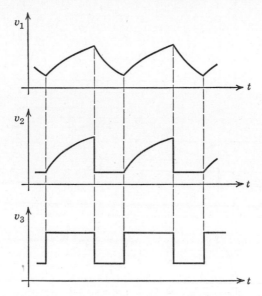

Fig. 8.36   Waveforms of the circuit of Fig. 8.35

rent i_Q, corresponding to the clamped valley potential v_Q, must lie in the astable region of operation if the multivibrator is to be free-running. From eqs. 8.62 and 8.63 the period of the complete cycle is

$$T = t_c + t_n \tag{8.64}$$

The ratio

$$S = t_c/(t_c + t_n) \tag{8.65}$$

is a measure of the symmetry of the square-wave output and may be varied by R_1 or R_2. The frequency of oscillation,

$$f = 1/T \tag{8.66}$$

may be varied by C, and this variation does not affect the symmetry of the waveform.

8.3.3 Pulse Oscillators

8.3.3.1 Blocking Oscillators

A junction-transistor blocking oscillator circuit is shown in Fig. 8.37. The regenerative feedback in this circuit is of such magnitude as to cause the transistor to become either saturated or cut off over a substantial part of the operating cycle. This feedback is obtained by using a pulse transformer equipped with windings W_1 and W_2. The circuit

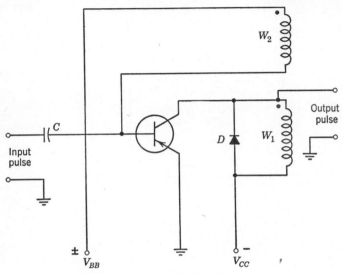

Fig. 8.37   Transistor blocking oscillator

usually is arranged to produce output pulses of large magnitude and short duration, either periodically in a free-running mode of operation or singly when the circuit is triggered by a suitable input. Capacitor C provides a path for input trigger pulses. The base supply voltage V_{BB} can be set for astable operation in which output pulses are periodically generated without the use of input pulses, or for monostable operation in which output pulses are obtained only when input pulses are present.

Circuit operation is as follows. With positive V_{BB} the transistor is in the "off" condition, and little current flows in the collector circuit. When a negative trigger pulse is impressed at the input, the transistor turns "on," and current flow is initiated in the pulse transformer winding W_1. The induced current in W_2 is regeneratively fed to the transistor base circuit, and the transistor impedance in series with W_1 is momentarily reduced to a low value. Magnetization of the transformer inductance continues until circuit saturation occurs, whereupon the induced voltages in the windings disappear, and the transistor base voltage returns to the positive value set by the supply voltage V_{BB}. The collector circuit then "opens," and the magnetic energy accumulated in the transformer core discharges in the diode circuit connected to winding W_1, thus completing the operating cycle. Astable operation can be achieved by setting the bias supply voltage V_{BB} to a slightly negative value. The blocking oscillator is discussed in further detail in Chapter 10.

8.3.3.2 Complementary-Transistor Pulse Oscillator

A junction-transistor analogue of the p-n-p-n transistor is illustrated in the circuit of Fig. 8.38. A common-base p-n-p transistor in direct cascade with a common-collector n-p-n transistor will exhibit approxi-

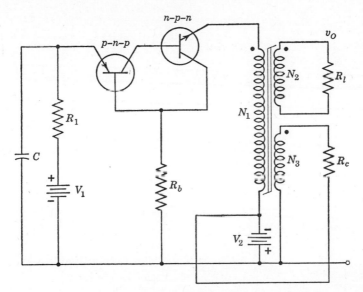

Fig. 8.38 Junction transistor negative-resistance pulse oscillator

mately the same negative-resistance characteristics as this transistor.[18] Figure 8.39 illustrates the input V,I static characteristic for the junction-transistor combination of Fig. 8.38. The peak and valley coordinates are given approximately by

$$(i_P, v_P) \cong (0, 0) \tag{8.67}$$

$$(i_Q, v_Q) \cong \left(\frac{V_2}{(R_b + R_l')\alpha_{c2}}, \frac{-V_2 R_b}{R_b + R_l'} \right) \tag{8.68}$$

where α_{c2} corresponds to the current amplification of the n-p-n transistor (common-collector) and R_i' represents the internal resistance of the transformer winding N_1.

In the circuit of Fig. 8.38, the capacitor C is charged through R_1 by V_1 until the peak-point potential v_P of the transistor combination is exceeded. At this point the transistors become unstable, and the operating point shifts along path PP' (see Fig. 8.39a) until the transistors saturate. When saturation occurs, and if R_b is very small, the battery supply V_2 is effectively switched across the transformer winding N_1, and an output signal appears in winding N_2. During the saturation interval, battery V_2 is in direct series with C since the saturated collector of the p-n-p transistor is effectively short-circuited to the emitter, owing to minority-carrier storage effects. Consequently, a negative potential rapidly develops across C until the valley-point potential is reached, at which time the transistor circuit again becomes unstable and switches from saturation into cutoff (along path QQ' in Fig. 8.39a), and the cycle repeats.

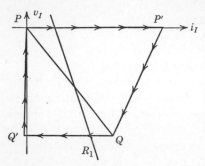

(a) Negative-resistance characteristic

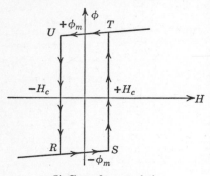

(b) Core characteristic

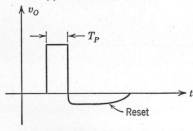

(c) Pulse waveform

Fig. 8.39 Operating characteristics of pulse oscillator

If the transformer core material has the square-loop hysteresis characteristic illustrated in Fig. 8.39b, a sharp pulse will be generated in the output winding N_2. The pulse shape and duration are determined by the magnitude of V_2 and by the properties of the transformer, provided that the transistor conduction time is larger than the time taken for the transformer core to saturate. Thus, the pulse waveform is essentially independent of saturation effects in the transistors.

When the transistor circuit is in the cutoff state, the transformer core is maintained in a condition of negative flux saturation by the bias current through the winding N_3. This operating point corresponds to point R in the hysteresis curve of Fig. 8.39b. The bias current required to provide a field intensity of $-H_c$ ampere-turns per meter for negative core saturation is

$$I_B = -H_c L/N_3 \cong V_2/R_c \text{ amperes} \qquad (8.69)$$

In eq. 8.69, I_B is defined as the coercive current in amperes, L is the mean magnetic path of the core in meters, N_3 is the number of turns on the bias winding, and H_c is the coercive field intensity in ampere-turns per meter. Thus, eq. 8.69 defines the requirements of the bias circuit.

When the transistor circuit switches from the cutoff state to saturation, enough current must be supplied to the primary winding N_1 to change the field intensity from $-H_c$ to $+H_c$. Consequently, the minimum peak-current requirement for the output transistor is

$$i_P = 2H_c L/N_1 \text{ amperes} \qquad (8.70)$$

If R_b is very small, the battery voltage V_2 will appear across N_1 almost instantaneously and the width of the pulse, T_P, which is generated during the interval in which the core switches from negative flux saturation $-\phi_m$ to positive flux saturation $+\phi_m$ is determined from the equation

$$\int_0^{T_P} V_2 \, dt = \int_{-\phi_m}^{+\phi_m} N_1 \, d\phi \qquad (8.71)$$

Solving eq. 8.71 for T_P gives

$$T_P = 2N_1\phi_m/V_2 \qquad (8.72)$$

In eq. 8.72, T_P will have the dimension of seconds if ϕ_m is expressed in webers and V_2 in volts. The energy dissipated in the core, per cycle, excluding the IR drop in the resistance of the winding, is

$$W/\text{cycle} = \oint H \, dB = 4B_s H_c AL \text{ joules} \qquad (8.73)$$

where B_s is the saturation flux density in webers per square meter, H_c is the coercive field intensity in ampere-turns per meter, A is the core area in square meters, and L is the mean core circumference (or magnetic path) in meters.

In the circuit of Fig. 8.38, the output pulse is developed across the secondary transformer winding N_2. The peak pulse power delivered to the load is approximately

$$\Gamma_P = (N_2/N_1)^2 (V_2^2/R_l) \tag{8.74}$$

The pulse waveform, illustrated in Fig. 8.39c, is determined by the transformer core properties and the repetition rate of the pulses is determined primarily by R_1 and C. Transistor saturation effects limit the maximum repetition rate of the oscillator but do not affect the pulse waveform.

8.3.4 Sawtooth Oscillators

Relaxation oscillators which generate sawtooth waveforms are based on the principle of charging a capacitor with a constant current or charging an inductance with a constant voltage. Examples of double-base diode and point-contact transistor sawtooth oscillators are illustrated in Fig. 8.40. In the double-base diode circuit, the capacitor is charged from battery supply V through resistor R_1. If R_1 is large, the current required to charge C to a potential equal to the peak-point potential of the negative-resistance characteristic is essentially constant,[19] hence, the potential across C builds up linearly until the double-base diode becomes unstable. At this point C will discharge through the forward-biased p-n junction. Since the resistance of the forward-biased junction is very low, the capacitor will discharge very rapidly, and the resultant voltage across C will be of sawtooth waveform. The circuit will be free-running if the input load line, determined by R_1, intersects the negative-resistance characteristic in the negative-resistance region only. The period of the sawtooth waveform is controlled by R_1 and is given by

$$T \cong R_1 C \ln [(V - v_Q)/(V - v_P)] \tag{8.75}$$

where v_Q and v_P are the valley- and peak-point potentials, respectively, of the double-base diode. Equation 8.75 neglects the discharge time of C.

The point-contact transistor circuit, illustrated in Fig. 8.40b generates a sawtooth voltage across C in approximately the same manner as described for the double-base diode. C is charged by V_1 through R_1 until the potential across C becomes equal to the peak-point potential of the negative-resistance characteristic. At this point, the capacitor discharges through the emitter of the transistor. If R_2 is small, the discharge of C will be very rapid, and the resultant voltage waveform at the emitter will be of the sawtooth type.

Circuits that generate a sawtooth current waveform are described in Chapter 11 in relation to television sweep circuits.

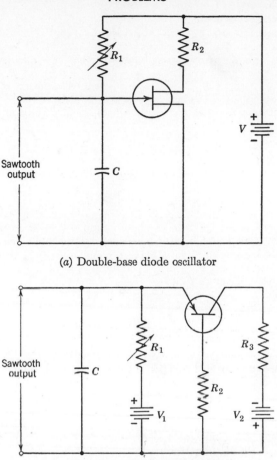

(a) Double-base diode oscillator

(b) Point-contact transistor oscillator

Fig. 8.40 Sawtooth relaxation oscillators

Problems

1. Determine the frequency of oscillation and oscillator starting condition for the Hartley oscillator of Fig. 8.8. Use the method described in Sec. 8.2.2 in the analysis.

2. A Hartley oscillator of the type shown in Fig. 8.9 is required to oscillate at a frequency of 1 mc. Determine the values of the inductance L_1 and capacitance C_1 that are necessary. Assume that the transistor output impedance is given by

$$z_o = 1/(10^{-4} + j\omega 25 \times 10^{-12}) \text{ ohms}$$

and that an oscillator load resistance of 10,000 ohms is connected to the transistor collector. It is desired that the loaded Q of the tank circuit be equal to 10. Neglect the loading effect of the feedback winding L_2.

3. An RC-type multivibrator is required to oscillate at a frequency of 5 kc with a voltage output of at least 5 volts. The circuit is to operate from an unregulated supply of 15 volts with ±5-volt variations possible and over a temperature range where I_{CO} of the transistors may vary from 1 μa to 0.2 ma. Transistors having the following parameters are available: $h_{21b} = -0.95$ to -0.99, $\omega_{ab} = 10^7$ radians per second, $v_{BE} = 0.1$ to 0.2 volt. Design a circuit that will meet the requirements for the operating conditions given above.

4. The driving-point impedance of a negative-resistance circuit, in the active region, is given by

$$Z_i = r_1 - r_2/[1 + (\omega/\omega_0)^2] - j\omega r_2/\omega_0[1 + (\omega/\omega_0)^2]$$

If it is desired to measure the static V,I characteristic at the driving-point terminals, what maximum value of lead inductance may be tolerated before instability occurs?

5. From eq. 8.14 it can be seen that at low frequencies h_{22b} and h_{11b} are the only transistor parameters that influence the frequency of oscillation appreciably. Determine the frequency change of the oscillator for (a) 20% variation of collector voltage and (b) 20% variation of ambient temperature. Use curves given in Chapter 2 to determine the corresponding variation of h_{22b} and h_{11b} with collector voltage and temperature. Assume that at room temperature $h_{22b} = 1.0$ μmho, $h_{11b} = 40$ ohms, and the circuit elements of the oscillator are as follows: $C_1 = 100$ $\mu\mu$f, $C_2 = 1000$ $\mu\mu$f, and $L = 10$ mh.

Bibliography

1. W. Edson, *Vacuum Tube Oscillators*, Wiley, New York, 1953.

2. J. B. Oakes, "Analysis of Junction Transistor Audio Circuits," *Proc. IRE, 42*, 1235 (1954).

3. E. A. Oser, R. O. Enders, and R. P. Moore Jr., "Transistor Oscillators," *RCA Rev., 13*, 369 (1952).

4. H. E. Hollman, "Transistor Oscillators," *Tele-Tech, 12*, 82 (Oct. 1953).

5. J. K. Clapp, "An Inductance Capacitance Oscillator of Unusual Frequency Stability," *Proc. IRE, 36*, 356 (1948).

6. G. G. Gouriet, "High Stability Oscillator," *Wireless Engr., 27*, no. 319, 105 (1950).

7. E. Keonjian, "Stable Transistor Oscillator," *IRE Trans., CT-3*, 38 (1956).

8. "Precision Transistor Oscillator," *Natl. Bur. Standards Tech. News Bull., 37*, no. 2 (1953).

9. E. Keonjian, "Variable-Frequency Transistor Oscillators," *Elec. Engr., 74*, 672 (1955).

10. E. R. Kretzmer, "An Amplitude Stabilized Transistor Oscillator," *Proc. IRE, 42*, 391–401 (1954).

11. J. J. Suran, "Circuit Properties of the Conjugate-Emitter (Hook-Collector) Transistor," Paper presented at IRE–AIEE Transistor Circuit Conference, University of Pennsylvania, February 1956.

12. R. F. Shea et al., *Principles of Transistor Circuits*, Wiley, New York, 1953.

13. J. J. Suran, "A Low-Frequency Equivalent Circuit of the Double-Base Diode," *IRE Trans., ED-2*, 40 (1955).

14. M. C. Kidd, W. Hasenberg, and W. M. Webster, "Delayed-Collector Conduction, a New Effect in Junction Transistors," *RCA Rev., 14*, no. 1 (1955).

15. J. J. Suran and F. A. Reibert, "Two-Terminal Analysis and Synthesis of Junction Transistor Multivibrators," *IRE Trans.*, *CT-3*, 26 (1956).

16. G. H. Royer, "A Switching Transistor D-C to A-C Converter Having an Output Frequency Proportional to the D-C Input Voltage," *Trans. AIEE, Communications and Electronics*, *74*, 322 (1955).

17. J. J. Suran and E. Keonjian, "A Semiconductor Diode Multivibrator," *Proc. IRE*, *43*, 814 (1955).

18. J. J. Ebers, "Four-Terminal *p-n-p-n* Transistors," *Proc. IRE*, *40*, 1361 (1952).

19. J. J. Suran, "Double-Base Expands Diode Applications," *Electronics*, *28*, 198 (March 1955).

Chapter 9

Modulation, Mixing, and Detection

9.1 Introduction

The processes of modulation, mixing, and detection may be grouped together in one chapter because of their basic similarity. In all three cases a device is operated in such a way that its output frequency spectrum differs from the input but is controlled by it. This implies the use of nonlinear elements. Semiconductor devices fortunately exhibit various nonlinear characteristics which may be utilized to achieve the desired output-input relationship.

The best-known nonlinear device, the diode, was also the first semiconductor device. Its use for modulation, mixing, and detection is now widespread, and the techniques involved are well known. The diode, therefore, will not be discussed as such in this chapter. However, the basic nonlinearity of a transistor, which is of significance in this chapter, is that of the emitter-base diode. A very brief discussion of its characteristics is therefore necessary.

9.1.1 Emitter-Base Diode Characteristics

It has been shown that for a junction transistor the nonlinear current versus voltage characteristic of the emitter-base diode is given by

$$I_D = I_S[\exp{(qV_D/kT)} - 1] \tag{9.1}$$

where I_S is the reverse saturation current of the diode, q = electronic charge, k = Boltzmann's constant, T = temperature in degrees Kelvin, I_D = total current through the emitter-base diode, and V_D = voltage across the emitter-base diode.

$$[kT/q \cong 25.9 \text{ mv (at } 25°C)]$$

Under static conditions the current-voltage plot appears as curve a in Fig. 9.1. However, because of hole storage, a junction diode which has been conducting in the low-resistance direction does not immediately

offer a high resistance when the potential across it is reversed.[1] At
the moment of potential reversal, the back characteristic resembles
curve b in Fig. 9.1.   If the reverse potential is applied for a sufficient
time, the back characteristic moves around in the direction of the arrow until it takes up its static position at a.   If the frequency of the
applied signal is very high, a complete negative half-cycle will be

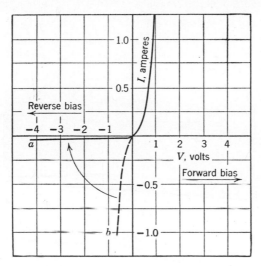

Fig. 9.1   Junction diode characteristic

passed by the diode, before the high back resistance represented by
curve a has established itself.   In this case the rectification efficiency
[defined as η = (d-c volts across load)/(a-c peak applied volts) $\times$ 100%]
of the diode is zero—it behaves as a very low impedance in either direction.   At frequencies between these extremes, the rectification
efficiency has an intermediate value.

Because of the above factors, when considering the effects of applying
a high-frequency signal to a transistor, caution must be exercised.   The
degree of nonlinearity that will be experienced is frequency-dependent
to a very marked extent.

9.2   Modulation

The process of modulation requires that some property of a relatively
high-frequency sinusoidal wave (the carrier) be varied in accordance with
the amplitude of a lower-frequency wave (the modulation).   There are
three properties associated with any sine wave: amplitude, frequency,
and phase.   This gives the possibility of modulating the carrier in any

one of three ways. Phase and frequency modulation are similar. In this chapter, therefore, only two types of modulation will be considered, amplitude modulation and frequency modulation. (Circuit techniques used for frequency modulation can be applied with little modification to produce phase modulation.)

9.2.1 Amplitude-Modulated Amplifier

The problem of amplitude modulation can be approached in two ways. The first is to change the amplitude of oscillation of a carrier-frequency oscillator by changing its operating point at the modulation frequency. The second is to pass the output of a constant-amplitude carrier-fre-

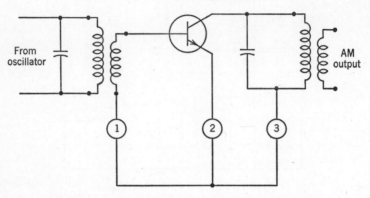

Fig. 9.2   Points at which modulation may be injected

quency oscillator through an amplifier, the gain of which is varied at the modulation frequency.

With the transistor connected in the common-emitter configuration, Fig. 9.2 shows the three points at which the modulation may be injected. These three cases will be treated individually.

Figure 9.3 shows a practical version of the first case, in which both modulation and carrier voltages are fed into the base of a common-emitter stage. The capacitor C_1 should be chosen so as to bypass resistor R_1 at the carrier frequency. If too large a value is chosen, the higher modulation frequencies will also be bypassed. Capacitors C_2, C_3, and C_4 should present a low reactance to the lowest modulation frequency. Consequently, at modulation frequencies the transistor appears as a common-emitter stage with the collector short-circuited to ground.

Let the d-c or the quiescent bias point of the modulator be $(I_E)_0 = I_0$ and $(V_{CE})_0 = V_0$. A modulation signal current $A_m \sin \omega_m t$ present in the base circuit will be amplified and appear in the emitter and collector

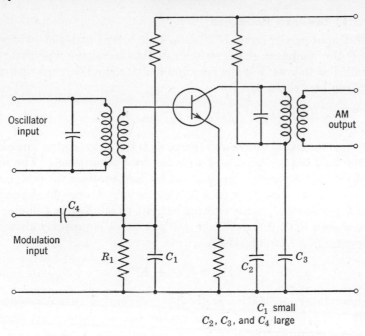

Fig. 9.3   Practical modulator circuit (injection in base)

circuits as $h_{21e}A_m \sin \omega_m t$, where h_{21e} is the common-emitter short-circuit current-amplification factor, A_m is the peak amplitude of the modulation signal current, and ω_m is the angular frequency of the modulation signal.

Since the bypass capacitors C_2 and C_3 are very large, the collector bias voltage remains practically constant. However the emitter bias current will be

$$i_E = I_0 + h_{21e}A_m \sin \omega_m t \qquad (9.2)$$

as shown in Fig. 9.4.

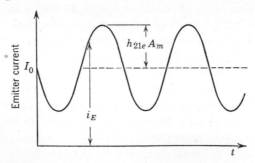

Fig. 9.4   Variation of i_E by modulation signal

9.2.1.1   Low-Level Modulation

If the input carrier signal is small in comparison with the emitter bias current, the nonlinear characteristics of this transistor modulator may be studied as follows: For the common-emitter amplifier, the transducer gain G can be written as

$$G = 4R_g G_l |h_{21e}|^2 / |(h_{11e} + Z_g)(h_{22e} + Y_l) - h_{12e}h_{21e}|^2 \qquad (9.3)$$

where R_g is the signal source resistance, Z_g is the signal source impedance, G_l is the load conductance, and Y_l is the load admittance. The square root of the gain expression (eq. 9.3) can be used to study the performance of a modulator. Let T_m represent this factor. Using the dependence of the h parameters on the emitter current as studied in Chapter 2, it can be shown that, if the emitter d-c bias point is properly chosen, we can operate in a region where

$$T_m \cong K'i_E + K'' \qquad (9.4)$$

i.e. where linear modulation is possible. K' and K'' are constants, K'' usually being very small. Therefore the output voltage or current is approximately proportional to i_E.

If the input carrier voltage or current is $A_c \sin \omega_c t$, where A_c is the peak amplitude of the carrier signal, and ω_c is the carrier angular frequency, the modulated output is

$$A_c T_m \sin \omega_c t \cong A_c K'(I_0 + A_m h_{21e} \sin \omega_m t) \sin \omega_c t \qquad (9.5)$$

Letting $h_{21e} A_m / I_0$ be m_a, the modulation factor, and writing $A_c K' I_0$ as A_c', the output appears in the familiar form

$$A_c'(1 + m_a \sin \omega_m t) \sin \omega_c t \qquad (9.6)$$

The qualitative behavior of T_m with i_E is shown in Fig. 9.5. The values of the coordinates of Fig. 9.5 depend on the individual transistor. Although it is a tedious and time-consuming process to obtain T_m versus i_E by analytical methods, this curve can be obtained rather easily by measuring the variation of power gain of the transistor amplifier as a function of i_E. For linear modulation, the emitter d-c bias current I_0 should be so chosen that the swing of i_E is in the linear region. This value of I_0 may range from about 0.1 ma to several milliamperes for the present high-frequency transistors.

Once the proper value of emitter d-c bias current I_0 is selected, the impedance seen by the modulation signal is h_{11e}. For 100% modulation, the modulation power required is

$$P_{mb} = [(I_0/\sqrt{2}\,)/h_{21e}]^2 h_{11e}$$

$$= I_0^2 h_{11b}(1 + h_{21b})/2(h_{21b})^2 \qquad (9.7)$$

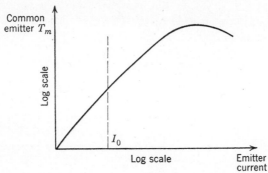

Fig. 9.5   Transfer function T_m of a modulator, emitter current modulation

The input impedance seen by the RF carrier varies according to the modulation signal.   If R_l is the load of the modulator, the quiescent impedance is

$$Z_{\text{carrier}} \cong (\Delta^h{}_e + h_{11e}/R_l)/(h_{22e} + 1/R_l) \qquad (9.8)$$

In the second case, illustrated in Fig. 9.6, the modulation is fed into the emitter circuit.   Capacitances C_1, C_3, and C_4 should present little

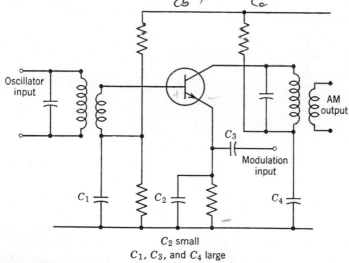

Fig. 9.6   Practical modulator circuit (injection in emitter)

reactance to the lowest modulation frequency. Capacitance C_0 is used to bypass RF signal only.

The analysis of this case is very similar to that for base modulation. The modulation signal current is now fed directly into the emitter circuit. The emitter d-c bias point should be chosen on the same basis as before. The modulation impedance is h_{11b}. The modulation power required to give 100% modulation is

$$P_{me} = (I_0/\sqrt{2}\,)^2 h_{11b} \qquad (9.9)$$

The input impedance seen by the carrier is the same as given in eq. 9.8.

Figure 9.7 shows plots of percentage modulation as a function of modulating voltage. Emitter modulation is seen to result in almost

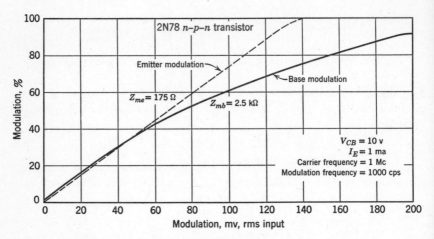

Fig. 9.7   Percentage modulation versus modulation voltage

perfect linearity up to about 92% modulation with only very slight curvature above that point, making this method of operation satisfactory for all normal applications.

In the third case the modulating signal is injected into the collector circuit as shown in Fig. 9.8. Capacitances C_1 and C_2 are large enough to present little reactance to the modulating signal. C_3 is the RF bypass capacitance.

In this method of modulation the emitter d-c bias current is kept constant. If the d-c or quiescent collector bias voltage is V_0, and if the carrier level is small, the collector bias voltage seen by the radio frequency is $v_{CE} = V_0 + B_m \sin \omega_m t$. The nonlinear properties of a transistor associated with a variation of the collector bias voltage can be studied in a manner similar to that for the case of variation of emitter

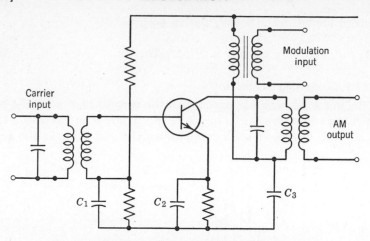

Fig. 9.8   Modulation injected into the collector circuit

current. The modulation transfer function T_m' can be expressed in terms of v_{CE}. If the d-c collector bias voltage is properly chosen, linear modulation is possible. The qualitative variation of T_m' with v_{CE} is shown in Fig. 9.9. For a given transistor, the T_m' versus v_{CE} curve can be obtained by measuring the variation of gain versus v_{CE}. Linear

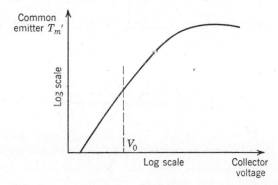

Fig. 9.9   Transfer function T_m' of a modulator (collector voltage modulation)

modulation can be obtained with high-frequency transistors. However, the proper bias voltage V_0 for linear modulation is often on the order of one tenth of a volt. Consequently the output of the modulator is limited to a low level.

The input impedance seen by the modulating signal at the secondary winding of the transformer in Fig. 9.8 is

$$Z_{mc} = h_{11e}/\Delta^h_e = h_{11b}/\Delta^h_b \qquad (9.10)$$

For 100% modulation, the modulation power is

$$P_{mc} = V_0^2 \Delta^h{}_b / 2h_{11b} \qquad (9.11)$$

9.2.1.2 Large-Signal Modulation

If the input RF signal is larger than the emitter bias, a partial rectification takes places as shown in Fig. 9.10. There is an increase of I_E by
ΔI_E, and this ΔI_E produces a small amount of distortion in the modu-

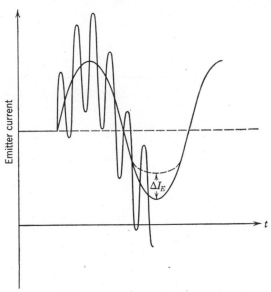

Fig. 9.10   Large-signal modulation

lated output. If the input RF signal is very much larger than the
emitter bias, then I_0 increases according to the input carrier level. When
emitter or base modulation is used, the distortion in the modulated output may increase rapidly, owing to the shift of bias point. However,
collector-circuit modulation can be used satisfactorily, even under this
larger RF signal condition.

A special case is shown in Fig. 9.11. C_1 is the RF bypass condenser.
There is no d-c or quiescent emitter bias. When the amplitude of the
unmodulated carrier is large enough, the emitter diode rectifies and
produces a d-c bias in the emitter circuit. Consequently a d-c collector
current flows. When the collector voltage increases, this current increases slightly. With initially small collector currents, this increase is
linear up to several hundreds of microamperes.

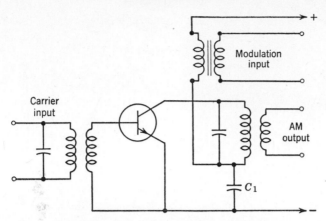

Fig. 9.11   Large-signal collector modulation

Although the small emitter bias current obtained from the rectification of the RF signal does not change, the collector current changes. The nonlinear properties required for modulation can be expressed in terms of I_C and in terms of V_{CE} to a small degree.   Curve a in Fig. 9.12

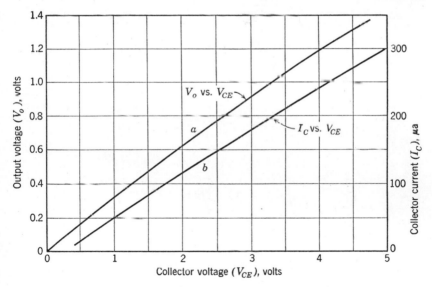

Fig. 9.12   High-level modulation

shows the relation between V_{CE} and the amplitude of RF output.   A nearly linear relationship exists except when the collector voltage is small.   Curve b shows the variation of d-c collector current as a function

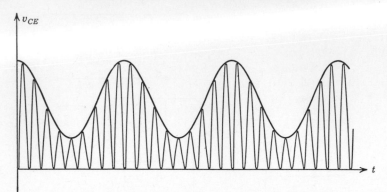

Fig. 9.13   Collector-to-emitter voltage waveform

of the modulating voltage.   Figure 9.13 shows the collector-to-emitter voltage waveform.   It consists of a modulated radio frequency, a modulation signal and a d-c voltage; thus

$$v_{CE} = V_0(1 + m_a \sin \omega_m t) \sin \omega_c t + m_a V_0 \sin \omega_m t + V_0 \quad (9.12)$$

Figure 9.14 shows the waveform of voltage across the tank circuit.

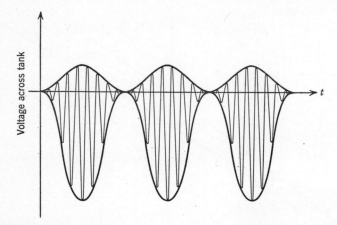

Fig. 9.14   Voltage waveform across tank circuit

For linear operation, the collector d-c bias voltage should be less than one half of the collector breakdown voltage.   The d-c emitter current is determined by the input RF level which may be on the order of 100 mv. The input impedance seen by the modulation signal is $h_{11b}/\Delta^h{}_b$.   For 100% modulation, the required modulation power is given by eq. 9.11.

9.2.2 Amplitude-Modulated Oscillator

If slight FM effects can be tolerated, amplitude modulation can be obtained by modulating the oscillator.

Figure 9.15 shows an amplitude-modulated oscillator. C_1 is the feedback capacitance, C_3 and C_4 are the bypass capacitances, and C_2 is the

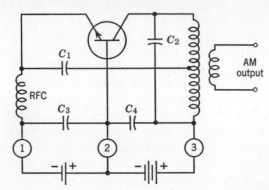

Fig. 9.15 Amplitude-modulated oscillator, general form

tank-circuit capacitance. There are again three possible points at which to modulate. Figure 9.16 shows an amplitude-modulated oscillator where the modulating signal is fed into the emitter circuit. C_3 is an RF bypass condenser. C_4 is large enough to bypass both the radio frequency

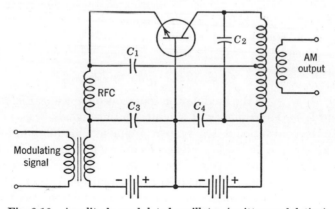

Fig. 9.16 Amplitude-modulated oscillator (emitter modulation)

and the lowest modulation signal frequency. C_1 and C_2 perform the same function as in Fig. 9.15.

Let the emitter-to-base d-c bias voltage be V_{EB}, the modulation signal voltage be $V_m \sin \omega_m t$, and the RF feedback voltage be $\beta V_c \sin \omega_c t$, where β is the feedback factor. The instantaneous emitter-to-base voltage is then

$$v_{EB} = V_{EB} + V_m \sin \omega_m t + \beta V_c \sin \omega_c t \tag{9.13}$$

The polarity of V_{EB} is such that the emitter diode is biased forward, in other words, so as to be conducting. Therefore V_{EB} is normally small, depending on the amount of d-c emitter current. If $V_m \sin \omega_m t + \beta V_c \sin \omega_c t$ is large enough, the emitter diode will be blocked during part of the negative cycle. Consequently, there is a slight increase of emitter bias current due to the rectification action of the diode.

Since the bypass capacitance C_4 is large, the collector bias voltage is practically constant.* Amplitude modulation is accomplished by changing the emitter bias current. Distortion in the modulated output is introduced in a manner similar to that discussed for the amplitude-modulated amplifier where the RF signal is large. This kind of distortion can be decreased by decreasing the feedback factor β.

The analysis of the amplitude-modulated oscillator is similar to that of the amplitude-modulated amplifier. The proper bias point is usually selected from a consideration of the frequency and stability requirements of the oscillator. The modulation impedance and the modulation power required can be calculated accordingly.

9.2.3 Frequency Modulation

In an FM system, the carrier is modulated by having its frequency varied on either side about a center frequency f_c. Let V_t be the instantaneous value and V_m the maximum amplitude of the modulating voltage. Then

$$V_t = V_m \sin [2\pi f_c t + m_f \sin (2\pi f_m)t] \tag{9.14}$$

where $m_f = \Delta f_c / f_m$ is the modulation index, also known as the deviation ratio, and f_m is the frequency of the modulating signal.

Unlike the conventional AM system, frequency modulation is accomplished at low power levels. Very often the FM carrier is then frequency-multiplied several times, up to the desired center frequency of the radiated FM signal. In electron-tube circuitry, frequency modulation may be obtained from a conventional tube oscillator having a tank circuit consisting of L, C, and a reactance tube modulator. Application of a modulating signal to the grid of the reactance tube changes the frequency of oscillation.

* The d-c collector bias voltage is assumed to be larger than the peak-to-peak value of the output voltage. Otherwise a decrease of collector d-c current will be observed when oscillation begins.

It was shown in Chapter 2 that the parameters of a transistor vary with operating point.   In particular, the reactive components of the input and output impedances of a transistor are functions of the operat-

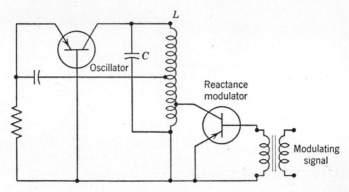

Fig. 9.17   Frequency modulation by reactance modulator (d-c circuit not shown)

ing point.   Consequently a transistor can be used as a reactance modulator.   Figure 9.17 shows a transistor oscillator with tank circuit L and C.   The output side of the reactance modulator is connected across part of the tank circuit.   The modulating signal is applied to the base of the modulator.   Variations of the modulating signal vary the reactive com-

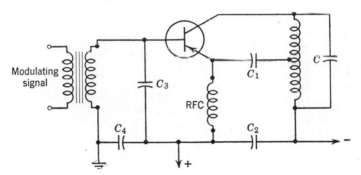

Fig. 9.18   Frequency-modulated oscillator.   Modulation fed to the base.

ponent of the output impedance of the modulator, and the frequency of the oscillator is changed accordingly.

A second approach is to modulate directly by varying the bias point of the oscillator.   Figure 9.18 shows an oscillator having the modulating signal fed into the base. C_1 forms the oscillator feedback connection.

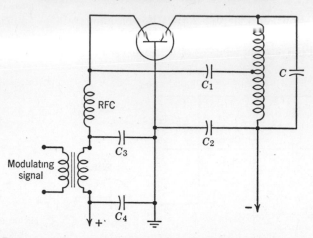

Fig. 9.19   Frequency-modulated oscillator.   Modulation fed to the emitter.

C_2, C_3, and C_4 are bypass capacitors.   Figure 9.19 shows a circuit where the modulation is fed to the emitter, while in Fig. 9.20 the modulating is done in the collector circuit.   In all three configurations, the modula-

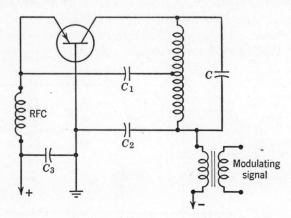

Fig. 9.20   Frequency-modulated oscillator.   Modulation fed to the collector.

tion may be introduced into the circuit by RC coupling in place of the transformers shown.

In the following, some experimental results are presented, obtained with a center frequency of 10.7 mc.   Excellent FM linearity can be obtained with any of the three modulator configurations.   Figure 9.21 shows that with a center frequency of 10.7 mc good linearity can be achieved with deviations in excess of 8 kc.   After suitable frequency multiplication, broadband frequency modulation can be readily obtained. Since the impedance across which the modulating voltage is measured is different in all three circuits, the curves shown in Fig. 9.21 are not indicative of the relative modulating powers required at the three modulating positions. In terms of modulating signal power required to produce a given frequency deviation, the most efficient ar-

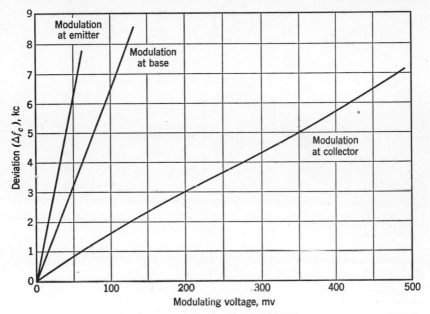

Fig. 9.21   Linearity of modulation

rangement is that in which modulation is fed to the base. Collector modulation is the least sensitive.

Together with the desired frequency modulation a 20 to 30% amplitude modulation is also produced. This amplitude modulation can be removed by using limiters.

9.3   Mixing

Mixing may be defined as a process that transforms a band of frequencies centering about one frequency f_1 to another related band of frequencies centering about some other frequency f_2.

Since, from the principle of superposition, the addition of two frequencies in a linear device never results in the generation of additional frequencies, nonlinear properties are essential to the process of mixing. One of the most important applications of mixing in a communications system is the heterodyne conversion of an RF signal to one at a relatively low, or as it is usually called, intermediate frequency (IF) Figure 9.22 shows a common-emitter transistor used as a mixer. Both the radio

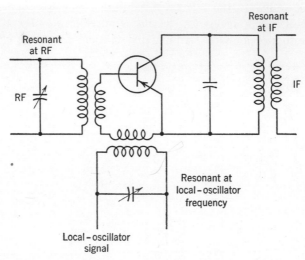

Fig. 9.22 Transistor mixer with both RF and local-oscillator signals fed into the base circuit

frequency and the local-oscillator voltages are fed into the base. A tank circuit, resonant at the intermediate frequency and connected in the collector circuit, forms the load. The resultant signal is therefore developed

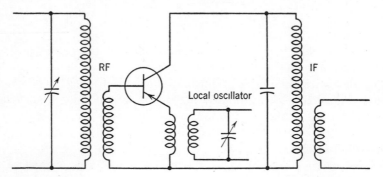

Fig. 9.23 Transistor mixer with RF fed into the base and the local-oscillator signal into the emitter

across this tank circuit. Figure 9.23 shows a variation of the circuit given in Fig. 9.22. In this case the local-oscillator voltage is fed into the emitter circuit but the radio frequency is still connected to the base.

In another variation, the local-oscillator voltage may be fed into the collector circuit. Further modifications may be made by feeding the radio frequency to the emitter and connecting the transistor in the common-base configuration.

The local-oscillator voltage can be either supplied by a separate transistor oscillator or generated by the mixing transistor. Figure 9.24 shows

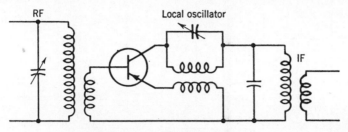

Fig. 9.24   Transistor converter

a transistor local-oscillator–mixer combination. The local oscillation is generated by the feedback provided between collector and emitter circuits. The RF signal is fed into the base and the intermediate frequency is obtained across the collector tank circuit. A variation is shown in Fig. 9.25. Here the local oscillation is produced by feedback between collector and base.

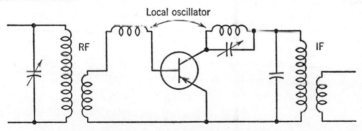

Fig. 9.25   Transistor converter

9.3.1   Optimum Local-Oscillator Level

Since the nonlinear properties of a transistor depend on the bias point, the conversion gain of a transistor mixer depends on the local oscillator level.[2] (The local-oscillator level partially determines the operating point.) Defining conversion gain as IF power output divided by RF power input, Fig. 9.26 gives a plot of conversion gain of the transistor-mixer circuit shown in Fig. 9.22 as a function of local-oscillator voltage and of emitter current. Initially gain increases rapidly with local-oscillator voltage but then levels off, further increase in voltage causing a slight reduction of gain. If the collector bias voltage is kept constant, an increase of emitter current from 50 μa to 250 μa increases the gain by about 15 db. The conversion gain of a transistor depends also upon the input signal frequency. However, over the range of frequencies represented by the broadcast band the variation in power gain is negligible.

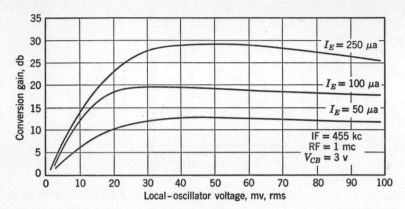

Fig. 9.26   Conversion gain versus local-oscillator output.   Base injection.

For a given transistor at a given operating point the conversion gain is about 6 to 8 db less than the power gain of the transistor used as an IF amplifier.

Figures 9.27a, b, and c show the variation of conversion gain with local-oscillator level for a transistor mixer of the type shown in Fig. 9.23.   The effects of signal frequency and local-oscillator level on the conversion gain are much more pronounced than in the circuit of Fig. 9.22.   The higher the frequency of the input signal, the larger the local-oscillator voltage required for the same conversion gain.   Similarly, the optimum local-oscillator level shifts upward with increased emitter bias current.

9.3.2   Noise in a Transistor Mixer

The fundamental limitation on the sensitivity of any radio receiver arises from sources of noise in the circuit elements or from external noise sources.   Sources of noise in the circuit elements, being the only ones over which he has any control, are the important factors to the designer of a receiver.   The output noise of a receiver consists of noise originating in the RF amplifier, in the mixer, and in the IF and AF amplifiers.   Noise introduced by the IF and AF amplifiers is normally so small compared with the amplified noise from the RF amplifier and mixer that it may be neglected.   When no RF stage is used, the mixer becomes the

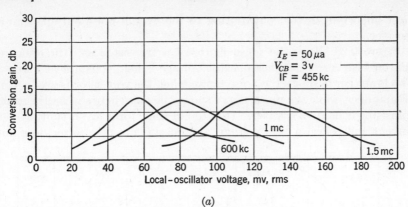

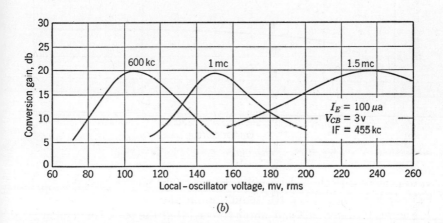

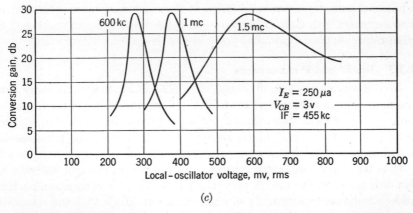

Fig. 9.27   Conversion gain versus local-oscillator output.   Emitter injection.

most important factor contributing to the overall noise output from a receiver.

Figure 9.28 shows the noise figure of a transistor as a function of emitter bias current. The collector voltage is held constant at 3 volts. The lower curve shows the noise figure when the transistor is used as an IF amplifier, while the upper curve shows the noise figure when the same transistor is used as a mixer. It is found that, for a given emitter bias current and collector bias voltage, the noise figure of a mixer does not

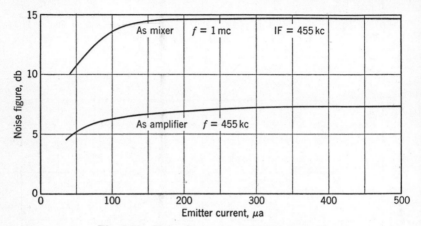

Fig. 9.28   Noise figure versus emitter current

vary greatly with the local-oscillator level. The noise figure also appears to be independent of the RF signal amplitude.

Figures 9.26 and 9.27a, b, and c showed that the peak conversion gain of a transistor mixer increases with increasing emitter bias current. This additional gain, however, is obtained at the expense of noise level, which also increases with emitter current. It is therefore necessary to reach a compromise between gain and noise in the design of a mixer stage.

9.3.3   The RF and IF Impedances

In the circuits shown in Figs. 9.22, 9.23, 9.24, and 9.25 there are resonant tank circuits tuned to the RF, IF, and local-oscillator frequencies. At frequencies other than the resonant frequencies, the impedance of the tank circuits may be considered as negligible for the purposes of calculation.

It is true that conversion results from the nonlinearity of the mixer, but this nonlinearity affects only the local-oscillator voltage. The RF and IF voltages are normally of such small amplitude that the relationship between them and the RF and IF currents is essentially linear.

The RF impedance looking into the transistor mixer at the quiescent bias point is given by the short-circuit input impedance h_{11e}. The IF impedance on the output side of the mixer is given by the output impedance of the transistor with zero source impedance.

$$(Z_o)_{\mathrm{IF}} = h_{11e}/\Delta^h{}_e \qquad (9.15)$$

The h parameters are those applicable to the quiescent bias point at the intermediate frequency used.

9.4   Detection

9.4.1   AM Detection

Amplitude-modulation detection can be achieved using semiconductor diodes.   There are, however, several advantages to detecting with a transistor.

(a) At small signal levels both transistors and diodes will give square-law detection.   However the power level at which detection changes from square-law to linear is slightly lower with transistors.

(b) The transistor detector has considerable power gain and, as with an electron-tube triode detector, acts in addition as a first audio stage.

(c) Where automatic gain control of transistor IF amplifiers is to be used, considerable control power is required.   Such power may be obtained from a transistor detector.

The gain of a transistor detector may be defined as

$$G = \frac{\text{audio power available at output}}{\text{power in both sidebands at input}}$$

$$= (V_o{}^2/R_l)(R_{\mathrm{in}}/V_c{}^2)(2/m_a{}^2) \qquad (9.16)$$

where V_o = audio voltage at output, V_c = unmodulated carrier amplitude at input, R_l = detector load resistor, R_{in} = detector input resistance and m_a = modulation factor. This gain equation applies for low-level inputs only.   At high signal levels this expression is an oversimplification due to the extremely nonlinear nature of R_{in}.   It is usually desirable to optimize the low-level detector gain.   Detection at higher levels of input signal does not normally present any problems.   Figures 9.29a and b show typical common-base and common-emitter detector stages, respectively.

The process of transistor detection may be divided into two phases. Initially, the incoming carrier must be rectified by the emitter-base diode.

For good rectification efficiency, the operating point must be chosen on the most nonlinear portion of the dynamic diode characteristic. Without a high cutoff frequency relative to the carrier frequency, the transistor, due to storage effects, will not exhibit a sharp knee in its dynamic char-

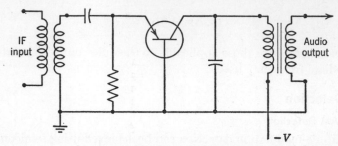

(a) Common-base detector stage

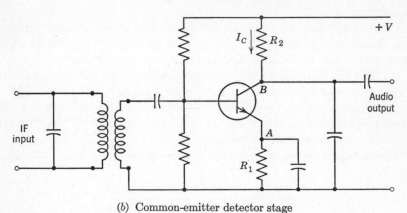

(b) Common-emitter detector stage

Fig. 9.29

acteristic. Consequently a good forward-to-reverse resistance ratio cannot be obtained.

The second phase of the detection process involves amplification of the audio modulation present on the original carrier. Thus, the transistor is required to have good audio-frequency gain. Since high gain is not associated with extremely low emitter current, operation of a transistor detector is a matter of compromise. Fortunately, with germanium transistors, the compromise between low emitter currents for maximum nonlinearity and relatively high currents in the interests of high gain can be made fairly successfully. With many silicon units, however, efficient low-level detection is not realizable. The input-diode curve for silicon transistors is similar in shape to that for germanium units, except that it is displaced on the voltage axis by about 0.5 volt. Consequently the nonlinearities available are similar. However, the gain of silicon transistors is often considerably lower at low emitter currents than that of germanium units, making a satisfactory compromise difficult for the silicon device.

For germanium transistors the optimum emitter current is in the region from 25 to 50 μa, depending on transistor type, as shown in Fig.

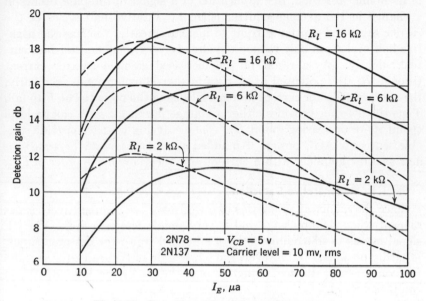

Fig. 9.30   Detection gain versus emitter current

9.30. The gain is shown to be nearly 20 db for a 16-kilohm load. With silicon units the optimum emitter current is on the order of 100 to 150 μa, and the gain, under similar conditions, is considerably lower. It is desirable to have as high a load resistor as possible, consistent with available bias supply voltages.

The input resistance of a detector is higher than that associated with an amplifying stage, being on the order of 20 kilohms. As stated earlier, this resistance must be nonlinear. At high signal levels, the value of R_{in} averaged over a complete cycle is higher than the zero-signal value of R_{in}. If, however, R_{in} is averaged over the conducting half-cycle, it will be found to have a lower value than its zero-signal value, which is to be expected. The zero-signal value of R_{in} is usually the one of interest since this is the resistance that must be matched to the output resistance of the preceding stage for maximum sensitivity.

Although a fuller treatment of automatic gain control will be found in Chapter 11, it should be pointed out here that a common-emitter detector provides control power in the following manner. Figure 9.29b shows a typical circuit. In the absence of a signal, the potential at point A with reference to ground is given by the product of the quiescent emitter current and the emitter resistor R_1. Similarly, the potential between point B and ground is $V - I_C R_2$. Since the transistor is biased in its nonlinear region, the application of a signal to the base results in a change in the average emitter current. Positive half-cycles of the carrier cause the emitter current to increase greatly, whereas the negative half-cycles can only reduce the already very small emitter bias current slightly. As a result of the increased average emitter current through R_1, the potential at A rises farther above ground. Similarly, the average collector current increases, causing the potential at B to fall. Thus the detector provides either a voltage increasing with carrier level (point A) or decreasing (point B). These varying voltages provide suitable sources of AGC power. An added advantage is that the transistor acts as a d-c amplifier with a current amplification on the order of h_{21e}.

9.4.1.1   Regenerative Detection

Since the nonlinear properties of a transistor are comparatively insignificant when the applied signal is very small, detection of an AM RF signal of only a few millivolts by a standard transistor detector circuit is hardly possible. If, however, the power gain of the transistor at radio frequency can be utilized, detection of an originally low-level RF signal can be achieved.

Figure 9.31 shows a regenerative detection circuit. The AM RF signal is fed into the base. The signal is amplified and appears across the collector tank circuit. The emitter circuit is inductively coupled to the tank circuit and provides regeneration. The result is that the amplified RF signal fed into the emitter is large in comparison to the d-c emitter bias. Rectification occurs at the emitter diode. An increase of emitter current causes an increase in collector current. Since the increase of emitter current is a function of the amplitude of the envelope of the RF signal, an audio signal will appear across the audio transformer TR. The resistance R_1 is used to obtain the proper emitter bias current. Capacitors C_1 and C_2 are RF bypasses.

The sensitivity of a regenerative detector depends on the gain of the transistor, its nonlinear properties at the radio frequency considered, and the original d-c bias point. The sensitivity increases as emitter current is decreased. The gain and the amount of feedback that may be used are limited by stability considerations. For stable operation the regen-

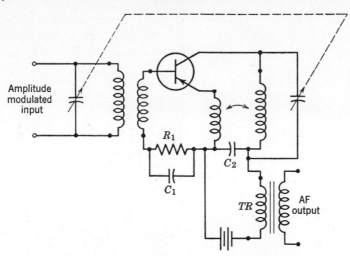

Fig. 9.31   Regenerative detection

erative detector is designed to operate with a small emitter bias current and a margin of stability such that the detector will not break into oscillation when the amplitude of the RF signal is increased.

The audio output will be somewhat distorted as a result of square-law detection. An increase of the quiescent bias current will usually reduce the distortion.

9.4.1.2   Superregenerative Detection

The sensitivity of a regenerative detector is limited by stability considerations. The sensitivity must be kept relatively low to prevent oscillation. This restriction does not exist with superregenerative detection.

A superregenerative detector is an RF oscillator whose oscillation is quenched periodically by another oscillation. This second oscillation is usually at some ultrasonic frequency known as the quench frequency. The quench frequency can be supplied by a second oscillator, called the auxiliary oscillator, or generated in the detector. The first case is termed "externally quenched superregenerative detection" and the second "self-quenched superregenerative detection."

Figure 9.32 shows a superregenerative detector having the output of the external-quench oscillator fed into the emitter circuit. In addition radio frequency is fed back into the emitter through the coupling capacitor C, thus producing oscillation. Capacitors C_1 and C_2 are the RF bypass capacitors. The quench oscillator is coupled to the emitter through a transformer. The detected audio signal is taken from the

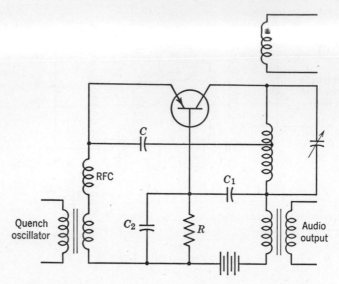

Fig. 9.32   Superregenerative detection.   Emitter injection.

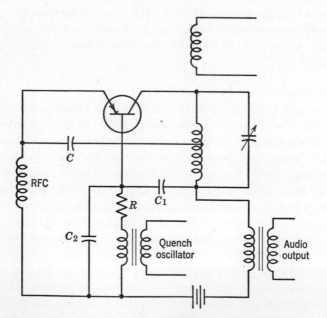

Fig. 9.33   Superregenerative detection.   Base injection.

collector circuit through an audio transformer. Resistance R may be adjusted for an optimum bias point. Figure 9.33 shows a superregenerative detector having the quench oscillator fed into the base.

Figure 9.34 shows a self-quenched superregenerative detector. The mechanism of the self-quenched oscillator is as follows: Initially, the emitter d-c bias current is very small. It is determined by the d-c voltage drop across the base resistor. Since the collector current is also

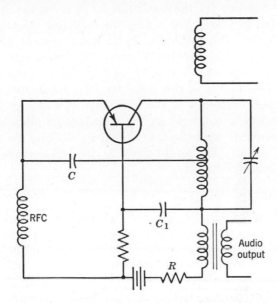

Fig. 9.34   Self-quenching superregenerative detection

small, the d-c voltage drop across the resistor R in Fig. 9.34 is negligible, and the collector bias voltage V_{CB} is practically equal to the battery supply voltage. If under this initial d-c bias condition the loop gain of the oscillator circuit is positive, oscillation begins. The amplitude of the oscillation builds up. At the same time, the instantaneous emitter current increases according to the envelope of the oscillation, as a result of rectification at the emitter diode. At first the effect of increased emitter current overcomes the effect of slightly decreased collector bias. Consequently, the loop gain is increased. The oscillation builds up at a high rate, and the emitter and collector currents increase correspondingly. Owing to the presence of the resistance R in the collector circuit, the collector voltage falls. The amplitude of oscillation soon reaches a point at which the emitter current is large and the collector bias voltage is small. The loop gain drops below unity. That is to say, the circuit has loss instead of gain. The oscillation dies down very rapidly, the emitter and collector currents decreasing at the same time. The collector bias voltage tends to recover, but, owing to the capacitances C and C_1, the instantaneous value of the collector voltage will be the same as the voltage across the capacitances. A finite time is required to build up the voltage across these two capacitances, charging through resistor R. If the time required to charge the capacitors C and C_1 is longer than the time required for the oscillation to stop (or the amplitude of oscillation to fall to a very low value) the oscillator behaves as a self-quenched oscillator. When there is an RF signal present, the period of the quench action is changed. In other words, the quench frequency is modulated by the envelope of the RF signal. Since the maximum amplitude of the oscillation is the same for all quench frequencies, the change in quench frequency is the indication of a change in the area under the oscillation envelope as the signal amplitude changes. I_C changes in accordance with the modulation and follows the envelope of the RF input signal. The audio signal is developed across the transformer in the collector circuit.

9.4.2 Limiters and Discriminators

Transistor limiters may be designed using various techniques, either based on normal electron-tube methods or utilizing new principles. Examples of both varieties are described in this chapter and in Chapter 12.

If a transistor is biased with a low emitter current, it will only act as a linear amplifier for low-level signals. For larger signals the transistor will be cut off on alternate half-cycles, producing a compression of the output. In order to restrict the amplification of the opposite half-cycle, a large resistor is placed in the collector circuit. In this manner, the collector voltage quickly falls to zero as the signal tends to increase the emitter current, and, consequently, the collector current.

Satisfactory operation can be obtained, provided that the required limiter characteristic does not have to be very flat and the range of input levels is not too great. At very high input levels the output falls off, owing to a shift in operating point resulting from rectification across the base-emitter junction. A typical characteristic is shown in Fig. 9.35.

When both the input and output are tuned, this type of transistor limiter is unsatisfactory. At high levels of input, a form of instability is encountered. If a high-level signal is applied to the circuit shown in Fig. 9.36, which is slightly lower in frequency than that to which the tank circuits are tuned, i.e. so that the collector load appears inductive, a form of instability results resembling the case of a tuned-grid tuned-plate oscillator being shocked into and out of oscillation. In this circuit, the feedback is through the transistor itself. The actual process is extremely complicated and nonlinear, involving the reversal of the collector-base diode for a portion of the cycle.

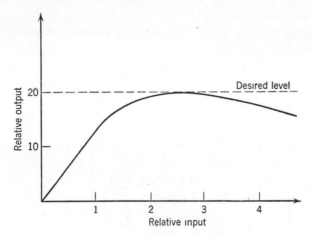

Fig. 9.35   Typical limiter characteristic

Satisfactory limiters have been built where this trouble has been eliminated by having the stages untuned. This, however, is associated with a somewhat different systems philosophy and is described in Chapter 11. If a tuned limiter is essential, a junction diode must be placed across the input of the transistor to prevent the signal from causing

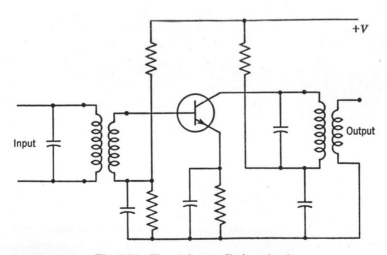

Fig. 9.36   Unsatisfactory limiter circuit

collector limiting. Such a circuit is shown in Fig. 9.37. The operation of this type of limiter is described in Chapter 12.

The design of discriminators suitable for use in transistorized receivers is quite straightforward, utilizing point-contact diodes in conventional circuits. Since the only problem is one of impedance levels dictated by the adjacent stages of the system, the reader is referred to Chapter 11 where such system aspects are discussed.

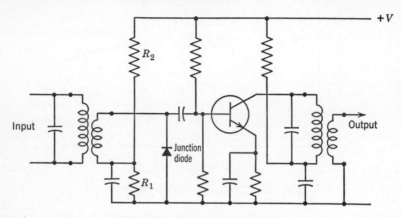

Fig. 9.37   Junction diode limiter

Problems

1. A combination of a resistor R in series with a capacitance C is connected across the emitter diode of a transistor. Assuming that eq. 9.1 represents the diode characteristic and that this expression is correct for all frequencies, discuss the behavior of the combined voltage-versus-current characteristic at low and at high frequencies.

2. From Chapter 2 derive the transfer functions T_m and T_m' as functions of i_E and v_{CE}.

3. Using a typical transistor as described in Chapter 4, Table 4.1, compare the amount of modulation power required for 100% modulation for the three cases of amplitude-modulated amplifiers.

4. If the modulation signal is injected into the base circuit of an amplitude-modulated oscillator, (a) study the mechanics of modulation, (b) derive an expression for modulation power, (c) derive an expression for the impedance seen by the modulation generator.

Bibliography

1. R. G. Shulman and M. E. McMahon, "Recovery Currents in Germanium p-n Junction Diodes," *J. Appl. Phys.*, *24*, no. 10, 1267–1272 (1953).

2. J. Zawels, "Transistor as a Mixer," *Proc. IRE*, *42*, 542–548 (1954).

3. W. F. Chow and A. P. Stern, "Automatic Gain Control of Transistor Amplifiers," *IRE Trans.*, *BTR-1*, no. 2, 1–15 (1955).

Chapter 10

Transient Response
and Pulse Circuits

10.1 Introduction

Pulse and switching circuits play an important role in such systems as television, radar, digital computers, telephone switchboards, sampling-type servomechanisms, pulse-code radio, and radiation detectors. Many of these systems require thousands of active elements per unit. Since reliability, size, heat dissipation, and power consumption are important in complex systems of this type, the transistor offers considerable advantages.

Pulse circuits may be classified into two general categories: linear and nonlinear. Linear pulse circuits are small-signal amplifiers which are required to reproduce the input pulse with little or no distortion of waveform. Nonlinear pulse circuits require wide excursions in the operating points of the active elements, and hence the output signals may be substantially different in waveform from the input or triggering signals.

The problems involved in the design of linear pulse amplifiers are similar to those encountered in the design of video amplifiers. Consequently, the principles outlined in Chapter 7 should be employed in the design of small-signal pulse amplifiers.

Nonlinear pulse circuits cover a wide range which includes such diverse applications as regenerative amplifiers, binary and decimal counters, shift registers, delay circuits, logic circuits, memory or storage systems. Since a comprehensive treatment of these applications is beyond the scope of this book, the discussion here will be restricted to fundamental considerations and several specific examples.

10.2 Small-Signal Transient Response

In general, the transient response of a transistor stage depends upon such factors as generator and load impedance, input and output impedances of the transistor, internal coupling effects, and the transport mechanism of carriers between the emitter and collector. If all these effects

299

were treated accurately in an attempt at exact analysis, the transient response calculations would be complicated and unwieldy. However, approximation techniques may be applied to the development of an equivalent circuit which will yield to linear analytical methods and which will give results that are compatible with experience. It will be informative, however, to begin with an analysis of the effect of diffusion upon the transient response.

10.2.1 Transient Solution of the Diffusion Equation

As was described in Chapter 2, the common-base short-circuit current amplification may be written as

$$\alpha_b = \alpha_{b0} \cosh p / \cosh \left[p(1 + j\omega\tau)^{\frac{1}{2}} \right] \tag{10.1}$$

Equation 10.1 is a fairly accurate expression, for most transistors, of the small-signal current-response function of a common-base transistor amplifier for the condition that the load impedance is negligible compared to the collector impedance. If the substitution, $j\omega = s$, is made in eq. 10.1, the current-transfer function may be expanded into a series of exponential terms which are readily transformable by the Laplace integral.[1] Thus, it is found that, if

$$i_E(s) = 1/s \tag{10.2}$$

i.e. if the emitter current is a unit step function, the collector-current response, $i_C(t)$, may be approximated by

$$i_C(t) \cong 2[1 - erf(1/2\omega_{\alpha b}t)^{\frac{1}{2}}] \quad \text{for} \quad t \to 0 \tag{10.3}$$

$$i_C(t) \cong 1 - \exp(-\omega_{\alpha b}t) \quad \text{for} \quad t \to \infty \tag{10.4}$$

In eq. 10.3, the error function [2] is defined by

$$erf\, y = \frac{2}{\sqrt{\pi}} \int_0^y e^{-x^2}\, dx$$

Equations 10.3 and 10.4 show that the response of the collector current to a step-type emitter current is composed of two parts. The first part of the response is a slowly rising function near $t = 0$ and is given approximately by eq. 10.3. This part of the response may be considered as a time delay which is due to the finite time it takes carriers to travel from the emitter to the collector. The second part of the collector-current response is approximated by an exponential function, given by eq. 10.4 and is due to charge-storage effects in the base region. The time it takes the collector current to reach a value of 10% of its final value may be found by equating the right-hand side of eq. 10.3 to 0.1. Thus

$$t_{0.1} \cong 0.04/f_{\alpha b} \tag{10.5}$$

The time required for the collector current to reach 63% of its final value, may be found from eq. 10.4 by equating $\omega_{\alpha b}t$ to unity and adding $t_{0.1}$. Thus

$$t_{0.63} \cong 0.16/f_{\alpha b} + 0.04/f_{\alpha b} = 0.2/f_{\alpha b} \tag{10.6}$$

An approximate equivalent circuit which may be used to represent the

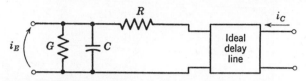

Fig. 10.1   Delay-line approximation of diffusion mechanism

delay and dispersion effects associated with the transit of minority carriers in the base region of a junction transistor is illustrated in Fig. 10.1.[3] The network parameters in this circuit are related to the transistor parameters as follows:

$$1/(1 + RG) \cong \alpha_{b0} \tag{10.7}$$

$$RC \cong 1/\alpha_{b0}\omega_{\alpha b} \tag{10.8}$$

Thus, the diffusion mechanism of the transistor may be represented approximately by a simple RC network in combination with an ideal delay line. The delay time of the latter is given by eq. 10.5.

10.2.2   Approximate Small-Signal Transient Analysis

When the transistor is operated as a small-signal amplifier, the emitter-base junction is biased in the forward direction and the base-collector junction in the inverse direction. In reference to the collector characteristics illustrated in Fig. 10.2, the transistor operating point is then in region II. An approximate equivalent circuit for the transistor operated in region II is illustrated in Fig. 10.3 and is identical to that of Fig. 2.15, except that h_{12b}' is neglected. This is justified for circuits operating into a small load impedance. For this circuit

$$z_\epsilon \cong r_\epsilon/(1 + j\omega C_\epsilon r_\epsilon) \tag{10.9}$$

$$C_\epsilon \cong 1/r_\epsilon\omega_{\alpha b} \tag{10.10}$$

and $$\alpha_b \cong \alpha_{b0}/(1 + j\omega/\omega_{\alpha b}) \tag{10.11}$$

As was indicated in Chapter 2, a closer approximation for the frequency variation of α_b may be obtained by multiplying the denominator of eq. 10.11 by an additional factor, $(1 + j\omega/4\omega_{\alpha b})$. Fairly simple trans-

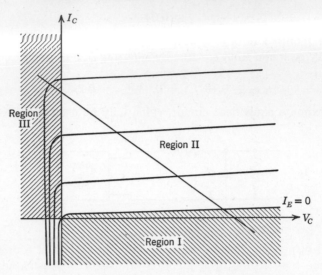

Fig. 10.2   Collector characteristics showing regions of transistor operation

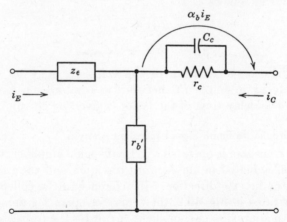

Fig. 10.3   Small-signal equivalent circuit of transistor in the active region

$$\alpha_b \cong \frac{\alpha_{b0}}{1 + j\omega_{\alpha b}} \qquad z_\epsilon \cong \frac{r_\epsilon}{1 + j\omega r_\epsilon C_\epsilon}$$

form equations may be derived for the circuit of Fig. 10.3 if it is assumed that the load impedance is very small. For the three transistor configurations, this assumption implies the following inequalities.

Common-base: $(R_l + r_b')/r_c \ll 1$ (10.12a)

$$\omega_{\alpha b} C_c R_l \ll 1 \qquad (10.12b)$$

Common-emitter and common-collector:

$$R_l/r_c \ll (1 - \alpha_{b0}) \tag{10.13a}$$

$$\omega_{ab} C_c R_l \ll 1 \tag{10.13b}$$

The validity of these conditions is quite realistic for a wide variety of applications. For example, if a transistor has the following parameter values: $r_c = 5 \times 10^6$ ohms, $r_b' = 200$ ohms, $C_c = 5$ μμf, $\alpha_{b0} = 0.99$, and $\omega_{ab} = 10^7$ radians per second, the conditions given by eqs. 10.12–10.13 restrict the load resistance R_l to values considerably below 20,000 ohms.

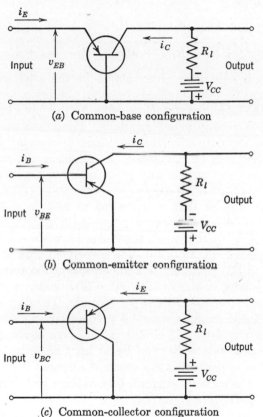

(a) Common-base configuration

(b) Common-emitter configuration

(c) Common-collector configuration

Fig. 10.4   Transistor configurations for transient analysis

From the equivalent circuit of Fig. 10.3, and for the conditions given by eqs. 10.12–10.13, the following transform equations may readily be derived for the circuits illustrated in Fig. 10.4.

Common-Base.

$$i_C(s)/i_E(s) \cong -\alpha_{b0}/(1 + s/\omega_{ab}) \tag{10.14a}$$

$$v_{EB}(s)/i_E(s) \cong [r_\epsilon + r_b'(1 - \alpha_{b0} + s/\omega_{ab})]/(1 + s/\omega_{ab}) \tag{10.14b}$$

Common-Emitter.

$$i_C(s)/i_B(s) \cong \alpha_{b0}/(1 - \alpha_{b0} + s/\omega_{ab}) \tag{10.15a}$$

$$v_{BE}(s)/i_B(s) \cong r_b' + r_\epsilon/(1 - \alpha_{b0} + s/\omega_{ab}) \tag{10.15b}$$

Common-Collector.

$$i_E(s)/i_B(s) \cong (1 + s/\omega_{ab})/(1 - \alpha_{b0} + s/\omega_{ab}) \tag{10.16a}$$

$$v_{BC}(s)/i_B(s) \cong r_b' + [r_\epsilon + R_l(1 + s/\omega_{ab})]/(1 - \alpha_{b0} + s/\omega_{ab}) \tag{10.16b}$$

The transform equations given above in the *a*-lettered equations represent current-transfer functions between the input and output terminals, while the *b*-lettered equations relate to the input impedances for each of the three transistor configurations. From each set of equations, the response of the output current or input voltage for a given input current waveform may be calculated. In addition, the response of the output and input currents for any given input voltage waveform may be found.

For example, suppose that it is desired to find the collector-current time response of a common-emitter transistor amplifier to a small-signal step in source voltage when the source impedance of the generator is R_g. In particular, the time constant associated with this response is required if $R_g = 300$ ohms, $R_l = 2$ kilohms, and the transistor parameters are $\alpha_{b0} = 0.98$, $r_\epsilon = 26$ ohms, $r_b' = 200$ ohms, $r_c = 5$ megohms, $C_c = 5$ $\mu\mu f$ and $\omega_{ab} = 10^7$ radians per second. The degree of accuracy of the short-circuit analysis may be predetermined from eqs. 10.13a and b. For the transistor and circuit values given above, it can be seen that these inequalities are satisfied by at least an order of magnitude. The next step is to determine the required response function from eqs. 10.15a and b. The collector-current–base-voltage transform is given by

$$i_C(s)/v_{BE}(s) = [i_C(s)/i_B(s)][i_B(s)/v_{BE}(s)]$$

$$\cong (\omega_{ab}\alpha_{b0}/r_b')/[\omega_{ab}(1 - \alpha_{b0} + r_\epsilon/r_b') + s] \tag{10.17}$$

Since the generator impedance R_g adds directly to the transistor base resistance r_b', the value of r_b' in eq. 10.17 should be replaced by R_b, where

$$R_b = r_b' + R_g \tag{10.18}$$

The Laplace transform of the step in source voltage is

$$v_{BE}(s) = \Delta v_{BE}/s \qquad (10.19)$$

Substituting eqs. 10.19 and 10.18 into eq. 10.17 and solving for $i_C(t)$ gives

$$i_C(t) \cong \alpha_{b0}\Delta v_{BE}\{1 - \exp[(1 - \alpha_{b0}$$
$$+ r_\epsilon/R_b)(-\omega_{\alpha b}t)]\}/[r_\epsilon + (1 - \alpha_{b0})R_b] \qquad (10.20)$$

Hence, the time constant $t_{0.63}$ is

$$t_{0.63} = \frac{1}{\omega_{\alpha b}(1 - \alpha_{b0} + r_\epsilon/R_b)} = \frac{1}{10^7(1 - 0.98 + 26/500)} = 1.30 \ \mu\text{sec}$$

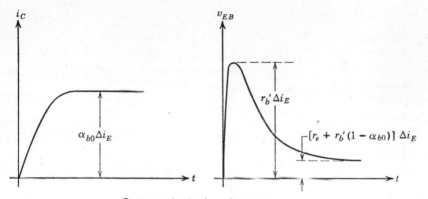

Responses to step in emitter current

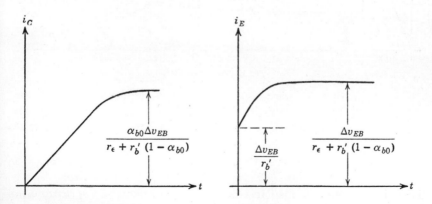

Responses to step in emitter voltage

Fig. 10.5   Transient response for common-base amplifier

Similar analyses may be applied to the other transistor configurations. Table 10.1 summarizes the time constants which are related to the response functions of the three transistor configurations for small-signal step input signals. The response functions for the common-base and

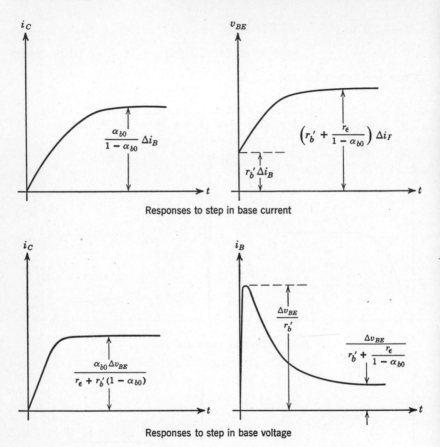

Fig. 10.6   Transient response for common-emitter amplifier

common-emitter amplifiers, as derived by J. L. Moll,[4] are illustrated in Figs. 10.5 and 10.6.

It should be noted that the short-circuit transient analysis given above leads to the most optimistic estimates of the transistor response times; i.e. the effect of load resistance will be to increase the rise and fall times. If the load resistance is increased to a value where the short-circuit approximations are no longer valid, the response times will be longer due to the $R_l C_c$ time constant.

Table 10.1

Time Constant of Response Functions for Transistor Amplifiers with Small-Signal Step Inputs

Response	Common-base Forcing Function		Common-emitter Forcing Function		Common-collector Forcing Function	
	Δi_E	Δv_{EB}	Δi_B	Δv_{BE}	Δi_B	Δv_{BC}
i_{OUT}	$\dfrac{1}{\omega_{ab}}$	$\dfrac{1}{(1-\alpha_{b0}+r_e/r_b')\omega_{ab}}$	$\dfrac{1}{(1-\alpha_{b0})\omega_{ab}}$	$\dfrac{1}{(1-\alpha_{b0}+r_e/r_b')\omega_{ab}}$	$\dfrac{1}{(1-\alpha_{b0})\omega_{ab}}$	$\dfrac{(r_b'+R_l)/\omega_{ab}}{r_e+R_l+r_b'(1-\alpha_{b0})}$
v_{IN}	$\dfrac{1}{\omega_{ab}}$	—	$\dfrac{1}{(1-\alpha_{b0})\omega_{ab}}$	—	$\dfrac{1}{(1-\alpha_{b0})\omega_{ab}}$	—
i_{IN}	—	$\dfrac{1}{(1-\alpha_{b0}+r_e/r_b')\omega_{ab}}$	—	$\dfrac{1}{(1-\alpha_{b0}+r_e/r_b')\omega_{ab}}$	—	$\dfrac{(r_b'+R_l)/\omega_{ab}}{r_e+R_l+r_b'(1-\alpha_{b0})}$

Configuration

10.3   Large-Signal Equivalent Circuit

When a transistor is operated as a switch, it is usually driven from a cutoff state to a saturated state, corresponding to an excursion from region I to region III in Fig. 10.2.   In this chapter, *cutoff* and *saturation* will refer to the state of the collector current; hence, when the transistor is cut off, or its operating point is in region I, the collector current is small and corresponds to zero or reverse emitter-base current. When the transistor is saturated, the collector current is high and the collector-base voltage is zero or reversed so as to bias the collector-base junction in the forward direction.[5]   A large-signal analysis of the transistor must therefore take into account the large variations of transistor parameters as the operating point of the device shifts over the entire range of the operating characteristics, from cutoff to saturation.   A convenient method of representing such nonlinear behavior is to make several linear approximations which apply over restricted regions of the overall operating characteristic.   This technique has been applied with considerable success to such devices as the point-contact transistor and the double-base diode.[6,7]

For example, the current through a rectifying junction has been given by (see eq. 9.1)

$$I_D = I_S[\exp (qV_D/kT) - 1] \qquad (10.21)$$

Equation 10.21 may be approximated by the equivalent circuit illustrated in Fig. 10.7.   Here D is an ideal diode, and R_f and R_s approximate the forward and reverse resistances, respectively, given by eq. 10.21.   A closer approximation represents the real diode by the equivalent circuit

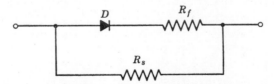

Fig. 10.7   Approximation for diode

of Fig. 10.7 in only a restricted region of the V,I curve, namely in the vicinity of the zero coordinate, and uses line segments to approximate the variation of the exponential curve for greater negative and positive values of V_D.   For the transistor, three linear approximations are usually sufficient, each of the approximations representing the device in one of the three regions of operation shown in Fig. 10.2.

In the simplest approximation, the large-signal equivalent circuit of the junction transistor may be represented by the back-to-back diode configuration illustrated in Fig. 10.8.[8]   When the transistor is active, i.e. the operating point is in region II of the I_C, V_C plane, the equivalent emitter diode is biased in the conducting, or forward, direction and the equivalent collector diode is biased in the nonconducting, or reverse, direction. The diodes in Fig. 10.8 can then be replaced by linear resistances as a first approximation. Thus, R_{fe} represents the forward resistance of the equivalent emitter-base diode, and R_{rc} represents the reverse resistance of the equivalent collector-base diode. The current-amplification factor is then α_{fb}, where the subscript f refers to the

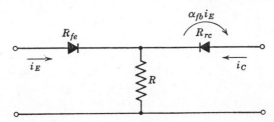

Fig. 10.8. Large-signal approximation for the p-n-p transistor

"normal" forward direction of current flow in the base region, i.e. diffusion from the emitter to the collector.

When the transistor is in the cutoff state, such that its operating point is in region I of the I_C, V_C plane, the equivalent emitter-base diode is biased in the reverse direction and may be represented by a linear resistance R_{re}. For this operating point the equivalent collector-base diode is still biased in the reverse direction, but the current-amplification factor α_{fb} is now zero. Similarly, when the transistor is biased into its saturation state, such that its operating point is in region III of the I_C, V_C plane, the equivalent collector diode is biased in the forward direction and may be represented by a linear resistance R_{fc}. Again, in the saturation region, the current-amplification factor is zero. Thus, an equivalent circuit of the type shown in Fig. 10.8 may be used to derive the approximate static characteristics of the transistor over a large segment of the I_C, V_C plane. However, a serious objection to the large-signal equivalent circuit of Fig. 10.8 is that it neglects the effects of saturation currents and reverse current-transfer in the transistor.

In order to derive a more general large-signal equivalent circuit, it is necessary to consider the nonlinear equations which describe the voltage and current relationships in a transistor. These may be written as follows for the common-base configuration: [9]

$$i_E = A_{11}[\exp(q\phi_E/kT) - 1] + A_{12}[\exp(q\phi_C/kT) - 1] \quad (10.22)$$

$$i_C = A_{21}[\exp(q\phi_E/kT) - 1] + A_{22}[\exp(q\phi_C/kT) - 1] \quad (10.23)$$

Here ϕ_E and ϕ_C represent the emitter and collector junction voltages, respectively. The similarity of the bracketed terms in eqs. 10.22 and 10.23 to the I,V relationship of a junction diode, as given by eq. 10.21, should be noted. Thus, the ensuing analysis is restricted to transistors having junctions which, separately, satisfy the diode equation. In addition, the analysis is restricted to transistors where space-charge layer widening effects may be neglected and where no significant voltage drops occur within the transistor other than those relating to the junctions.

The coefficients A_{ij} in eqs. 10.22 and 10.23 may be related to the saturation currents and current-amplification factors of the transistor, which are defined as follows: I_{CO} is the current that flows in the collector for zero emitter current; I_{EO} is the current that flows in the emitter for zero collector current; α_{fb} is the normal transistor current-amplification factor, i.e. the current-transfer function when carriers are emitted from the emitter junction and collected by the collector junction; α_{rb} is the reverse transistor current-amplification factor, i.e. the current-transfer function when carriers are emitted from the collector junction and collected by the emitter junction in inverted operation of the transistor.

When the transistor is operated in the normal manner and the operating point is in region II of the I_C, V_C plane, ϕ_C is negative, and hence the corresponding exponential argument is comparatively large and negative. The equations are then reduced to

$$i_E = A_{11}[\exp{(q\phi_E/kT)} - 1] - A_{12} \tag{10.24}$$

$$i_C = A_{21}[\exp{(q\phi_E/kT)} - 1] - A_{22} \tag{10.25}$$

Solving for the bracketed term in eq. 10.24 and substituting in eq. 10.25 results in

$$i_C = (A_{21}/A_{11})i_E + (A_{21}A_{12}/A_{11}) - A_{22} \tag{10.26}$$

The relationship between collector current and emitter current for a transistor in the active region of operation is usually given by

$$i_C = -\alpha_{fb}i_E + I_{CO} \tag{10.27}$$

Hence, the coefficients in eq. 10.26 may be related to α_{fb} and I_{CO} in eq. 10.27 by direct comparison. Similarly, when the transistor is operated in an inverted direction, i.e. with emitter functioning as collector and collector as emitter, the following relationship may be derived from eqs. 10.22 and 10.23:

$$i_E = (A_{12}/A_{22})i_C + (A_{12}A_{21}/A_{22}) - A_{11} \tag{10.28}$$

For the inverted operation,

$$i_E = -\alpha_{rb}i_C + I_{EO} \tag{10.29}$$

By comparing coefficients of eqs. 10.26 and 10.27, and also of eqs. 10.28 and 10.29, it can be shown that

$$A_{11} = -I_{EO}/(1 - \alpha_{fb}\alpha_{rb}) \tag{10.30}$$

$$A_{12} = \alpha_{rb}I_{CO}/(1 - \alpha_{fb}\alpha_{rb}) \tag{10.31}$$

$$A_{21} = \alpha_{fb}I_{EO}/(1 - \alpha_{fb}\alpha_{rb}) \tag{10.32}$$

$$A_{22} = -I_{CO}/(1 - \alpha_{fb}\alpha_{rb}) \tag{10.33}$$

Ebers and Moll have shown that, for even the most general transistor geometry, $A_{12} = A_{21}$.[10] A result of this equality is that

$$\alpha_{rb}I_{CO} = \alpha_{fb}I_{EO} \tag{10.34}$$

From the results derived above, large-signal equivalent circuits may be obtained.[10] For example, when the transistor is operated in regions I and II of the I_C, V_C plane, the collector junction is reverse-biased and eqs. 10.22 and 10.23 (with the coefficient values given by eqs. 10.30–10.33 substituted for the A's) may be written as

$$i_E = -[I_{EO}/(1 - \alpha_{fb}\alpha_{rb})][\exp(q\phi_E/kT) - 1] - \alpha_{rb}I_{CO}/(1 - \alpha_{fb}\alpha_{rb}) \tag{10.35}$$

$$i_C = [\alpha_{fb}I_{EO}/(1 - \alpha_{fb}\alpha_{rb})][\exp(q\phi_E/kT) - 1] + I_{CO}/(1 - \alpha_{fb}\alpha_{rb}) \tag{10.36}$$

Using the equality given by eq. 10.34, eq. 10.35 can be simplified to yield

$$i_E = [I_{EO}/(1 - \alpha_{fb}\alpha_{rb})][-\exp(q\phi_E/kT) + (1 - \alpha_{fb})] \tag{10.37}$$

Furthermore, eq. 10.36 can also be written in the form of eq. 10.27, i.e. as

$$i_C = -\alpha_{fb}i_E + I_{CO} \tag{10.38}$$

From eqs. 10.37 and 10.38, it is seen that both the emitter and collector currents are composed of two components, these being due to the forward-transfer characteristics of the junction and to reverse leakage effects. The equivalent circuit which results from these equations, and which is valid in only regions I and II of the I_C, V_C plane, is illustrated

in Fig. 10.9a. Linear resistances have been included in the equivalent
circuit to account for the finite resistivity of the base region (R_b') and
for the finite resistivity of the junction regions (R_e and R_{rc}).

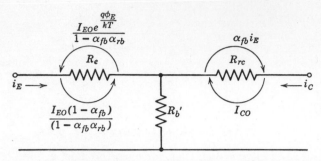

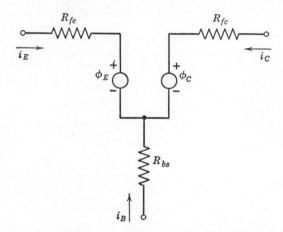

(a) Large-signal equivalent circuit valid in regions I and II

(b) Large-signal equivalent circuit valid in region III

Fig. 10.9

In region III, the transistor is saturated, and both the emitter and
collector junctions are virtually biased in the forward direction. Since
the emitter and collector junctions are of very low impedance, the external circuitry is essentially responsible for current limiting. It is convenient, therefore, to derive the junction voltages, from eqs. 10.22 and
10.23, in terms of the emitter and collector currents. Thus

$$\phi_E = (kT/q) \ln [1 - (i_E + \alpha_{rb} i_C)/I_{EO}] \qquad (10.39)$$

$$\phi_C = (kT/q) \ln [1 - (i_C + \alpha_{fb} i_E)/I_{CO}] \qquad (10.40)$$

From eqs. 10.39 and 10.40, the equivalent circuit illustrated in Fig. 10.9*b* may be obtained for region III. Linear resistances R_{fe}, R_{fc}, and R_{bs} have been added to account for the bulk resistances of the emitter and collector regions and the base-spreading resistance, respectively, under saturated conditions.

The results obtained above may be applied directly to the common-emitter configuration. If the positive sense of the emitter, base, and collector currents is defined as flowing into the transistor terminals,

$$i_E + i_B + i_C = 0 \qquad (10.41)$$

Substituting for i_E in eq. 10.41, from eq. 10.22, results in

$$i_C = [\alpha_{fb}i_B/(1 - \alpha_{fb})] - I_{CO}[\exp(q\phi_C/kT) - 1]/(1 - \alpha_{fb}) \qquad (10.42)$$

Equation 10.42 applies to the common-emitter configuration in regions I, II, and III. Since, in the common-emitter connection,

$$v_{CE} \cong \phi_C - \phi_E \qquad (10.43)$$

the application of eqs. 10.39 and 10.40 to eq. 10.43 results in

$$v_{CE} \cong kT/q \ln \{[\alpha_{rb}(1 - i_C/i_B)(1 - \alpha_{fb})/\alpha_{fb}]/[1 + (i_C/i_B)(1 - \alpha_{rb})]\} \qquad (10.44)$$

For *n-p-n* transistors, the right-hand side of eq. 10.44 is multiplied by −1. Note that eq. 10.44 is valid only in region III and that v_{CE} represents the voltage drop across the transistor output terminals when it is saturated.

In applying the above equations to practical cases, it should be remembered that the current-amplification factors are functions of the operating point and that, in general, the theoretical equations apply to low emitter-current densities. The type of transistor may also be involved in the accuracy of the analysis; for example, *n-p-n* alloy transistors follow the theoretical predictions more closely than *p-n-p* alloy types.

10.4 Large-Signal Transient Response

When a transistor is used as a switch or in a regenerative pulse circuit it is usually operated from the cutoff to the saturation states. (This may not be true in high-frequency applications, as will be discussed later.) Since the operating point traverses the I_C, V_C plane from region I to region III, both emitter and collector junctions reverse their normal functions. In region I, therefore, the emitter of the transistor is reverse-biased and presents a high-impedance input to the source while in region

III the collector is forward-biased and requires current limiting by the external circuit. When the transistor is turned on, it is driven from region I to region III and the parameters of region II predominantly determine the switching speed. However, in region III, the collector voltage has dropped to a near-zero value, and in turning the transistor off an appreciable time is required before the reverse collector potential can be restored. This time depends upon the rate of decay of carriers in

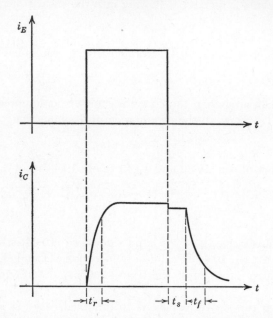

Fig. 10.10   Transient response of common-base transistor

the base region, and is a storage phenomenon that is governed by such factors as the lifetime of the minority carriers. Hence, the response of a common-base transistor circuit to a square-wave current input appears as is illustrated in Fig. 10.10. The rise time t_r is calculated by the linear-response equations for the active transistor (eqs. 10.14a and b). The storage time t_s is the time it takes the reverse collector-junction potential to recover and is, in effect, the time required to shift the transistor operating point from region III to region II. Once the transistor has become active again, the fall time t_f is determined by the active transistor parameters.

The rise, storage, and fall times of the transistor have been calculated [4] and are summarized below. It should be noted that rise or fall time is defined as the time it takes the output current to reach 90% of its final value; these times are calculated from the active-region current transforms given by eqs. 10.14a, 10.15a, and 10.16a. The final values of the output current are limited to the saturation and cutoff values, which are approximately V_{CC}/R_l and 0, respectively. The forward and reverse common-base α-cutoff frequencies are denoted by $\omega_{\alpha fb}$ and $\omega_{\alpha rb}$, respectively.

Common-base Configuration:

$$t_r = [1/\omega_{\alpha fb}] \ln [i_E/(i_E - 0.9i_C/\alpha_{fb})] \tag{10.45a}$$

$$t_s = \left[\frac{\omega_{\alpha fb} + \omega_{\alpha rb}}{\omega_{\alpha fb}\omega_{\alpha rb}(1 - \alpha_{fb}\alpha_{rb})} \right] \ln \left[\frac{i_{E1} - i_{E2}}{i_{C1}/\alpha_{fb} - i_{E2}} \right] \tag{10.45b}$$

$$t_f = [1/\omega_{\alpha fb}] \ln [(i_{C1} + \alpha_{fb}i_{E2})/(0.1i_{C1} + \alpha_{fb}i_{E2})] \tag{10.45c}$$

Common-emitter Configuration:

$$t_r = \left[\frac{1}{(1 - \alpha_{fb})\omega_{\alpha fb}} \right] \ln \left[\frac{i_B}{i_B - 0.9(1 - \alpha_{fb})i_C/\alpha_{fb}} \right] \tag{10.46a}$$

$$t_s = \left[\frac{\omega_{\alpha fb} + \omega_{\alpha rb}}{\omega_{\alpha fb}\omega_{\alpha rb}(1 - \alpha_{fb}\alpha_{rb})} \right] \ln \left[\frac{i_{B1} - i_{B2}}{i_{C1}(1 - \alpha_{fb})/\alpha_{fb} - i_{B2}} \right] \tag{10.46b}$$

$$t_f = \left[\frac{1}{(1 - \alpha_{fb})\omega_{\alpha fb}} \right] \ln \left[\frac{i_{C1} - \alpha_{fb}i_{B2}/(1 - \alpha_{fb})}{0.1i_{C1} - \alpha_{fb}i_{B2}/(1 - \alpha_{fb})} \right] \tag{10.46c}$$

Common-collector Configuration:

$$t_r = \left[\frac{1}{(1 - \alpha_{fb})\omega_{\alpha fb}} \right] \ln \left[\frac{\alpha_{fb}i_B}{i_R - 0.9(1 - \alpha_{fb})i_E} \right] \tag{10.47a}$$

$$t_s = \left[\frac{\omega_{\alpha fb} + \omega_{\alpha rb}}{\omega_{\alpha fb}\omega_{\alpha rb}(1 - \alpha_{fb}\alpha_{rb})} \right] \ln \left[\frac{i_{B1} - i_{B2}}{i_{B2} + i_{E1}(1 - \alpha_{fb})} \right] \tag{10.47b}$$

$$t_f = \left[\frac{1}{(1 - \alpha_{fb})\omega_{\alpha fb}} \right] \ln \left[\frac{i_{E1} - i_{B2}/(1 - \alpha_{fb})}{0.1i_{E1} - i_{B2}/(1 - \alpha_{fb})} \right] \tag{10.47c}$$

In the b- and c-lettered equations given above, the subscripts 1 and 2 refer to current values immediately before and immediately after the turn-off step is applied at the driving terminal, respectively. It should be noted that these equations are based upon the assumption that collector capacitance does not significantly affect the rise and fall times, i.e. that

$$R_l C_c \omega_{\alpha fb} \ll 1$$

If this condition is not true, the effect of collector capacitance will be to increase the switching times. In addition, in the calculation of storage time, it has been assumed that the carrier density in the base region of the transistor has reached an equilibrium condition. For this assump-

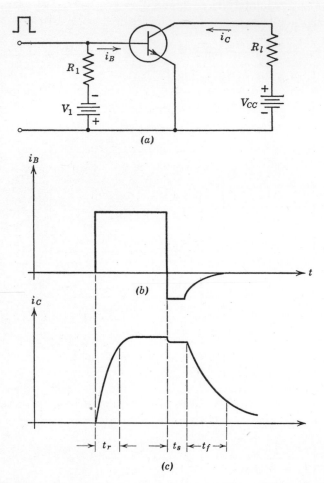

Fig. 10.11   Transient response of common-emitter switching circuit

tion to be true, the width of the turn-on pulse must be at least equal to the lifetime of minority carriers in the base. Since this is in the same order of magnitude as the time constant associated with the α_e cutoff frequency, the equilibrium condition implies that

$$t_d \geq 1/(1 - \alpha_{fb})\omega_{\alpha fb}$$

where t_d is the duration of the driving pulse.

Example. Suppose that it is desired to calculate the large-signal transient response of the common-emitter amplifier illustrated in Fig. 10.11. The transistor has the following parameters: $\omega_{\alpha fb} = 10^7$ radians per second, $\omega_{\alpha rb} = 10^6$ radians per second, $\alpha_{fb} = 0.98$, $\alpha_{rb} = 0.70$. In addition, when the transistor saturates, the collector current is

$$i_C \cong V_{CC}/R_l = 10 \text{ ma}$$

The base drive i_{B1} is 3 ma, and at the termination of the turn-on pulse the reverse base-bias current, due to V_1, is $i_{B2} \cong V_1/R_1 = -0.5$ ma. From eq. 10.46a, the rise time of the amplifier is

$$t_r = [1/(1 - 0.98)(10^7)] \ln \{3/[3 - 0.9(1 - 0.98)10/(0.98)]\}$$

$$= 0.32 \ \mu\text{sec}$$

From eq. 10.46b, the storage time is calculated as

$$t_s = [(1.0 + 0.1)(10^7)/(10^7)(10^6)(1 - 0.686)]$$

$$\times \ln \{3.5/[(10)(0.02/0.98) + 0.5]\} = 5.62 \ \mu\text{sec}$$

And, from eq. 10.46c, the fall time is

$$t_f = [1/(1 - 0.98)(10^7)] \ln \{[10 + (49)(0.5)]/[1 + (49)(0.5)]\}$$

$$= 1.5 \ \mu\text{sec}$$

It is seen that, the stronger the base drive, the shorter will be the turn-on time. However, because of the larger carrier density injected with strong base drives, the storage effects will be more severe and the turn-off time will be longer. Thus, in the above example, if the turn-on current were reduced to $i_{B1} = 1$ ma and the turn-off drive were increased to $i_{B2} = -1$ ma, the rise, storage, and fall times would be $t_r = 1.0 \ \mu\text{sec}$, $t_s = 1.75 \ \mu\text{sec}$, and $t_f = 0.8 \ \mu\text{sec}$.

10.5   Gate and Logic Circuits

An example of a transistor switch was illustrated in Fig. 10.11a. Here the transistor is driven into saturation by an input signal and driven back to cutoff, upon the termination of the signal, by the reverse bias supply V_1. Figures 10.11b and c show the input and output current waveforms. The state of the transistor, therefore, is determined by the presence and duration of the input signal, and the operation is similar to that of a simple relay.

A transistor switching circuit which may be used to gate an input signal from a common input terminal to one of two output terminals is illustrated in Fig. 10.12. The input signal is applied at terminal A and may be routed to the collector output of either transistor T_1 (B terminal) or T_2 (D terminal), depending upon the polarity of the gating signal applied at G. Thus, if a positive potential is applied at G, transistor T_1 is biased into cutoff and a positive pulse applied at A will cause an output signal to appear at D only. However, if a negative potential is applied at G the input pulse will cause T_1 to conduct, and hence the signal output will appear at B but not at D, since the negative potential at G back-biases the emitter of T_2 but forward-biases the emitter of T_1.

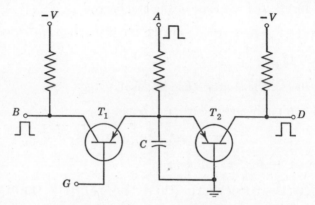

Fig. 10.12   Bidirectional transistor gate

Once T_1 conducts, transistor T_2 is clamped into a cutoff state by the negative gate potential at G. Similarly, once T_2 conducts, transistor T_1 is clamped into cutoff by the positive potential at G. Hence, either transistor may be driven from cutoff to saturation without the possibility of losing the routing action, and full advantage may be taken of the nearly ideal switching characteristics of the transistors.

By directly coupling several transistor switching stages, multiterminal gates which are applicable to logic networks may be constructed. The basic functions required in logical networks used in digital equipment may be divided into "or," "and," and "inhibit" operations. An n-terminal "or" gate will have an output when *any* one of its n input terminals is energized. However, an n-terminal "and" gate will have an output only when *all* of its n input terminals are energized. An "inhibit" circuit is an "or" or "and" gate with an additional input terminal which, when energized, prevents an output signal from occurring, even when the other input terminals are activated.

Logic gates may be constructed with only passive elements, such as diodes, but amplifiers are then required to make up for energy losses in the logic circuits.[11]　Transistor logic circuits combine the switching and amplifying properties of transistors and thus eliminate the need for additional amplifying stages.　A *series*-connected transistor "and" gate is illustrated in Fig. 10.13.　Transistors T_1 and T_2 are biased into cutoff by the negative potential V_1.　When positive pulses are applied to terminals A *and* B at the same time, both transistors are driven into saturation and the output potential at terminal C drops to a near-zero value. However, pulses applied to terminal A or B separately will have no effect upon the output potential at C since one of the transistors remains

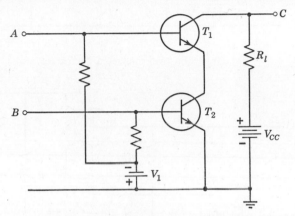

Fig. 10.13　Series-connected "and" gate

cut off.　By reversing the polarity of the bias supply V_1, so that a positive bias is applied to the bases of the transistors, the series-connected circuit of Fig. 10.13 is converted to an "or" gate.　For this connection, the transistors are maintained in saturated states by V_1, but negative pulses applied at either A *or* B terminals will cut one of the transistors off and thus cause the output potential at C to rise from a near-zero value to a value almost equal to the battery supply potential V_{CC}.

　　A *parallel*-connected transistor "or" gate is illustrated in Fig. 10.14. Transistors T_1 and T_2 are maintained in cutoff states by the negative bias supply V_1.　A positive pulse applied at either A *or* B terminals will drive either T_1 or T_2 into saturation, thus causing the output potential at terminal C to fall to a near-zero value.　By reversing the polarity of the bias supply the parallel-connected circuit of Fig. 10.14 may be converted to an "and" gate.　For this condition both transistors are biased into saturation by V_1, and thus, only when negative pulses are applied to A *and* B terminals simultaneously, forcing both T_1 and T_2 into cutoff states, can the potential at C rise from a near-zero value to a value approximately equal to V_{CC}.

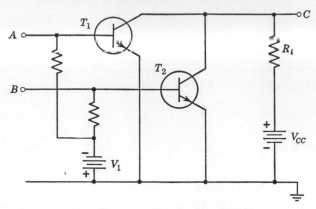

Fig. 10.14   Parallel-connected "or" gate

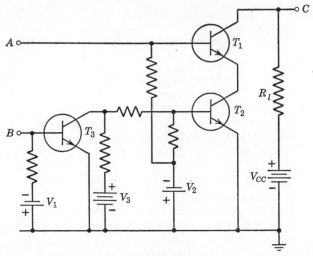

Fig. 10.15   "Inhibiting" gate

Figure 10.15 illustrates a series-connected "inhibit" gate. If the B terminal is not energized, the negative bias supply V_1 maintains T_3 in a cutoff state, and hence the collector potential of T_3 is very nearly equal to the positive potential V_3. The potential at the base of T_2 is then positive enough to drive T_2 into saturation. For this condition, a positive pulse applied to the A terminal will drive T_1 into saturation and will cause the output voltage at C to fall from a value almost equal to the battery supply V_{CC} to a near-zero value. Thus, as long as the B terminal is not energized, the potential at C responds to pulses applied at A. However, if a positive signal is applied at B, transistor T_3 is driven into saturation, and the potential at the base of T_2 falls to a negative value owing to the bias supply V_2. Transistor T_2 is then driven into cutoff, and positive pulses applied at A are no longer effective in changing the potential at the output terminal C. Consequently, positive signals applied at B inhibit the effect of pulses at A.

10.5.1 Clamping Circuits

Transistor storage effects encountered during saturation seriously limit the maximum repetition rate at which switching or gating circuits may be driven. A method for preventing saturation is by the use of a diode clamp as illustrated in Fig. 10.16a. When the collector potential

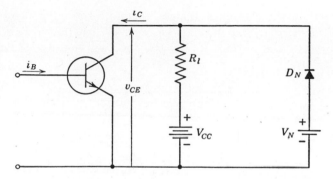

(a) Clamping circuit to prevent saturation

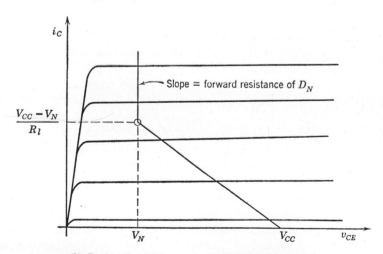

(b) Broken load-line representation of clamp effect

Fig. 10.16   Collector clamp to prevent saturation effects

v_{CE} falls to a value equal to the clamping potential V_N, the diode D_N begins to conduct, and hence the transistor collector voltage cannot fall below the value V_N. A broken load line representation of the clamping action is shown in Fig. 10.16b. The current through the load resistance R_l is limited to the value

$$i_{LM} = (V_{CC} - V_N)/R_l \qquad (10.48)$$

where the subscript M denotes the maximum value of the current. However, the collector current of the transistor is limited only by the driving current i_B; i.e.

$$i_{CM} \cong \alpha_e i_{BM} \qquad (10.49)$$

The current in the clamping diode is therefore the difference between the collector current and the load current. When the driving current i_B is reduced to zero, current through the load will continue to flow until

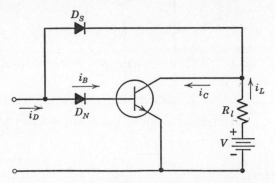

Fig. 10.17   Low-dissipation, high-speed clamp

the collector current has decayed to a value just equal to the load current given by eq. 10.48. Thus, pulse widening or "stretching" may occur even when transistor saturation is prevented by clamping.

In order to maintain high switching efficiency when the transistor is fully conducting, the clamping voltage V_N should be as low as feasible, i.e. as close to the saturation voltage of the transistor as is practicable. Since clamping voltages less than one volt are difficult to obtain in practice, an alternative clamp procedure has been developed [13] which utilizes the low voltage drop across a conducting diode. This low-dissipation clamp circuit is illustrated in Fig. 10.17. A requirement of the circuit is that the diode D_N have a higher forward-voltage drop than the feedback diode D_S. In practice, this condition can generally be assured by using a silicon diode for D_N and a germanium diode for D_S. The potential at which the collector will clamp is

$$v_{CE} = v_{BE} + v_{fN} - v_{fS} \tag{10.50}$$

where v_{BE} is the base-to-emitter voltage drop of the conducting transistor, v_{fN} is the forward-voltage drop of the diode D_N, and v_{fS} is the forward-voltage drop of the diode D_S. The maximum current in the load is then limited to

$$i_{LM} = [V - (v_{BE} + v_{fN} - v_{fS})]/R_l \tag{10.51}$$

In practice, the transistor may be clamped to within a few tenths of a volt of its saturation value, and hence the internal dissipation of the fully conducting transistor is only slightly higher than it would be if the transistor were saturated.

Another important feature of the clamping circuit illustrated in Fig. 10.17 is the degenerative effect of the feedback diode D_S *after* the clamping action has taken place. Before the clamping action occurs, the base current of the transistor is equal to the drive current i_D since the diode D_S is nonconducting. The load current, which is then equal to the collector current, is given by

$$i_L \cong \alpha_e i_D \tag{10.52}$$

and hence is driven "hard" (by virtue of the common-emitter current-amplifying factor in eq. 10.52) to its limiting value of eq. 10.51. After clamping has occurred, D_S conducts and the base current drive in the transistor is now less than i_D as a result of the base-to-collector path through D_S. After clamping,

$$i_B = i_D - (i_C - i_L) \tag{10.53}$$

Since the transistor is still active,

$$i_C \cong \alpha_e i_B \tag{10.54}$$

Substituting eq. 10.53 into eq. 10.54 and solving for the rate of change of i_C as a function of drive current i_D results in

$$di_C/di_D \cong \alpha_e/(1 + \alpha_e) = \alpha_b \tag{10.55}$$

Thus, immediately after clamping, the ratio of collector- to drive-current falls from α_e to α_b. The degenerative action of the clamp circuit minimizes the effect of overdrive *after* the clamping action has taken place, thus allowing a very rapid load-current response in the switching-on process while minimizing the "pulse-stretching" effect during the switching-off interval.

10.6 Bistable Pulse Circuits

Many useful switching applications require bistable circuit configurations in which the switching element is triggered "on" by a pulse and remains "on" even after the pulse has terminated. An example of such a circuit is the well-known Eccles-Jordan bistable flip-flop, which is a regenerative-feedback configuration having two stable states. Single active elements which exhibit internal regeneration, such as the double-base diode, may also be employed in pulse circuits having two stable states.[16] The principal characteristics of these circuits, whether they employ nonregenerative active devices with external positive feedback or devices with internal regeneration are:

(a) They have two stable operating states.

(b) The regenerative action carries the circuit from one state to another, and this action is essentially independent of the amplitude of the trigger pulse (provided that the trigger pulse has reached a certain critical minimum amplitude) except in high-speed operation.

(c) The circuit remains in a stable state for an arbitrarily long time, when no trigger signal is applied, and this state is determined by the preceding pulse.

This last condition is a property associated with "memory," and is, in effect, a condition required of all bistable devices and circuits.

10.6.1 Eccles-Jordan Flip-Flop

A bistable transistor multivibrator is illustrated in Fig. 10.18. This circuit employs common emitter coupling and is analogous to the well-known cathode-coupled electron-tube configuration. The circuit may be triggered into on-off operation by applying the trigger signal at either point H or points F and G. The coupling resistors R_{k1} and R_{k2} provide the transistors with a d-c bias, and the coupling capacitors C_{k1} and C_{k2} are used to bypass the coupling resistors for maximum regenerative drive during the switching transients. The emitter coupling resistance R_f is used to supply the turn-off action on the transistor stage which is being driven from a conducting state to a nonconducting state, but C_f bypasses R_f during the switching transient in order to insure maximum transistor gain during the regeneration process.

It is convenient to analyze the circuit of Fig. 10.18 in terms of a two-terminal negative-resistance characteristic which may be obtained by breaking the circuit at any point and then calculating the V,I characteristic associated with these two terminals.[12] This technique is illustrated in Fig. 10.19, where the multivibrator circuit has been broken between the common emitter impedance Z_f and the emitter of the first transistor. When a current i_{E1} is forced through the emitter of T_1 and the resultant voltage between the two terminals v_{E1} is measured, a static curve of the

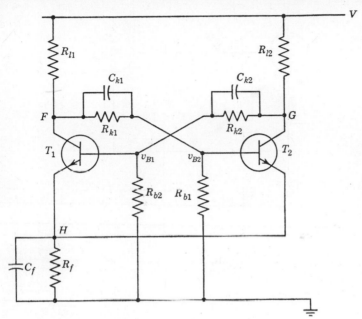

Fig. 10.18   Bistable transistor flip-flop

form illustrated in Fig. 10.20 is obtained.   The negative-resistance curve thus obtained consists of four regions.   If, for example, T_1 and T_2 are p-n-p transistors and i_{E1} is negative, T_1 will be cut off, and the resistance between terminals E and H in Fig. 10.19 will be very high. As the current into the emitter of T_1 is increased in the positive direction, a peak point P is reached (see Fig. 10.20) when T_1 becomes conducting.   A negative-resistance region is then encountered which corresponds to both T_1 and T_2 in active conduction states.   A valley point Q is then obtained when T_2 is just driven into cutoff, but T_1 is still active. As the emitter current is increased in T_1, a current value will be reached at the saturation point S when T_1 saturates, and hence the resistance between terminals E and H will change again.

The points P, Q, and S may readily be calculated from the circuit of Fig. 10.19 if it is assumed that T_1 and T_2 are ideal current generators

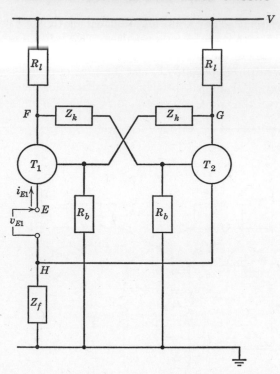

Fig. 10.19   Bistable configuration for design analysis

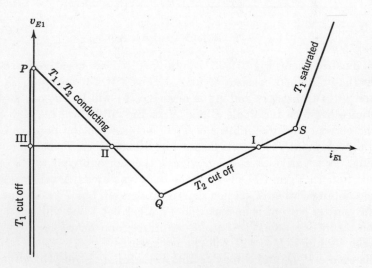

Fig. 10.20   Static negative-resistance characteristic

and if the current-amplification factors (d-c) of the transistors are assumed constant over the active region.[12] For these conditions, the approximate current and voltage coordinates of P, Q, and S for a symmetrical circuit are as follows:

Peak Point: $i_P \cong 0$ (10.56a)

$$v_P \cong -KV[\alpha_b KX(1 - \psi) - \psi]$$ (10.56b)

Valley Point: $i_Q \cong -(V/R_f)[K/(1 + \alpha_b KX)]$ (10.57a)

$$v_Q \cong KV[\alpha_b KX/(1 + \alpha_b KX) - \psi]$$ (10.57b)

Saturation Point:

$$i_S \cong -(Y - K)V/\alpha_b XYR_f$$ (10.58a)

$$v_S \cong KV[1 - (Y - K)/(\alpha_b KXY) - \psi]$$ (10.58b)

In eqs. 10.56–10.58, K, X, Y, and ψ are defined as follows:

$$K = R_b/(R_b + R_k + R_l)$$ (10.59a)

$$X = R_l/R_f$$ (10.59b)

$$Y = (R_b + R_k)/(R_b + R_k + R_l)$$ (10.59c)

$$\psi = |v_{BE}/KV|$$ (10.59d)

where v_{BE} is the internal base-to-emitter voltage drop of the conducting transistor.

If the terminals E and H in Fig. 10.19 are now short-circuited, which is the requirement imposed by the circuit of Fig. 10.18, the operating load line associated with the negative-resistance characteristic of Fig. 10.20 is the i_{E1} axis. The two stable operating points are I and III, corresponding to T_1 conducting and cutoff, respectively. Operating point II is potentially unstable since it is in the negative-resistance region. From Fig. 10.20 and eq. 10.57b, it is apparent that the valley voltage v_Q must always have the same sign as V (e.g. negative for *p-n-p* transistors) if the circuit is to be bistable. Thus,

$$\psi < \alpha_b KX/(1 + \alpha_b KX)$$

However, the saturation voltage v_S may be either positive or negative, depending on the sign of the bracketed term in eq. 10.58b. If the conducting transistor is to be prevented from saturating under steady-state conditions, v_S must have the opposite sign of V (e.g. positive for *p-n-p* transistors).

It should be noted that the analysis given above, for a symmetrical circuit, is the same whether the circuit is broken at the emitter of T_1 or at the emitter of T_2. Hence, the analysis that applied to T_1 also applies to T_2, with the exception that T_2 operates in a mode conjugate to that of T_1. Thus, when T_1 is at operating point III, T_2 is at operating point I.

Referring to the circuit of Fig. 10.18, when T_1 switches from cutoff to a conducting state, the potential at point F in the circuit falls by an amount Δv_C. This negative step is transmitted to the base of T_2 through the coupling capacitor, C_{k1}. The negative transient must be large enough to drive T_2 into cutoff. Now, when T_1 was cut off, the potential at F was approximately equal to the battery voltage V minus the potential drop in R_{l1} due to the current flow in the coupling network; i.e.

$$v_{C1} = V[(R_{b1} + R_{k1})/(R_{b1} + R_{k1} + R_{l1})] \qquad (10.60)$$

Similarly, the potential v_{B2} is

$$v_{B2} = KV \qquad (10.61)$$

Equation 10.61 assumes that the d-c input resistance of T_2, when the latter conducts, is much greater than R_{b1}. When T_1 conducts, the potential at F falls to

$$v_{C1}' = v_{C1} - \Delta v_C \qquad (10.62)$$

where Δv_C is the voltage-amplitude change at the collector of T_1. Correspondingly, the potential at the base of T_2 falls to

$$v_{B2}' = K(V - \Delta v_C) \qquad (10.63)$$

The effect of the coupling network upon the transient behavior of the potential v_{B2} may then be calculated from the equivalent circuit illustrated in Fig. 10.21. If it is assumed that $v_{C1} - \Delta v_C$, as given by eq.

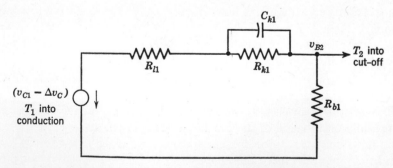

Fig. 10.21   Equivalent circuit of coupling network during switching transient

10.62, is a step function, the potential at the base of T_2 is

$$v_{B2}(s) = [(v_{C1} - \Delta v_C)R_{b1}/(R_{b1} + R_{l1})]$$

$$\times \{(s + \omega_k)/s[s + \omega_k/K(1 + R_{l1}/R_{b1})]\} \quad (10.64)$$

where $$\omega_k = 1/R_k C_k$$

By making the following definitions,

$$B = R_b/(R_b + R_l)$$

$$\gamma = B\omega_k/K$$

the variation of v_{B2} with time is obtained:

$$v_{B2}(t) = B\,\Delta v_C[(K/B)(1 - e^{-\gamma t}) + e^{-\gamma t}] - KV \quad (10.65)$$

The time it takes v_{B2} to recover to a value of zero is defined as the recovery time t_R, and may be calculated by setting eq. 10.65 equal to zero. Thus,

$$t_R = (-K/B\omega_k) \ln \{(1 - A)/A[(B/K) - 1]\} \quad (10.66)$$

where $$A = |\Delta v_C/V| \quad (10.67)$$

The variation of v_{B2} with time during the switching transient is illustrated in Fig. 10.22.

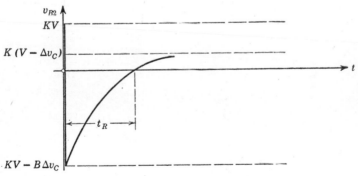

Fig. 10.22   Variation of base potential during switching transient

The ratio of collector voltage swing Δv_C to the battery supply V, which is denoted by A in the preceding equation, is given by

$$A = \alpha_{b0}(KX)(1 - KX/U)(1 - \psi) \quad (10.68)$$

where $$U = R_b/R_f \quad (10.69)$$

Several design procedures may be developed from the negative resistance analysis given above. In a symmetrical multivibrator circuit of the type illustrated in Fig. 10.18, there are seven circuit unknowns; these are R_l, R_b, R_k, R_f, V, C_k, and C_f. Seven conditions are therefore required to determine uniquely the circuit parameters. In a general design problem, only three or four conditions may be supplied by the circuit requirements, and hence several degrees of design freedom are usually available. An example of a design procedure is given below.

Circuit Requirements.   (a) V (available voltage supply) specified.

(b) Δv_C (desired collector voltage swing) specified.

(c) f_M (maximum pulse repetition rate) specified.

In addition, it is desired that the conducting transistor not be saturated during steady-state conditions. Thus, referring to Fig. 10.20,

(d) $$v_S > 0$$

It may also be required that the transistor leakage current I_{CO} not materially affect the output voltage. For this condition to be realized under any circumstances, it can be shown that

(e) $$i_{E1M} \gg I_{CO}(U - KX)(1 - \psi)$$

where i_{E1M} is the maximum steady-state emitter current for the conducting transistor.

Problem.   Determine: R_l, R_b, R_k, R_f, C_k, C_f.

Design Procedure.   1. Select K. To insure bistable operation:

$$(1 - A) \quad \text{and} \quad A > K \gg (1/A)(v_{BE}/V)$$

2. Select U. For design realizability:

$$\alpha_{e0} \gg U > A/(1 - \psi)(A - K)(1 + K - A)\alpha_{b0}$$

3. Calculate KX:

$$KX = U/2 - [(U/2)^2 - UA/\alpha_{b0}(1 - \psi)]^{1/2}$$

4. Select i_{E1M}:

$$i_{E1M} \gg I_{CO}(U - KX)(1 - \psi)$$

5. Calculate R_f:

$$R_f = (V/i_{E1M})(K - |v_{BE}/V|)$$

6. Calculate R_l:

$$R_l = XR_f$$

7. Calculate R_b:

$$R_b = UR_f$$

8. Calculate R_k:

$$R_k = [(U/K) - U - X]R_f$$

9. Calculate C_k:

$$C_k = 1/[\pi f_M R_k K(1 + X/U)]$$

10. Select C_f. This is accomplished by specifying that the switching time should be primarily determined by ω_{ab}. In addition, C_f must be small enough to permit the degenerative effect of R_f to occur within the pulse period. Thus [12,14]

$$(1/f_M \pi R_f) > C_f \gg (1/R_f \omega_{ab})$$

The design is thus completed. It is noted that the circuit requirements, which specified a given collector voltage output and a desired circuit recovery time, left the designer with four degrees of freedom. These were exercised in design steps 1, 2, 4, and 10. However, the degrees of freedom were not completely arbitrary since additional circuit requirements relating to steady-state nonsaturation and insensitiveness to I_{CO} were given. The degrees of freedom were still further restricted by realizability criteria resulting from approximations made in the analysis (eqs. 10.56–10.68) and by the requirement that the circuit be bistable.

Example. Suppose that it is desired to design a bistable multivibrator of the type illustrated in Fig. 10.18 such that $\Delta v_C = 5$ volts, $f_M = 100$ kc, and $V = 10$ volts. Transistors of the p-n-p type having the following parameters will be employed: $v_{BE} = 0.2$ volt, $\omega_{ab} = 10^7$ radians per second, $\alpha_{b0} = 0.98$. (Note: Since v_{BE} is actually a function of i_E, the particular value indicated is a "working figure" which applies approximately to a given current region.) The circuit will be operated over a temperature range where I_{CO} may reach a maximum of 25 μa. The design procedure is then as follows:

1. Select K. For bistable operation, $0.5 > K \gg (0.98/0.5)(0.02)$. Thus, select $K = 0.15$.

2. Select U. For design realizability:

$$50 \gg U > (0.5)/(0.98)(0.87)(0.35)(0.65)$$

Thus, select $U = 10$.

3. Calculate KX:

$$KX = 5 - (25 - 5.86)^{1/2} = 0.63$$

4. Select i_{E1M}:

$$i_{E1M} \gg (25)(10^{-6})(9.37)(0.87)$$

Thus, select $i_{E1M} = 2$ ma.

5. Calculate R_f:

$$R_f = (10/2)(0.15 - 0.02)(1000) = 650 \text{ ohms}$$

6. Calculate R_l:

$$R_l = (0.63/0.15)(650) = 2.73 \text{ kilohms}$$

7. Calculate R_b:

$$R_b = (10)(650) = 6.5 \text{ kilohms}$$

8. Calculate R_k:

$$R_k = [(10/0.15) - 10 - 4.2](650) = 34.1 \text{ kilohms}$$

9. Calculate C_k:

$$C_k = \frac{(10^{-5})(10^{-3})}{(3.14)(34.1)(0.15)(1.42)} = 0.00044 \ \mu\text{f} = 440 \ \mu\mu\text{f}$$

10. Select C_f:

$$10^{-5}/(\pi)(650) > C_f \gg 1/(650)(10^7)$$

Thus, select $C_f = 0.001 \ \mu\text{f}$.

Hence, the design of the multivibrator circuit is complete from a theoretical point of view. However, it is usually desirable to use standard resistance values in the circuit, and the closest standard values to the theoretical calculations are as follows: $R_f = 680$ ohms, $R_l = 2700$ ohms, $R_b = 6800$ ohms and $R_k = 33,000$ ohms. It is apparent, therefore, that the parameters K and U should be selected with enough tolerance to allow at least as much as 20% variation in the final design values without upsetting the validity of the design criteria.

10.6.2 High-Efficiency Multivibrators

In many pulse applications, particularly where portable energy sources may be required, it is desirable to utilize circuits of maximum efficiency. The conventional transistor flip-flop circuit of Fig. 10.18 is of comparatively low efficiency due to the considerable power losses in the common-emitter resistance R_f. Additional problems are encountered when this circuit is heavily loaded since the collector swing of the conducting transistor may be reduced. Consequently, buffer stages between the load and the multivibrator transistors are often used to prevent overloading, and hence considerable power is wasted in the collector resistors R_l.

A method for increasing the power efficiency of the conventional multivibrator (which is defined as the ratio of the signal power delivered to the load to the total power drain of the circuit) is to eliminate R_f by returning the emitters to ground and by utilizing a separate battery supply in series with R_{b1} and R_{b2} to provide the cutoff potential for the nonconducting transistor. However, the efficiency of the multivibrator may still be well below 50% owing to the power dissipation in R_l.

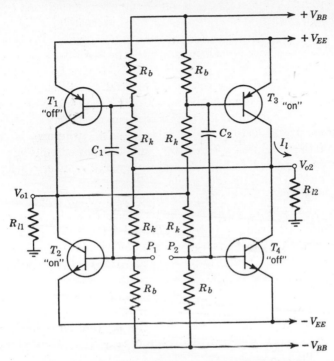

Fig. 10.23   High-efficiency flip-flop

It is possible to replace the collector resistance R_l in the conventional multivibrator circuit by complementing transistors in a circuit configuration similar to the bridge circuits described in Chapter 4. A circuit of this type is illustrated in Fig. 10.23.[13]

Transistors T_1 and T_3 are p-n-p types which are cross-coupled in the conventional manner. Coupling capacitors C_k are omitted but may be used to increase the trigger sensitivity of the circuit. Transistors T_2 and T_4, which are of the n-p-n type, constitute a second conventionally-coupled flip-flop pair. The two flip-flop circuits are then paralleled by directly coupling the collectors together. A negative bias V_{EE} is connected to the emitters of the n-p-n transistors while a positive bias is connected to the emitters of the p-n-p transistors. Cutoff biases are supplied to the bases of the transistors to provide the cutoff voltage due to R_f in the conventional circuits.

One of the two stable states of the bridge-type multivibrator is indicated by the "on" and "off" notations in Fig. 10.23. The complementary transistor pairs T_1 and T_4 and T_2 and T_3 operate "on" and "off" together. Thus, when T_3 is supplying current to a load connected to terminal V_{o2} so that the potential at V_{o2} is positive, T_2 is supplying current to a load at terminal V_{o1} so that the potential at V_{o1} is negative. If the transistors are allowed to saturate, the terminal voltages at V_{o1} and V_{o2} swing between $+V_{EE}$ and $-V_{EE}$. It may be noted that the load resistors are effectively connected between the collector points V_{o1} and V_{o2}, and hence the multivibrator may be thought of as a symmetrical bridge circuit in which the bridge arms are nearly ideal switches. The current available to the load is $(\alpha_{e0} - 1)i_B$, where i_B is the base current of the conducting transistor, and the power efficiency of the circuit approaches a limiting value given by α_{b0}. Power efficiencies in excess of 90% are readily attainable.

In the high-efficiency flip-flop circuit of Fig. 10.23, trigger pulses are applied to the bases of T_2 and T_4 at terminals P_1 and P_2. The capacitors C_1 and C_2 couple the bases of T_1 and T_2 and T_3 and T_4, respectively, so that a pulse applied to the base of T_1 is also routed to the base of T_2, and similarly a pulse applied to the base of T_3 is also routed to the base of T_4. Thus, for the "on-off" conditions illustrated, a positive pulse applied at P_2 will reverse the state of the multivibrator (by triggering T_4 "on" and T_3 "off").

Typical circuit values for this multivibrator are as follows: $V_{BB} = 6.5$ volts, $V_{EE} = 5$ volts, $R_k = 6800$ ohms, $R_b = 4700$ ohms, and $C_1 = C_2 = 0.1$ μf.

10.6.3 Direct-Coupled Multivibrators

In conventional multivibrators of the type illustrated in Fig. 10.18, the transistors are gated "on" and "off" by appropriate division of the collector voltages through the voltage-dividing networks consisting of R_b, R_k, and R_l. These networks are designed so that the collector voltage of the nonconducting transistor provides sufficient bias to the base of the conducting transistor to forward-bias its emitter. Conversely, the collector voltage of the conducting transistor must be divided down sufficiently at the base of the nonconducting transistor to insure that the latter is in a cutoff state.

If the collector-to-emitter saturation voltage of a transistor is less than the base-to-emitter drop, v_{BE}, it is possible to eliminate the voltage dividing networks in a flip-flop and thus obtain a directly coupled stage as illustrated in Fig. 10.24a. If T_1 is saturated, the base of T_2 is held at a low enough potential to prevent T_2 from conducting while the current flow through R_2 is sufficient to hold T_1 in saturation. Although the collector voltage swing is very small, being the difference between the collector-to-emitter saturation potential and v_{BE}, the collector current

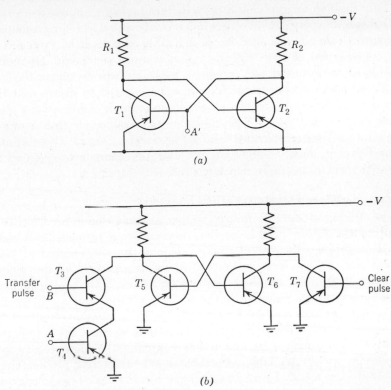

Fig. 10.24   Direct-coupled transistor logic circuits: (a) Direct-coupled flip-flop. (b) Clear and transfer circuit.

swing between the cutoff and saturation states can be quite large. Direct-coupled flip-flops offer considerable economy in component parts, viz. capacitors and resistors, and lend themselves to computer circuits which utilize direct-coupled transistor logic (sometimes abbreviated as DCTL) of the type described in Sec. 10.5. An example of such a circuit, which may be used for clear and transfer operations in the arithmetic units of digital computers, is illustrated in Fig. 10.24b.

In the circuit of Fig. 10.24b, the flip-flop is set into an initial reference state by applying a "clear" pulse to the base of T_7. Thus, T_5 is cut off, and T_6 is saturated. Transistors T_3 and T_4 constitute an "and" circuit such that, when terminals A and B are energized, the base of T_6 is pulled to ground, and hence T_6 is cut off and T_5 becomes conducting. If the base of T_4 is connected directly to the base or collector of one of the transistors in a control flip-flop, e.g. to point A' in the circuit of Fig. 10.24a, the state of the control flip-flop can be "read" into the transfer flip-flop by applying a pulse at terminal B.

Owing to the very small voltage differentials with which direct-coupled transistor logic circuits operate, considerable care must be exercised in the construction of such circuits. For example, if careful grounding techniques are not used, line transients may accidentally trigger the flip-flops. In addition, the transistors must be selected to insure that the saturation voltages are within proper limits. Since the pertinent transistor characteristics vary with ambient temperature changes, suitable temperature constraints must also be imposed. Despite these limitations, however, direct-coupled circuits offer such component economy as to make their use attractive in large digital systems.[18, 19]

10.6.4 High-Speed Operation of Multivibrators

The driving of bistable multivibrators at repetition rates which exceed the α_e cutoff frequencies of the transistors may be considered high-speed operation. In general, three problems are encountered at high frequencies. These are: (a) reliability of triggering, (b) frequency-response limitations imposed by the transistor, and (c) frequency-response limitations imposed by the circuit configuration.

The first problem may be particularly severe in cascaded multivibrator circuits, such as counters, where the output of one stage is required to drive a succeeding stage and where, consequently, unlimited trigger amplitudes are not available. Fortunately, the triggering problem may be solved quite readily by adding gating or routing diodes to the conventional circuit. This solution is illustrated in the circuit of Fig. 10.25. Diodes D_G and D_G' are connected from the collectors of the transistors to the battery supply V. Consequently, the diode connected to the cutoff transistor will be the first to conduct when a negative trigger pulse occurs at T, whereas the diode connected to the conducting transistor will be nonconducting. A pulse applied to the trigger terminal T is routed to the cutoff transistor through the conducting diode but is blocked from appearing at the collector of the conducting transistor. In addition to the steering diodes D_G and D_G', a third diode D_T has been added to the trigger circuit. Diode D_T allows the coupling capacitor C_T to discharge rapidly at the termination of the negative trigger pulse, and so prevents the build-up of excessive charge across C_T which would tend to buck the trigger potential. Thus, the diode combination illustrated in the circuit of Fig. 10.25 routes the trigger pulses to the correct circuit points and prevents the trigger pulses from being unduly attenuated by a charge accumulation on the trigger coupling capacitor.

The problem of frequency limitations due to transistor large-signal transient effects may be met by preventing saturation of the conducting transistor. The clamping techniques described in Sec. 10.5.1 are directly applicable to the transistors in a multivibrator circuit. However, it

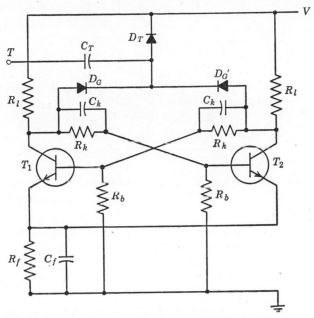

Fig. 10.25   Bistable multivibrator with steering diodes for high-speed triggering

should be remembered that, although clamping diodes prevent storage effects in the transistors, storage effects may nevertheless be encountered in the diodes. Consequently, the clamping diodes must be selected for short recovery time in order to insure high-speed recovery from the conduction state.

A method for routing pulses in a transistor multivibrator and providing simultaneously a clamp to avoid saturation is illustrated in Fig. 10.26.[14] Breakdown diodes D_{BS} and D_{BS}' are connected in back-to-back cascade between the collectors of T_1 and T_2. Under steady-state conditions, one transistor is in a high-conducting state and the other is in a low-conducting state. Hence, a potential difference exists between the collectors, and, if this potential difference is enough to break down diode D_{BS} or D_{BS}', the voltage difference between the collectors will be

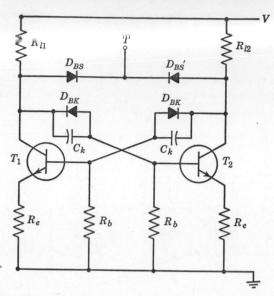

Fig. 10.26   Nonsaturating flip-flop using breakdown diodes

just equal to V_{BS}, which is the breakdown voltage of either D_{BS} or D_{BS}'. The breakdown diodes in the coupling circuits, D_{BK}, are continuously broken down and thus maintain a constant-voltage difference between the collector of T_1 and the base of T_2 and between the collector of T_2 and the base of T_1. Consequently, the diodes D_{BS} and D_{BS}' prevent the collector potentials of T_1 and T_2 from falling to zero while the reference potentials established by D_{BK} and D_{BK}' fix the stable points of the bistable circuit. When a trigger pulse is applied to point T in the circuit of Fig. 10.26, the diodes D_{BS} and D_{BS}' perform a routing function somewhat similar to the routing diodes of the circuit of Fig. 10.25.

When the transistors in a bistable circuit are prevented from saturating, their switching time may be calculated from an approximate equivalent circuit which represents the transistors as current generators and the coupling networks as short circuits. Such a circuit is illustrated in Fig. 10.27. It can then be shown [14] that the transient response is determined by the two time constants given approximately by

$$t_1 \cong 1/[(2\alpha_{b0} - 1)\omega_{\alpha b} - 2G_l/C_e] \qquad (10.70)$$

$$t_2 \cong 1/[G_e/C_e - G_l/C_e] \qquad (10.71)$$

Equation 10.71 is associated with a decaying transient while eq. 10.70 is associated with the growing component of the transient. The time re-

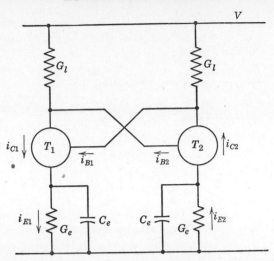

Fig. 10.27 Approximate equivalent circuit for rise and fall time calculations of flip-flop

quired by the growing component to increase to a value ten times greater than some reference value is $2.3/\omega_{ab}$ sec, if $(2G_l/C_e) \ll (2\alpha_{b0} - 1)\omega_{ab}$. (Note: $e^{2.3} = 10$.) If this rise time is defined as the time required by the transient to reach its final value from the time the transient was 0.1 of its final value, the 90% rise time of the transient is

$$t_{0.9} = 2.3/\omega_{ab} \tag{10.72}$$

Thus, a transistor having an ω_{ab} of 10^7 radians per second should switch in approximately 0.23 μsec when employed in a nonsaturating multivibrator configuration. Load conditions, and particularly the amplitude of the trigger pulse, will, of course, affect this value.

A requirement imposed on the trigger pulse is that it deliver enough charge to the nonconducting (or low-conduction) transistor to establish the specified conducting current. A very rough estimate of the charge requirement is

$$q \cong i_{CM}/\omega_{ab} \tag{10.73}$$

where i_{CM} is the maximum steady-state current that flows in the collector of the conducting transistor. Hence, if $i_{CM} = 1$ ma and $\omega_{ab} = 10^7$ radians per second, the required trigger charge is 10^{-10} coulomb.

Although the switching time of the transistors in a multivibrator configuration may be fast, as indicated by eq. 10.72, the maximum repetition rate at which the circuit can be driven is a good deal less than the α_b cutoff frequency. In essence, the maximum repetition rate depends on the phase-shift characteristics of the regenerative mechanism of the circuit. It can be shown, for example, that the maximum fundamental frequency of a multivibrator is [12]

$$f_{max} \cong (f_{\alpha b} f_{\alpha e})^{1/2} \tag{10.74}$$

The derivation of eq. 10.74 neglects the effects of collector capacitance and the recovery time of the cross-coupling networks. The maximum frequency of a multivibrator, therefore, is approximately the geometric mean of the α_b and α_e cutoff frequencies. Since $f_{\alpha b} \cong f_{\alpha b}/\alpha_{e0}$, eq. 10.74 may be written

$$f_{max} \cong f_{\alpha b}/(\alpha_{e0})^{1/2}$$

Consequently, a transistor having an $f_{\alpha b}$ of 10 mc and an α_{b0} of 0.98 may be expected to have a maximum permissible fundamental frequency on the order of 1.4 mc, or a maximum regenerative pulse driving rate, in bistable applications, of 2.8 mc.

10.6.5 Cascaded Binary Counters

Any bistable circuit that can be triggered from a unipolar pulse source may be used as a binary counter. The basic Eccles-Jordan configuration has found wide application to counting functions because of the circuit's inherent reliability and ruggedness. The flip-flop is a binary counter, or count-by-two circuit, because it requires two input pulses of a given polarity to generate one output pulse of the same polarity. Thus, n cascaded stages of flip-flops will count down by a factor of 2^n. Cascading such binary counters, particularly when routing diodes are used in each stage, is not difficult. Figure 10.28 illustrates the cascaded connection of two bistable stages, which results in a count-by-four circuit. The only requirement of such counting chains is that the collector swing in each stage be sufficient to provide a trigger pulse of sufficient power to drive the succeeding stage.

Counting in other than binary steps is very often required in pulse systems. For example, television sync generators require counters that divide the 31.5-kc output of a stabilized reference oscillator by a factor of two to supply the 15.75 kc necessary for the horizontal circuits and by a factor of 525 ($15 \times 7 \times 5$) to supply the 60 cycles for the vertical circuits. Counters fulfill these functions in studio equipment, and it is apparent that scaling by 2, 3, 5, and 7 must be accomplished.

Scaling by a factor of $(2^n - 1)$ requires n binary counters with one feedback path between the output and input stages. The feedback path advances the count of the first stage by an additional pulse so that only $(2^n - 1)$ input pulses are required to obtain one output pulse. For

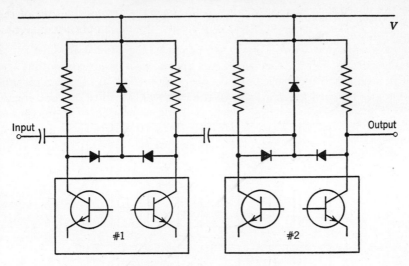

Fig. 10.28   Count-by-four circuit

example, a ternary counter requires two binary stages with feedback from the second to the first stage such that every three input pulses to the circuit generates one output pulse. A ternary counter is illustrated in Fig. 10.29a. A single feedback diode between the collector of T_3 and the collector of T_1 supplies the feedback pulse. The diode is connected

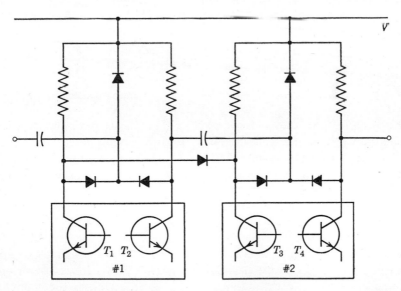

Fig. 10.29(a)   Count-by-three circuit

such that, whenever the collector of T_3 goes down, a negative signal is fed back to T_1 causing the first stage to advance a count. The collector waveforms for the transistors in the circuit of Fig. 10.29a are illustrated in Fig. 10.29b. From the waveform diagrams, it is apparent that the diode used in the feedback path between the second and first stages prevents any forward transmission of the input pulses to the second stage.

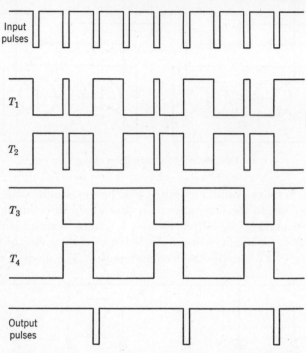

Fig. 10.29(b)   Collector waveforms in ternary counter

This is so because the collector of T_3 is always at maximum positive potential whenever the collector of T_1 is at maximum potential.

To obtain scaling by factors of $(2^n - 3)$, n binary stages with two feedback paths are required. Feedback from the last stage to the first stage is necessary to advance the count by one, and feedback from the last stage to the second stage is then required to advance the count by an additional two. A count-by-five circuit is illustrated in Fig. 10.30. Here the diode D_1 provides a feedback path from the collector of T_5 to the collector of T_1 and thus allows the count of the circuit to be advanced by one. In addition, diode D_2 provides a feedback path from the collector of T_5 to the collector of T_3 which advances the count of the circuit by two. Thus, for every five input pulses, one output pulse

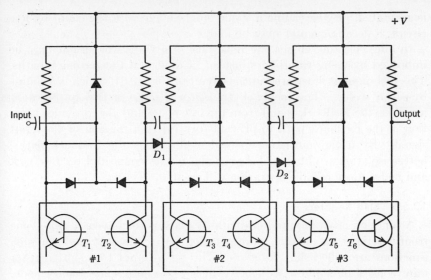

Fig. 10.30   Count-by-five circuit

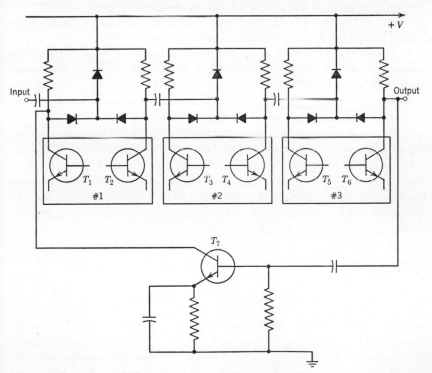

Fig. 10.31   Count-by-seven circuit

is generated. By cascading a single binary stage with the count-by-five circuit, a decade counter may be built.

In long counting chains the reliability of a transistor circuit may be improved by using transistors instead of diodes in the feedback paths. This technique is illustrated in the circuit of Fig. 10.31, which is a count-by-seven scaler. The feedback transistor T_7 serves two purposes; it amplifies the feedback signal from the last stage and also provides isolation in the feedback path to prevent forward transmission of the input signal. By using transistors instead of diodes in the feedback paths, better isolation is obtained between the points connected by feedback and hence more reliable operation will result.

10.6.6 Shift Registers

A function often required in digital systems is to convert a pulse code from a serial to a parallel representation. Circuits that perform such functions are called shift registers. The signal input to a shift register may consist of a pulse sequence which represents some binary code. The shift register then stores the binary information in such a way that the pulse sequence may be read out in parallel. Since "memory" is inherent in the serial-to-parallel conversion, one bistable element is required for each bit of information that must be stored.

Shift registers consist of cascaded flip-flops which are coupled in such a way that, when a shift pulse is applied simultaneously to all the stages, each individual stage is set in a state identical to that held by the preceding stage just before the application of the shift signal. One stage of a transistor shift register is illustrated in Fig. 10.32. Transistors T_1 and T_2 are connected in a bistable multivibrator configuration of the type described in Sec. 10.6.1. The base resistor R_b of the second transistor is connected to a reset line which permits the multivibrator to be reset (or preset) to a desired reference state. Shift pulses are routed to the bases of the transistors through capacitors C_t and diodes D_1 and D_2. The diodes act as gates which are controlled by the preceding register stage and are always in opposite states of conduction, i.e. when D_1 is nonconducting, D_2 is conducting. Consequently, the shift pulse is routed to one or the other of the two transistors, depending upon the state of the preceding multivibrator. Resistors R_1 and R_2 form voltage dividing networks which are connected to the collectors of each of the transistors. The tap points of the dividing networks, which are terminals 5 and 6 in Fig. 10.32, are connected to the diode gates of the succeeding register stage (terminals 1 and 2) and thus provide a bias to the succeeding stage gate. Thus, the gates of successive stages are controlled by the collector potentials of previous stages. The interstage coupling scheme for a shift register is illustrated in Fig. 10.33. Battery

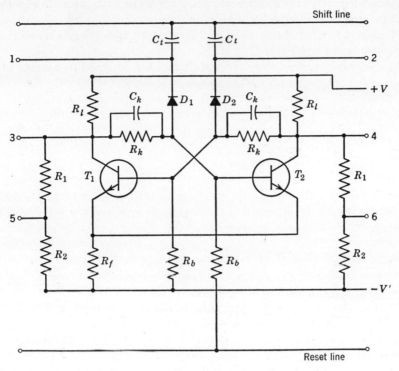

Fig. 10.32　Single stage for shift-register circuit

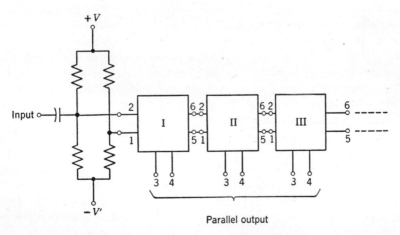

Fig. 10.33　Intercoupling scheme for shift register

supplies V and V' are of opposite polarities in order to provide collector swings between positive (or zero) and negative values for indicating the "0" and "1" states of the register. The output indication is taken from collector terminals 3 and 4.

Typical parameter values for a shift register designed to operate at a shift-pulse frequency up to 500 kc are as follows:

$$R_f = 1000 \text{ ohms,} \qquad R_b = 4.7 \text{ kilohms,} \qquad R_k = 22 \text{ kilohms}$$

$$R_l = 4.7 \text{ kilohms,} \qquad R_1 = 47 \text{ kilohms,} \qquad R_2 = 22 \text{ kilohms}$$

$$C_k = 120 \ \mu\mu\text{f,} \qquad C_t = 120 \ \mu\mu\text{f,} \qquad V = +5 \text{ volts,} \qquad V' = -20 \text{ volts}$$

For this design, the collector swing is from 0 to -10 volts, and a shift-pulse amplitude of approximately 5 volts is required for reliable triggering.

10.7   Monostable Pulse Circuits

A *monostable* pulse circuit is a regenerative circuit that has one stable operating point but can be triggered into unstable operation by the application of an input signal. Monostable circuits are used widely as regenerative pulse amplifiers in such applications as pulse-type digital computers [15] and delayed-pulse generators.

Two types of monostable pulse circuits will be described here. The first type is a two-transistor circuit, similar to the Eccles-Jordan configuration, where regenerative action is supplied by positive feedback from the output transistor to the input transistor. The second monostable circuit is a single transistor configuration of the blocking-oscillator type which utilizes a transformer to supply the required positive feedback. Many other configurations are possible, particularly with negative-resistance devices such as the p-n-p-n transistor or the double-base diode.[16] However, space limitations do not permit a thorough survey of the field.

10.7.1   Monostable Multivibrators

Monostable multivibrators are flip-flops which are triggered by an input pulse and generate an output pulse of prescribed width. The width of the output pulse is essentially independent of the trigger signal and is determined by the RC time constants of the circuit. Any of the conventional multivibrator configurations may be made monostable by unbalancing the circuit. For example, the bistable flip-flop illustrated in Fig. 10.18 can be unbalanced by inserting a resistance in series with the emitter of T_1. The resulting monostable circuit is illustrated in

Fig. 10.34a. Emitter resistance R_{e1} unbalances the circuit such that T_1 is nonconducting under steady-state conditions. R_{e1} must be sufficiently large to insure only one stable operating point; this condition is

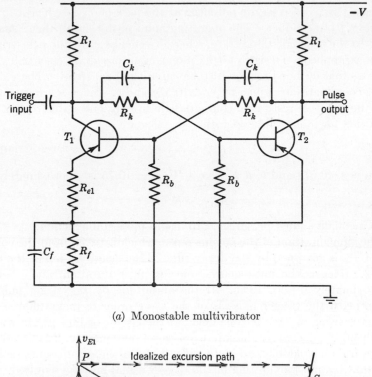

(a) Monostable multivibrator

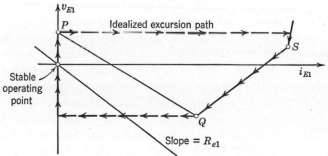

(b) Monostable operation characteristic

Fig. 10.34

illustrated in Fig. 10.34b where R_{e1} is shown intersecting the v_{E1}, i_{E1} negative-resistance characteristic in only one stable region.

A negative pulse applied to the collector of T_1 will be transmitted to the base of T_2, causing the latter to cut off. The potential rise at the collector of T_2 then drives T_1 into a conduction state. The circuit will remain in this state until the negative step at the base of T_2 decays through the coupling network. Since the emitter current in T_1 decays to a value less than the valley-point current i_Q, the circuit becomes regenerative as soon as the potential at the base of T_2 is sufficiently low to allow T_2 to conduct. The operating point of the circuit then "snaps" back to the original stable state, where it remains until the next trigger pulse is applied. Design of this monostable circuit is essentially the same as that outlined for the bistable circuit in Sec. 10.6.1. The valley-point coordinates are given by eqs. 10.57a and b. Since R_{e1} must intersect the negative-resistance characteristic in only one stable region, the condition for monostable operation is

$$|R_{e1}| > |v_Q/i_Q| \qquad (10.75)$$

From eqs. 10.57a and b, if $K \gg |v_{BE}/V|$, eq. 10.75 is, approximately,

$$|R_{e1}| > |KXR_f|$$

This inequality must be satisfied to insure monostable action.

The time duration of the output pulse, which is taken from the collector of T_2, is governed by the decay time of the negative step at the base of T_2. This is the pulse-delay time, or pulse duration, and is given approximately by eq. 10.66. If the amplitude of the trigger pulse is large, i.e. if the trigger pulse is of the same order of magnitude as the collector swing of T_1, the time delay of the circuit of Fig. 10.34a will be significantly affected by the input pulses. Consequently, if large trigger pulses are unavoidable and if the delay time of the circuit must be held constant, amplitude limiting of the trigger signal may be required.

A monostable circuit which permits the delay time of the generated pulse to be adjusted by means of a potentiometer is illustrated in Fig. 10.35. Under steady-state conditions, i.e. with no trigger pulse applied, T_2 is conducting and T_1 is cut off. When a negative trigger pulse is applied, T_2 is cut off and T_1 is turned on. The negative step thus generated at the collector of T_1 is transmitted to the base of T_2 and maintains the second transistor in a cutoff state until the potential across C_k' can decay. When T_2 becomes conducting again, T_1 cuts off and the circuit reverts to its initial steady-state condition until the next trigger pulse occurs. Since the charge stored in C_k' must leak off through R_l and $(R_b' + R_p)$, the variable resistance R_p may be used to control the delay time.

Typical circuit parameters for the monostable multivibrator of Fig. 10.35 are as follows: $R_{b1} = 8.2$ kilohms, $R_{b2} = 68$ kilohms, $R_f = 2.2$ kilohms, $R_l = 6.8$ kilohms, $R_b' = 100$ kilohms, $R_k = 22$ kilohms, $C_k =$

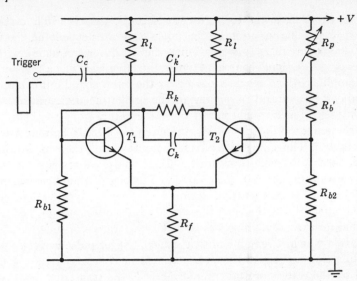

Fig. 10.35   Variable-delay (monostable) circuit

0.1 μf, $C_k' = 1000$ $\mu\mu$f, $V = 50$ volts, and R_p is a 100-kilohm potentiometer.   For this particular circuit, the time delay, or pulse duration,
is adjustable from 50 to 200 μsec, and the pulse amplitude at the collector of T_2 is 20 volts.

10.7.2   Pulse Generators and Regenerative Amplifiers

Although any monostable circuit of a regenerative nature is inherently
a pulse amplifier, the circuit to be described here specifically consists
of a single transistor with positive feedback supplied by a transformer.
The basic form of this circuit is that of a blocking oscillator and is illustrated in Fig. 10.36.   When the emitter-base bias V_1 is of such polarity

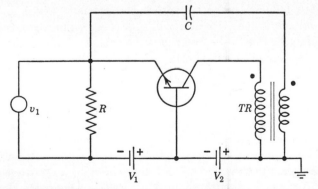

Fig. 10.36   Blocking-oscillator-type pulse generator

as to cause the emitter to be forward-biased, the circuit is *astable* or *free-running*. The function of the pulse generator supplying the input signal to the circuit is to synchronize the oscillator frequency with the frequency of the signal source. Hence, the circuit acts as a regenerative pulse amplifier which is synchronized by the input signal but can operate only above the natural frequency of the oscillator configuration. This circuit is useful as a synchronized pulse oscillator.

By reversing the polarity of V_1, the circuit of Fig. 10.36 may be made monostable. The d-c emitter-base potential will then maintain the emitter in a cutoff condition until a trigger pulse causes current to flow in the forward direction of the emitter. The circuit then becomes regenerative, and this regenerative action is essentially independent of the trigger signal. If, at the time the regenerative action ceases, the trigger pulse has decayed to a value less than V_1, the transistor reverts to a cut-off state in which it remains until the next trigger pulse arrives.

In blocking oscillators the pulse waveform characteristics are determined by the transistor and transformer. If the transistor is prevented from saturating, reasonably sharp pulses may be generated at comparatively high repetition rates by proper selection of the pulse transformer. The transistor may be prevented from saturating by clamping the collector as described in Sec. 10.5.1. In addition, care must be exercised to prevent collector breakdown due to inductive "kick-back" effects in the transformer. For example, in the circuit of Fig. 10.36, during the regeneration cycle, the potential supplied by the battery V_2 will be transferred from across the collector of the transistor to across the primary winding of the transformer. At the end of the switching interval, the entire potential of the battery V_2 will be across the transformer primary winding, and the transistor will be in a saturated state. However, the energy stored in the magnetic field of the transformer must now be discharged back to the circuit. The transformer discharge action reverses the induced potential across the primary winding, and the collector voltage of the transistor will suddenly rise to several times V_2. If this voltage exceeds the peak inverse rating of the transistor, the collector junction will break down. Since the collector breakdown is of a transient nature, this effect may actually be used to discharge the magnetic energy stored in the transformer, provided that proper current-limiting means are used in the collector circuit. However, the collector breakdown effect may be deleterious to high-speed operation and should therefore be avoided in high-frequency applications.

A blocking oscillator circuit which utilizes collector clamping to prevent transistor saturation and transformer clamping to prevent collector breakdown effects is illustrated in Fig. 10.37. Diode D_1 clamps the collector to the potential value of V_1 while diode D_2 prevents the collector potential from exceeding $(V_1 + V_2)$. Thus, the voltage change across the primary winding of the transformer is limited to V_2.

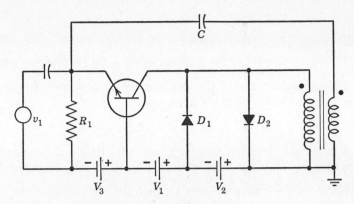

Fig. 10.37   Nonsaturating blocking oscillator

The circuit of Fig. 10.37 may be analyzed using linear approximation techniques.[17]   By assuming that the emitter resistance r_ϵ and the collector conductance g_c are negligible and that $\alpha_{b0} = 1$, the circuit of Fig. 10.37 may be replaced by the approximate equivalent circuit illustrated in Fig. 10.38 *during the switching interval*.   The switching interval

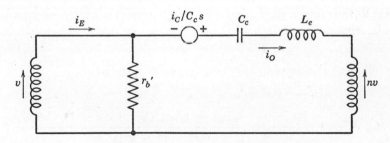

Fig. 10.38   Approximate equivalent circuit during switching interval

is that period of time required for the pulse to build up from zero to its final voltage value, and hence the clamping diodes D_1 and D_2 are open-circuited.   The transistor is approximated by an ideal current source i_C, shunted by the collector capacity C_c.   This is equivalent to a voltage source $i_C/C_c s$ in series with C_c.   In addition, the transformer is approximated by an ideal transformer having a voltage step-down ratio (primary-to-secondary) of $n:1$ and a leakage inductance L_e. The following equations may then be written for the equivalent circuit of Fig. 10.38.

$$i_E = (1 + s/\omega_{ab})i_C \qquad (10.76a)$$

$$i_E = ni_O \qquad (10.76b)$$

$$v = (i_E - i_O)r_b' \qquad (10.76c)$$

$$i_C/C_c s = (i_O/C_c s) + L_e s i_O + nv - (i_E - i_O)r_b' \qquad (10.76d)$$

If the leakage inductance of the transformer L_e is related to the magnetizing inductance L_m by the equation

$$L_e = (1 - k^2)L_m \qquad (10.77)$$

where k is the coefficient of coupling, and eqs. 10.76a–d are combined, the following equation for the circuit of Fig. 10.38 may be derived.

$$(1 - k^2)s^3 + [(1 - k^2)\omega_{ab} + (n - 1)^2/g_b'L_m]s^2$$
$$+ [\omega_{ab}(n - 1)^2/g_b'L_m + 1/C_cL_m]s - \omega_{ab}(n - 1)/L_mC_c = 0 \qquad (10.78)$$

In eq. 10.78, $g_b' = 1/r_b'$. It can be shown that, for $n > 1$, one of the roots of eq. 10.78 must be positive-real. This positive-real root, denoted by s_r, is associated with the regenerative term of the solution of eq. 10.78, whereas the effect of the other roots can be neglected. s_r is related to the 90% rise time of the pulse by

$$t_{0.9} = 2.3/s_r \qquad (10.79)$$

If eq. 10.78 is solved for L_m in terms of the normalized frequency parameter x, where

$$x = s/\omega_{ab} \qquad (10.80)$$

the following relationship between L_m and n is derived.

$$L_m = \frac{\left\{\begin{array}{l} -(n - 1)^2 x^2/g_b'\omega_{ab} \\ \quad - [(n - 1)^2/g_b'\omega_{ab} + 1/\omega_{ab}^2 C_c]x + (n - 1)/C_c\omega_{ab}^2 \end{array}\right\}}{(1 - k^2)x^3 + (1 - k^2)x^2} \qquad (10.81)$$

A second equation involving the transformer parameters L_m and n may be derived by analyzing the blocking oscillator circuit for the conduction time of the transistor, which is, in effect, the duration of the output pulse, T. An approximate equivalent circuit for the conduction period is illustrated in Fig. 10.39. The regenerative, or switching, interval ends when the potential at the collector is clamped through the diode D_1 by the battery V_1. At the instant the regenerative action is terminated, the magnetizing inductance L_m is carrying a negligible amount of current, and the voltage across the primary winding is V_2. Since the voltage drop between the emitter and base of the transistor is approximately $i_E[r_\epsilon + r_b'(1 - \alpha_{b0})]$, where the bracketed term is the

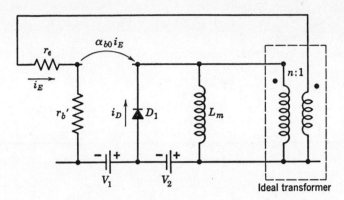

Fig. 10.39 Approximate equivalent circuit during conducting period

input resistance of the common-base transistor stage, the magnitude of the emitter current is given by

$$i_E = -V_2/n[r_\epsilon + r_b'(1 - \alpha_{b0})] \qquad (10.82)$$

However, since i_E flows through the secondary winding of the transformer, the current entering the primary winding is i_E/n. The current carried by the diode D_1 in the equivalent circuit of Fig. 10.39 must be the difference between the collector current and the current entering the primary winding of the transformer. Thus, i_D, at the beginning of the conducting period, is

$$i_D = \alpha_{b0}i_E - i_E/n = i_E(\alpha_{b0} - 1/n) \qquad (10.83)$$

and i_E is given by eq. 10.82. The pulse width T is the amount of time required to transfer the current i_D, given by eq. 10.83, to the transformer primary winding having the equivalent inductance L_m. Since

$$V_2 = L_m \, di_D/dt$$

a linear approximation gives the pulse width T as

$$T = L_m i_D/V_2 \qquad (10.84)$$

Combining eqs. 10.82, 10.83, and 10.84 results in

$$L_m = n^2[r_\epsilon + r_b'(1 - \alpha_{b0})]T/(\alpha_{b0}n - 1) \qquad (10.85)$$

Thus, from eqs. 10.81 and 10.85, the transformer parameters L_m and n may be calculated by specifying the required pulse rise time in terms of the transistor cutoff frequency x and the required pulse width T for a given transistor. This may be done most readily by a graphical technique where L_m is plotted against n and the intersection of the curves obtained from eqs. 10.81 and 10.85 gives the transformer parameters required for a desired pulse rise time and pulse width.

The effect of loading the transformer secondary winding with a resistance R_l is to increase the pulse rise time; for a finite load conductance G_l these equations are modified as follows: [17]

$$L_m = \frac{\dfrac{g_b'(n-1)}{(g_b' + G_l)\omega_{ab}{}^2 C_c} - \dfrac{(n-1)x^2}{\omega_{ab}(g_b' + G_l)} - \left[\dfrac{(n-1)^2}{(g_b' + G_l)\omega_{ab}} + \dfrac{1}{\omega_{ab}{}^2 C_c}\right]x}{(1 - k^2)(x^3 + x^2)}$$

(10.86)

$$T = L_m\{(\alpha_{b0}n - 1)/n^2[r_\epsilon + r_b'(1 - \alpha_{b0})] - G_l/n^2\}$$ (10.87)

For a typical design, where the coupling coefficient is approximately 0.95 to 0.98, $\omega_{ab} = 10^7$ radians per second, $r_b' = 200$ ohms, $C_c = 10$ $\mu\mu$f, $L_m = 1$ mh, $n = 7$, $R_l = 500$ ohms, and $r_\epsilon = 30$ ohms, pulse rise times on the order of 0.1 to 0.2 μsec have been obtained for pulses of 2 to 5 μsec width.

10.8   Magnetic-Core Driver Circuits

The development of magnetic and dielectric materials having square-loop hysteresis characteristics has resulted in a growing number of applications of ferrite and dielectric materials to pulse circuitry. Wherever square-loop components can perform the same functions as transistors, the former have some advantages. For example, a magnetic core which is used as a bistable storage element requires no power to maintain either of the two stable states. In addition, the magnetic core can operate at higher temperatures than semiconductor devices and may be potentially more reliable and less expensive than the transistor.

Although a detailed description of magnetic and ferroelectric devices is beyond the scope of this book, it is instructive to consider the problems that are encountered when transistors and magnetic cores are combined in pulse circuits. A typical application is one that utilizes the transistor as an amplifying device to drive a magnetic core. Such a circuit is illustrated in Fig. 10.40. The transistor operates as an on-off switch which is driven by the input pulse v_I. In Fig. 10.41, the excursion of the operating point of the transistor is illustrated in the collector I,V plane

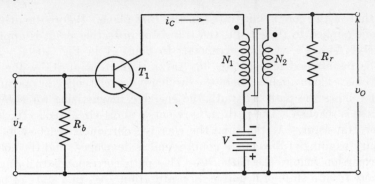

Fig. 10.40   Transistor-magnetic core circuit

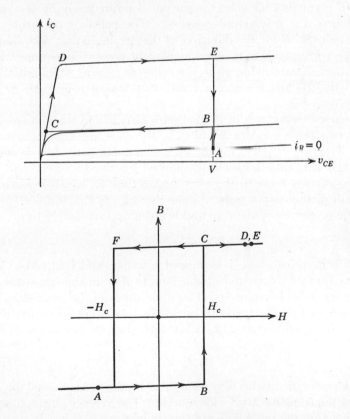

Fig. 10.41   Transistor and core excursion paths

and that of the core is illustrated in the B,H plane. Before the driving pulse is applied to the circuit, the transistor operating point is approximately (I_{CEO}, V), which corresponds to point A in Fig. 10.41. The core is maintained in negative flux saturation at point A by the d-c reset bias. Upon application of the driving pulse, the collector operating point follows the path AB until the coercive magnetizing force H_c of the core is reached. The path AB presents a short-circuit collector load to the transistor. At the time the coercive current is reached in the primary winding of the core, a counter emf is developed, and the collector excursion follows the path BC. This path corresponds to bringing the core from a state of negative flux saturation $-\phi_m$ to a state of positive flux saturation $+\phi_m$, and during this excursion the transistor load is a very high a-c impedance. When the core saturates in the positive sense, the collector load impedance suddenly drops to near-zero, and the collector operating point follows the path marked CDE. During the CDE excursion, the collector current is limited only by the current limitation of the driving-pulse source. The collector operating point then remains at E for the duration of the driving pulse; note that this condition corresponds to maximum collector power dissipation. At the termination of the driving pulse the collector returns to its initial state along path EA, and the core is reset along magnetizing path EFA by the core-reset bias.

The current waveform in the collector circuit and the voltage waveform across the secondary winding of the core are illustrated in Fig. 10.42. The time required for the excursion along path ABC is denoted by t_1, and this time is primarily limited by the transistor rise time. Coercive current flows in the core during time t_2, which is essentially the width of the output pulse. Time duration t_2 is determined by the magnetic properties of the core and is given approximately by

$$t_2 = 2N_1\phi_m/V \qquad (10.88)$$

where t_2 is in seconds if ϕ_m is expressed in webers and V in volts. When the core saturates, current will continue to flow in the transistor until the driving pulse is removed. This time duration is denoted by t_4 in Fig. 10.42, and during t_4 the transistor is dissipating maximum power. If the pulse repetition period t_p is low such that the duty cycle is small, i.e. if

$$t_4/t_p \ll 1 \qquad (10.89)$$

the peak power dissipation may sometimes be allowed to exceed the rated power of the transistor by a wide margin. The average power, however, must be within the rated limits of the transistor and it is this considera-

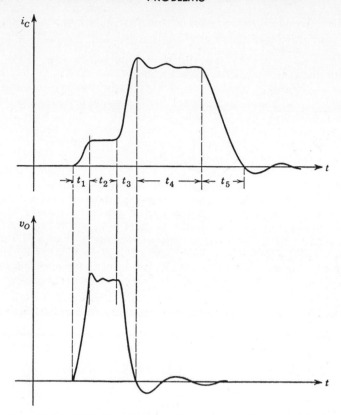

Fig. 10.42   Collector-current and secondary-voltage waveforms

tion that usually limits the upper repetition rate at which the core can be driven. At the termination of the driving pulse the rate of decay of collector current is limited by the fall time of the transistor, and this time is denoted by t_5 in Fig. 10.42.

Problems

1. A transistor amplifier is operated from a square-wave voltage generator having an internal resistance of 300 ohms, and the transistor is terminated by a load resistance of 2000 ohms. The transistor parameters are as follows: $r_\epsilon = 26$ ohms, $r_b' = 200$ ohms, $\alpha_{b0} = 0.98$, $g_c = 0.2 \times 10^{-6}$ mho. Also, $C_c = 5$ $\mu\mu$f, and $\omega_{ab} = 10^7$ radians per second. Calculate the small-signal time response of the output current when the transistor is connected in the common-base, common-emitter, and common-collector configurations.

2. A common-emitter transistor is connected to a 20-volt battery supply through a 1000-ohm load resistance. The transistor, which is driven by a 1-ma pulse of 10

μsec duration, has the following parameters: $\omega_{\alpha fb} = 10^7$ radians per second, $\omega_{\alpha rb} = 10^6$ radians per second, $\alpha_{fb} = 0.98$, $\alpha_{rb} = 0.75$. (a) Calculate the rise, storage and fall times of the collector-current waveform. (b) If the collector is clamped through an ideal diode by a 1.5-volt battery to prevent saturation, e.g. as in Fig. 10.16a, calculate the pulse-stretching effect due to the clamp.

3. Silicon transistors are selected for use in a bistable multivibrator circuit which will operate from a 12-volt supply. An output voltage of 6 volts and a maximum (steady-state) emitter current of 3 ma are desired. The transistor parameters of interest are as follows: $V_{BE} = 0.6$ volt, $\alpha_{b0} = 0.95$, $\omega_{\alpha b} = 2 \times 10^7$ radians per second. If a pulse period of 2 μsec is specified, calculate the circuit parameters that are required for a steady-state nonsaturating design.

4. A count-by-six circuit is required to operate from an unregulated voltage supply which may vary ±5 volts around a nominal 15-volt rating. Germanium alloy-type transistors are available having the following parameters: $v_{BE} = 0.05$ to 0.15 volt, $\alpha_{b0} = 0.95$ to 0.99, $\omega_{\alpha b} = 1 \times 10^7$ to 3×10^7 radians per second. The circuit is expected to operate over a temperature range of -25 to $+75°$ C, and I_{CO} may vary from 0.5 to 200 μa as a result of these temperature changes. A collector-voltage swing of at least 5 volts is desired, and the maximum input pulse repetition rate is 50 kc. Illustrate a circuit design that will satisfy the operational requirements.

5. A transistor blocking oscillator of the type illustrated in Fig. 10.37 utilizes a transformer having a magnetizing inductance of 1 mh. A transistor having the following parameters is used: $r_b' = 200$ ohms, $r_e = 26$ ohms, $\alpha_{b0} = 0.98$. (a) What is the maximum pulse width that the circuit can generate? (b) What is the transformer turns ratio required to generate these pulses?

6. A square-loop ferrite core having a saturation flux of 3×10^{-6} webers and a coercive mmf of 1 ampere-turn is wound with 50 turns and is driven from a common-emitter transistor stage. The maximum allowable transistor dissipation is 150 mw, and the transistor is driven into saturation by a 20-μsec-wide square pulse of 2 ma peak amplitude applied at the base. Neglecting dissipation losses during transistor saturation, calculate the maximum rate at which the core can be driven from a transistor having a common-emitter current-amplification factor of 20 and operating from a voltage source of 30 volts. (Assume that the core is driven from positive to negative flux saturation by the transistor and is reset by other means.)

Bibliography

1. J. S. Schaffner and J. J. Suran, "Transient Response of the Grounded-Base Transistor Amplifier with Small Load Impedance," *J. Appl. Physics, 24,* no. 11, 1355–1357 (1953).

2. E. Jahnke and F. Emde, *Tables of Functions*, 4th Ed., Dover Publications, New York, 1945.

3. W. F. Chow and J. J. Suran, "Transient Analysis of Junction Transistor Amplifiers," *Proc. IRE, 41,* 1125–1129 (1953).

4. J. L. Moll, "Large Signal Transient Response of Junction Transistors," *Proc. IRE, 42,* 1773–1784 (1954).

5. A. E. Anderson, "Transistors in Switching Circuits," *Proc. IRE, 40,* 1541–1548 (1952).

6. A. W. Lo, "Transistor Trigger Circuits," *Proc. IRE, 40,* 1531–1541 (1952).

7. J. J. Suran, "Low-Frequency Circuit Theory of the Double-Base Diode," *IRE Trans.*, *ED-2*, no. 2, 40–48, (1955).

8. R. B. Adler, "A Large Signal Equivalent Circuit for Transistor Static Characteristics," RLE, MIT Transistor Group, Oct. 2, 1951.

9. W. Shockley, M. Sparks, and G. K. Teal, "The *p-n* Junction Transistors," *Phys. Rev.*, *83*, 151–162 (July 1951).

10. J. J. Ebers and J. L. Moll, "Large-Signal Behavior of Junction Transistors," *Proc. IRE*, *42*, 1761–1772 (1954).

11. B. J. Yokelson and W. Ulrich, "Engineering Multistage Diode Logic Circuits," *Trans. A.I.E.E.*, *Commun. & Electronics*, 466 (1955).

12. J. J. Suran and F. A. Reibert, "Two-Terminal Analysis and Synthesis of Transistor Multivibrators," *IRE Trans.*, *CT-3*, 26 (1956).

13. R. H. Baker, "Maximum Efficiency Switching Circuits," *MIT Lincoln Lab. Rept. TR-110* (1956).

14. J. G. Linvill, "Non-Saturating Pulse Circuits Using Two Junction Transistors," *Proc. IRE*, *43*, 1826–1834 (1955).

15. J. H. Vogelsong, "A Transistor Pulse Amplifier Using External Regeneration," *Proc. IRE*, *41*, no. 10, 1444 (1953).

16. J. J. Suran and E. Keonjian, "A Semiconductor Diode Multivibrator," *Proc. IRE*, *43*, no. 7, 814 (1955).

17. J. G. Linvill and R. H. Mattson, "Junction Transistor Blocking Oscillators," *Proc. IRE*, *43*, no. 11, 1632 (1955).

18. R. H. Beter, et al., "Directly Coupled Transistor Circuits," *Electronics*, *28*, 132 (June 1955).

19. A. Cavalieri, "What's Inside Transac—I and II," *Electronic Design*, 22 and 30 (July 1 and 15, 1956).

Chapter 11

Systems

11.1 Introduction

As is being more and more widely realized, transistorizing a piece of equipment does not end with the simple replacement of electron tubes by transistors, with suitable modifications to the power supply. In order to take full advantage of the unique characteristics of transistors and to minimize their disadvantages, a new approach to most equipment design problems is required.

The advantages to be derived from the use of transistors may be divided into two classes. The first group arises from the mechanical features of the device and its associated circuitry. These include small size, light weight, and immunity to mechanical shock. Into the second category fit advantages inherent in the electrical properties of the transistor. Besides the obvious savings in power consumption, there are various circuit operations which can be performed far more simply by using transistors or other semiconductor devices. As an example, the use of transistors in audio output stages makes possible the direct feeding of the voice coil, eliminating the usual output transformer with its attendant size, weight, and cost.

Against the advantages must be weighed the difficulties. It is justifiable to assume that many of the existing limitations will be overcome. However, the designer is always faced with the problem of how best to utilize devices currently available. Limitations of frequency response, power-handling capabilities, ambient temperature range, and the fact that a transistor has to draw power from the signal source are all disadvantages which, although rapidly diminishing in severity, will be of concern to the circuit designer during the forseeable future.

Many of these advantages and disadvantages are closely related. The advantages to be derived from using transistors in an audio amplifier—small size and very low current drain—would be largely nullified if, owing to power-handling limitations of transistors, it was necessary to use a pair of large electron tubes in the output stage. In order to decide whether or not to use a transistor in a particular circuit, it is necessary to view that circuit and its relationship to the rest of the system in which it will be used. The purpose of this chapter is to discuss some of the most widely known "systems" and to show how transistors may be incorporated advantageously in their design.

11.2   AM Receivers

One of the first pieces of equipment to be selected for possible application of transistors was the AM broadcast receiver.[1-6] The choice was a good one since the advantages to be gained from transistorization were many, particularly in the field of portable receivers. Not only could every advantage of transistors be realized, but, because of the relatively modest requirements, none of the limitations of transistors were too serious.

Although the block diagram of a tube receiver and that of a receiver using transistors would probably be the same, the thought behind the design of the individual blocks and their relationships to other blocks would be considerably different. Before discussing the system aspects as they affect individual stages in the block diagram, it is well to examine the altered relationships between the various blocks.

If we commence at the second detector, which may be regarded as the center of a superheterodyne receiver, and work out in both directions, several significant factors become apparent. As mentioned in Chapter 9, a transistor detector has several advantages over a diode. One of the advantages listed is that a transistor will give linear detection at lower power levels. Coupled with the fact that greater gain per stage can be achieved at audio frequencies, the conclusion to be drawn is that as much of the gain as possible in a transistor receiver should be placed in the audio section. Between antenna and second detector there is need for just enough selective gain to amplify the weakest signal the receiver is intended to handle until it is of sufficient magnitude to be detected linearly.

The component parts of a broadcast receiver have been described in detail elsewhere in this book. It is desirable, however, in this chapter to look at them in relation to each other.

11.2.1   RF Amplifiers

Radio-frequency amplifiers may be divided into two broad types: inductively tuned and capacitively tuned. From the standpoint of circuit design, there is more difference between these two types than merely which element in the tuned circuit is made variable. The choice of

tuning element depends mainly on the type of antenna to be used and
space considerations. Whatever conclusions are reached concerning
these features, it is necessary to use certain circuits along with them in
the interest of satisfactory performance.

If it is intended to use a ferrite "loop" antenna, capacitive tuning is
preferable. A transistor cannot be placed directly across the tuned circuit, in the manner that is normally used with tubes, because of its low
input impedance. For good power transfer, impedance matching is necessary and can be obtained by winding a few secondary turns on the

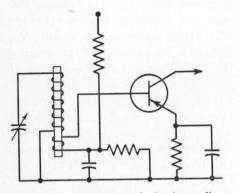
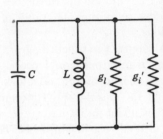

Fig. 11.1   Typical method of coupling   Fig. 11.2   Equivalent circuit of
            ferrite-loop antenna   Fig. 11.1

loop (or by tapping the antenna coil) as shown in Fig. 11.1. The selectivity requirements can be satisfied by using a loop with high unloaded
Q. This solution yields the equivalent circuit of Fig. 11.2 where g_l is
the equivalent parallel loss conductance of the tuned circuit and g_i' is
the transformed conductive component of the transistor input admittance. The loop Q is fairly constant over the RF band with an
average value on the order of 150 ($= Q_0$). Consequently, g_l ($= 1/\omega L Q_0$)
is a decreasing function of frequency, while g_i' is an increasing function
of frequency. Since g_l and g_i' are different functions of frequency, exact
impedance matching is possible only at one frequency. It is often desirable to match at the highest frequency in the band since the transistor
gain is lowest at this point. The optimum frequency at which to match
will depend, however, on the manner in which the unloaded Q of the
loop varies with frequency.

Assuming Q_0 is constant, g_i' an increasing function of ω, and matching
at the highest frequency (1620 kc), it can be shown that, although the
gain characteristics of the circuit of Fig. 11.1 are adequate, the RF
bandwidth varies substantially with frequency (increases by a factor of

approximately 10, going from the lower to the upper end of the RF band). If impedances are matched at the lower end of the band (520 kc), the resulting gain characteristic is undesirable (the gain drops at the high end), and the bandwidth variation is even worse. In extreme cases, the bandwidth is roughly proportional to $\sqrt{\omega^5}$.

Variation in RF bandwidth is undesirable because of (a) variation of image rejection with operating frequency, (b) problems of intermodulation at the high-frequency end, (c) problems that arise if reasonable selectivity is expected at the upper end of the band, namely, tracking at

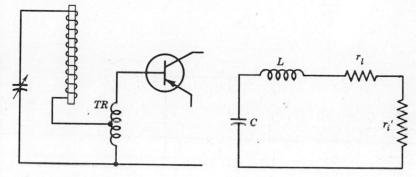

Fig. 11.3 Modified antenna coupling   Fig. 11.4 Equivalent circuit of Fig.
circuit   11.3

the lower end becoming extremely difficult, and the audio bandwidth too narrow.*

To overcome the problem of variable bandwidth in transistor receivers, the arrangement shown in Fig. 11.3 has been developed. In this circuit TR is an autotransformer (or two-winding transformer) with its input winding placed in series with the tuned circuit. The equivalent circuit of Fig. 11.4 results. r_l is the equivalent series resistance of the tuned circuit ($r_l = \omega L/Q_0$ with Q_0 approximately independent of frequency), while r_i' is the transformed resistive component of the transistor input impedance. Assuming that Q_0 is independent of frequency, and that r_i' decreases with ω and is matched to the tuned circuit at the high-frequency end, calculations show that the variation of RF bandwidth with frequency is very small. In practice, the variation in bandwidth is less than 3:1, compared to the conventional circuit where a variation in excess of 10:1 may be obtained.

* This situation does not apply to the same extent in tube receivers where the problem of power transfer does not arise and g_i is very small, g_l being the determining factor for bandwidth.

If inductive tuning is to be used, a different situation arises. In the first place, inductive tuning requires a rod or throw out wire antenna, because of the practical difficulty of varying the inductance of a ferrite loop. Inductive tuning permits the use of an antenna coupling circuit as shown in Fig. 11.5. The RF bandwidth remains more nearly constant with this arrangement than it does if the series arrangement, recommended above for capacitive tuning, is used. For a desirable bandwidth, the inductance L must be quite small, varying between 3 and 30 μh over the broadcast band. Miniature two- and three-gang inductive

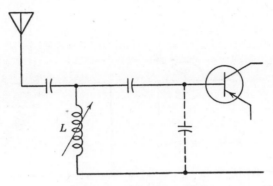

Fig. 11.5 Inductive tuning

tuners can be built using high-Q ferrites. By enclosing the coils in ferrite cups, feedback troubles due to the proximity of the coils can be eliminated.

11.2.2 Local Oscillators

Oscillators have been discussed in detail in Chapter 8. The local oscillator of a superheterodyne broadcast receiver must satisfy several very specific requirements:

(a) Adequate power output is needed for efficient converter operation. The oscillator feeds a transistor converter, the input impedance of which is quite low and therefore constitutes an appreciable load.

(b) The amplitude of oscillation should be reasonably uniform throughout the frequency range from 1 to 2 mc (assuming an intermediate frequency of 455 kc), in order that the converter output be essentially independent of the signal frequency. (On the other hand, to compensate for a possible frequency dependence of the RF amplifier or converter gain, it might be desirable that the oscillator amplitude vary slightly in a predetermined fashion with frequency.) Independence of the oscillation amplitude from battery-voltage changes is also desirable, but difficult and expensive to realize. It is, however, necessary in practice that the oscillator function reliably at 50% of the nominal battery voltage. Reasonable amplitude stability with ambient temperature variations is also desirable.

(c) The frequency of oscillation must be essentially independent of supply voltage and temperature variations. A change in collector voltage due to falling battery voltage causes a change in collector capacitance with the possibility of shifting the oscillator frequency. Temperature changes may have a similar effect by changing the operating point.

Methods of stabilizing oscillators have been discussed in Chapter 8, and local-oscillator amplitude requirements are covered in Chapter 9. From the system aspect it must be decided whether to use a combined local-oscillator–mixer or a separate local oscillator. By combining both functions in one transistor, savings in space, expense, and, to a lesser degree, battery drain can be realized. However, separate transistors are usually preferable if optimum performance is desired. The operating point of the mixer can then be chosen for optimum conversion gain, and similarly there is greater freedom in the design of the local oscillator.

11.2.3 Mixers

Both mixers and converters have been described in Chapter 9. The chief system consideration applicable to mixers is noise. As with electron tubes, transistor mixers are inherently noisier (by 7 to 10 db) than amplifiers. Most of the noise in a receiver is attributable to the first stage. It is therefore desirable, in a receiver designed to have high sensitivity, to include an RF stage ahead of the mixer. Image rejection is also improved in this way. By careful design of the head end, sensitivities of a few microvolts per meter can be obtained.

11.2.4 IF Amplifiers

It has been pointed out previously that transistors are low-impedance devices and that the impedance levels depend on a number of factors. In the common-emitter configuration at 455 kc, if the emitter current is approximately 1 ma and the collector voltage is in excess of 1 volt, the parallel resistive component of the input impedance is on the order of 500 ohms (200 and 2000 ohms being the extremes), and the resistive component of the output impedance is approximately 5 kilohms (2 to 20 kilohms being the extremes). Both input and output impedances have considerable reactive components which are usually tuned out by the interstage-coupling networks. Both input and output impedances are capacitive.

In the common-base circuit, the resistive component of the input impedance is considerably smaller (typical value 50 ohms) and the resistive part of the output impedance larger (typical value 50 kilohms). The input impedance is inductive and the output impedance capacitive in this configuration. It is usual to use interstage impedance-matching networks in order to take advantage of the available gain. The common-emitter configuration gives greater gain up to several megacycles and is now ordinarily used.

The most important factors in the operation of the IF amplifier are selectivity and gain. Concerning selectivity, the requirements for a broadcast receiver can be met using normal techniques. For equipment with more stringent requirements other approaches are necessary and are discussed in Sec. 11.3.3.

The maximum available gain of a transistor amplifier stage for a given degree of stability is determined by the transistor and cannot be increased. In order to make full use of the available gain of an IF stage, it is necessary to transfer almost the entire output power of this stage to the input of the next one. This means that only a small fraction of the power should be consumed in the interstage-coupling network. To satisfy this requirement, the unloaded Q of the coupling network (Q_0) should be greatly reduced by the output impedance of the first stage and the input impedance of the second. It has been shown in Chapter 6 that, for interstage-coupling networks consisting of a single-tuned circuit with some type of impedance matching, the maximum obtainable power-transfer efficiency η_{max}, as a function of the required fractional 3 db bandwidth B_1' and Q_0 is

$$\eta_{max} = (1 - 1/B_1'Q_0)^2 \qquad (11.1)$$

Consequently the required Q_0 for a given η and B_1' is

$$Q_0 = 1/B_1'(1 - \sqrt{\eta}) \qquad (11.2)$$

This equation shows that, even for moderate operating Q's, the required unloaded Q's may be very high. If, for instance, $\eta = 0.64$ (corresponding to a 2-db loss) and $B_1' = 0.03$ (3-db bandwidth of 13.6 kc at 455 kc), we require $Q_0 = 170$. A similar but somewhat more complicated relationship has been derived for double-tuned circuits in Chapter 6. Values of Q_0 in excess of 150 and, if possible, 200 are desirable. These Q_0's must be realized with miniaturized coils, and, consequently, the use of high-quality ferrites is indicated.

Many types of coupling networks are possible. The gain of transistors being lower than that of tubes, more transistors than tubes will usually be required for comparable performance. Consequently single-tuned circuits may be used as interstage-coupling networks without sacrificing selectivity.

Computations of the coupling circuit elements show that for adequate performance high Q_0's are necessary with very small values of L (20 μh or less). This is difficult and consequently expensive to realize in practice. High Q_0's are, however, readily obtainable with larger values of L. Consequently, the first transistor may be connected across only a portion of the tuned circuit. The resultant circuit is shown in Fig. 11.6. The

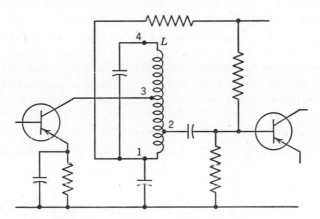

Fig. 11.6   Interstage-coupling transformer

total inductance (1–4) may be chosen arbitrarily. The ratio of the portions (1–3) and (1–2) are determined by the ratio of output resistance to input resistance. Typical values might be (1–2) 2μh, (1–3) 20 μh, (1–4) 500 μh. For good efficiency, the coupling between the three coil sections must be very tight.

The collector capacitance of a transistor, C_c, decreases with increasing collector voltage. This influences the output capacitance of the transistor, which is in turn part of the interstage-coupling tuned circuit. In battery-operated receivers, where the collector voltage may vary appreciably during the useful lifetime of the battery, it is important that this should not result in detuning the interstage-coupling networks. In order to insure that the output capacitance has only a very small influence on the tuning, it is necessary to place a restriction on the value of inductance between points 1 and 3 (Fig. 11.6) even if this results in a value of η appreciably less than η_{max}.

A satisfactory method of constructing the interstage transformers is to wind the coils and place them in ferrite cups so that they are surrounded by core material. In this way, not only is very close coupling achieved, but IF transformers of subsequent stages may be located very close together without danger of oscillation.

The internal feedback associated with transistors is, with many currently available types, of sufficient amplitude and in the correct phase to cause oscillation at the customary intermediate frequency of 455 kc.[7] Various neutralization techniques [8-10] may be used, as well as a method of stabilizing an IF amplifier by mismatching. These are described in some detail in Chapter 6.

11.2.5   Second Detectors

As pointed out in Chapter 9, transistor detection is often preferable to diode detection. Diodes may be used to advantage, however, under certain circumstances. (In reflex circuits, to be described in Sec. 11.2.8, it is customary in the interests of space and cost reduction to keep the number of transistors to an absolute minimum. Here a diode is the

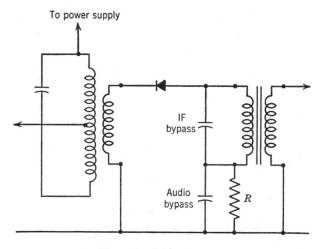

Fig. 11.7   Diode detector

customary detector.) A suitable circuit is shown in Fig. 11.7. For linear detection, it is necessary for the output of the IF amplifier to be at a relatively high voltage and impedance level. To obtain reasonable efficiency an audio transformer should be used, transforming the low-impedance input of the first audio stage up to a high value (100 kilohms or higher preferably). The resistor R is provided in order to develop a small d-c bias, 10 kilohms being a typical value. If a resistive load is used in place of the transformer R is not required.

11.2.6 Automatic Gain Control

The gain of a transistor amplifier may be varied by shifting its d-c operating point in a number of different ways. The significant parameters are emitter current and collector voltage.[11] The gain of a transistor stage decreases with decreasing emitter current (in the region of small emitter currents, i.e., <500 μa) or decreasing collector voltage (in the region <500 mv). The values of emitter current or collector voltage below which gain decreases sharply depend somewhat on the type of transistor being considered. Control of the emitter current or of the

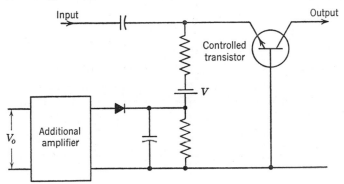

Fig. 11.8   Emitter current gain control

collector voltage requires AGC *power* in contrast to AGC *voltage* in the case of an electron tube. This point was mentioned in Chapter 9 to indicate the desirability of using a transistor detector, the available AGC power of which is considerably greater than that obtainable from a diode.

Before discussing practical circuits, the diagram of Fig. 11.8 should be considered. The controlled transistor is connected in the common-base configuration. Its emitter current is derived from the battery V. The output of the main IF amplifier V_o is amplified by the additional IF amplifier in the AGC loop and is then rectified. The rectified voltage is opposite in polarity to that of the battery so that the emitter current will be reduced with increasing V_o. Since the gain of a transistor is a function of emitter current, it too will be reduced.

To control the emitter current directly requires a great deal of power. These power requirements may be reduced by making the controlled stage a common-emitter stage and applying the AGC voltage to the base. The controlled transistor then acts not only as an IF amplifier but also as its own AGC d-c amplifier. In this case, to obtain AGC action it is necessary that the AGC voltage applied to the base of the controlled transistor be such that it decreases with increasing carrier level. In order to achieve this effect the circuit of Fig. 11.9 may be used.

To obtain the necessary control power, the AGC signal is amplified by the detector and then by the controlled transistor. This circuit has the disadvantage that a second or tapped battery is necessary. This need arises from the fact that the collector voltage of the detector, which is essentially the base potential of the controlled transistor, cannot fall all the way to ground potential. In order, therefore, to be able

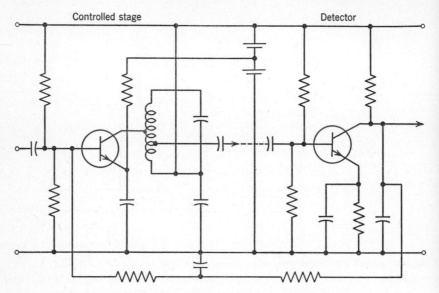

Fig. 11.9   Automatic gain control by emitter current

to reduce the base-to-emitter potential of the controlled transistor to the vicinity of zero, the emitter of that transistor must be returned to some intermediate voltage, comparable to that which the detector collector would reach on the strongest signals.

This circuit requires a control voltage which decreases with increasing carrier. Such a voltage will, however, decrease with decreasing battery voltage. Consequently, battery aging will not only cause a normal reduction in gain but will also reduce the amount of the AGC delay by bringing the quiescent operating point nearer to the region where gain falls sharply. A more important disadvantage is that control of the emitter current is only effective as long as the emitter current is small. Small emitter current restricts the signal-handling capability of the stage if input clipping and consequent distortion of the modulation envelope is to be avoided.

An entirely different form of gain control of high-frequency stages is based on variation of collector voltage. The system may be understood by referring to Fig. 11.10. If V_{DC} increases, the emitter and collector currents increase, causing the voltage at point X to decrease. This decreases the collector voltage and, consequently, the gain. This method of control requires an increasing voltage with increasing carrier which is the reverse of the previous system.

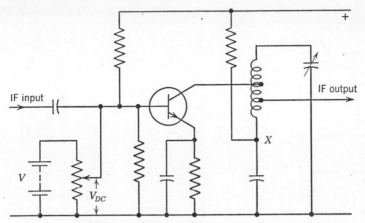

Fig. 11.10   Collector-voltage gain control

To obtain this control voltage, one may employ the common-emitter detector. As described in Chapter 9, the potential between emitter and ground increases with increasing carrier level. Connecting the detector emitter via an RF choke to the base of the controlled transistor completes the AGC loop. The complete circuit is shown in Fig. 11.11. In

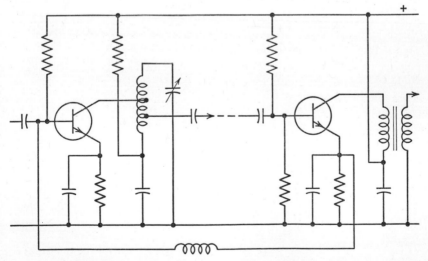

Fig. 11.11   Automatic gain control by collector voltage

this case an extra battery is not required. Furthermore, in contrast to emitter control, discharge of the battery tends to increase the AGC delay rather than to decrease it. However, owing to the low collector voltage (<0.5 volt), this method limits the signal level that can be handled without clipping, even more severely than emitter-current control.

Several variations on the two basic systems of automatic gain control described above have been used successfully. One method [12] of collector-voltage control relies on the presence of a resistor, in the collector circuit

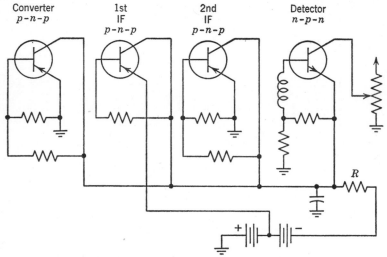

Fig. 11.12   Collector-voltage control by common resistor

of the detector, which is common to the collector circuits of the IF amplifiers and converter. The detector draws an increased current as the carrier level increases. This increased current produces an increased voltage drop across the common resistor (R in Fig. 11.12), thereby reducing the collector voltage available to the earlier stages. The percentage reduction in collector voltage of any individual stage, and hence the amount of AGC delay it experiences, can be designed judiciously by returning the emitter lead to a point of suitable potential.

An alternative form of emitter-current control [4,5] is provided by feeding the IF amplifier which is to be controlled and the detector through a common emitter resistor. The IF amplifier is biased so that it keeps the current through the common resistor essentially constant. The detector passes an increasing current as the carrier level increases. Since the total current through the resistor is kept nearly constant, the emitter current, and consequently the gain of the IF amplifier, is reduced with increasing carrier level.

Changing the operating point of a transistor alters the reactive components associated with its input and output impedances.   Application of an AGC signal to a tuned stage results, therefore, in some change in the frequency characteristics of the stage.   The degree to which the changes in resonant frequency and bandwidth are significant depends on the circuit design.

Because of the limitations and undesirable second-order effects introduced by applying automatic gain control to a transistor directly, cir-

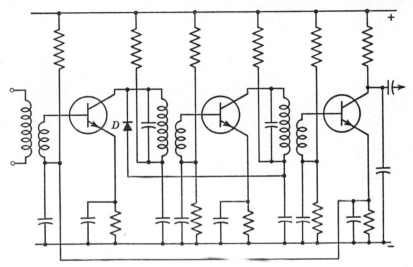

Fig. 11.13   Diode automatic gain control

cuits have been suggested where the properties of some other element, usually a diode, are controlled in order to reduce the gain of an amplifier on strong signals.   One such circuit is shown in Fig. 11.13.   Under quiescent conditions, the diode D is biased in the reverse direction and has no effect on the circuit.   A strong signal at the detector produces an AGC signal which is fed back to the first IF stage, increasing its collector current in the normal way.   The increased current increases the voltage drop across the collector resistor, reversing the bias across the diode D which shunts a portion of the signal developed across the IF transformer to ground.

In cases where it is of great importance to maintain a constant input impedance to the controlled stage, a junction diode may be connected in parallel with, but in the opposite polarity to, the emitter-base diode of the transistor.[13]   Gain is varied by controlling the sharing of a total constant current, between the diode and the transistor.

A consequence of collector-voltage automatic gain control arises from the fact that on strong signals the emitter current is increased. This lowers the input impedance of the controlled transistor. Since the tuned circuit is in parallel with the transformed input impedance, a strong signal results in a lowered operating Q which, in turn, increases the bandwidth. This may be very desirable as it is only on weak signals that narrow bandwidth is normally required. In practice, this effect can be arranged to give a bandwidth of 3 kc on weak stations where adjacent channel interference might be troublesome and 8 kc bandwidth on local stations, thereby taking better advantage of the radiated spectrum. Emitter-current automatic gain control exhibits the reverse effect, which can be undesirable. The effect may be rendered unimportant by making the bandwidth of the controlled stage broad under any operating conditions, the selectivity being provided by tuned circuits which are not directly adjacent to a controlled stage.

11.2.7 Audio Stages

The audio section of a transistor receiver is usually designed to have considerable gain, which is relatively easy to obtain at these frequencies. The number of audio stages is determined by the desired output level and the level of the signal available at the output of the second detector. The design procedure for audio stages is fairly straightforward and is adequately described in Chapter 4. Frequently a low-noise preamplifier follows the detector, feeding either the output stage or, perhaps, a driver supplying a push-pull stage.

Since the detector functions best with a high load impedance, it is desirable that the input impedance of the preamplifier be high. This may be accomplished by any of the standard techniques. Impedance matching is not recommended where the only consequence of mismatching would be loss of gain. It is desirable to match, however, where factors other than gain are important. Such a case arises in the preamplifier, where the linearity of the detector might be affected by working into too low an impedance.

Since transistors are particularly advantageous for portable receivers, operation is generally from batteries. The voltage requirements for all stages except the driver and output amplifiers rarely exceed 3 volts. For reasonable output power from the high-level stages, 6 volts may be considered as a desirable minimum.

A special circuit [12] can be used to improve the efficiency of class-A output or driver stages, thereby materially reducing the total power drain of the receiver. The bias current drawn by the stage may be adjusted automatically along with the gain-control setting. If the gain control is turned to its maximum position, the class-A driver or output stage draws its full current. With the gain control turned down, the drain is also reduced, but in such a way that linear amplification is still obtained for the reduced signal amplitude. Figure 11.14 shows how a combination of *n-p-n* and *p-n-p* transistors may be used to effect this purpose. With the slider at the grounded end of the gain control, no emitter bias is applied to the second transistor which consequently passes only a small collector current. As the slider is moved upward, the collector current of the detector passes through the lower portion of the gain control, producing a forward bias on the second transistor.

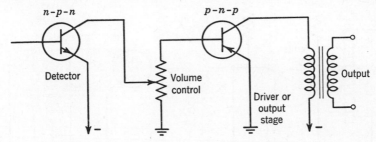

Fig. 11.14   Circuit to reduce battery drain at low volume control settings

Component values are such that the second transistor always passes sufficient current to amplify the input signal power which is fed to it without significant distortion. On very strong signals the slider will usually be set fairly near the lower end of the gain control. Sufficient bias is still developed for the second transistor because the collector current of the detector increases with increased carrier level.

11.2.8 Reflex Circuits

When size and cost are of extreme importance, reflex circuits may be used. A typical receiver using two transistors might contain two RF am-

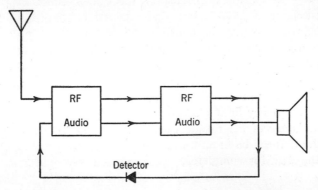

Fig. 11.15   Block diagram of typical reflex circuit

plifiers and a diode detector, the resultant audio being fed back through the two transistors which then provide two stages of audio amplification. Such an arrangement is shown in Fig. 11.15. A practical circuit of such a receiver is given in Fig. 11.16. Many other types of reflex circuits could be built, for example, reflexing the audio back through the IF stages of a superheterodyne receiver.

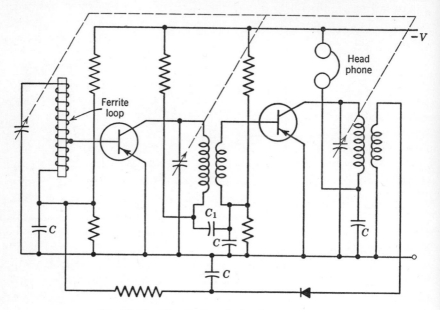

Fig. 11.16   Circuit of typical reflex receiver

11.3   FM Receivers

11.3.1   General Considerations

Transistors are capable of performing most of the functions pertaining to FM receivers of both the broadcast and communications types. However, transistorizing the head end of FM receivers presents some difficulties due to the frequency limitations of transistors commercially available to receiver designers. Transistors having adequate gain over the normal FM broadcast band of 88 to 108 mc and, in the various bands allocated to FM communication systems, are in an experimental stage. The upper frequency limit of transistors appears to have increased by roughly an order of magnitude every year. The development of the *p-n-i-p*, the diffused-base, and the melt-back transistor will, no doubt, prepare the way for completely transistorized FM and television receivers.

In high-quality FM receivers where an RF stage is needed, partial transistorizing provides a satisfactory interim solution. This is particularly true of mobile communication or walkie-talkie-type installations.[14] In such systems the receiver is turned "on" continuously, to receive calls. Substituting transistors for as many tubes as possible results in a very appreciable reduction in power consumption, thereby greatly prolonging battery life.

11.3.2 Local-Oscillator–Mixers

It is possible to obtain reasonable performance from a transistor mixer producing an intermediate frequency of 10.7 mc or lower in broadcast receivers, or a "high" intermediate frequency of 8 to 10 mc in communication receivers. The local oscillator should, in the interests of simplicity, be separate from the mixer. To ease the local-oscillator requirements slightly, its frequency can be made equal to the radio frequency minus the intermediate frequency rather than to the sum. Frequently these installations incorporate double conversion, the second or "low" IF mixer being the point at which transistors become economically advantageous.

11.3.3 IF Amplifier–Limiters

The use of transistors in the IF stages demands serious consideration of a new system approach. It was mentioned in Chapter 9 that transistor limiters introduce instability problems when the limiting stage has both its input and output tuned. Furthermore, severe limiting causes a shift in the transistor operating point, resulting in changes in transistor impedance levels with consequent variations in selectivity of the associated tuned circuits. In an FM IF amplifier–limiter, the limiting requirements are usually quite stringent and the selectivity requirements must be quite precise. The relatively poor limiting and danger of instability resulting from the conventional approach, coupled with a selectivity curve which will change with signal level, indicate the necessity of a new method of attack.

By placing all the selectivity in one filter the need for tuned interstage-coupling networks throughout the IF stages is removed. Selectivity is consequently independent of signal level, and simple RC-coupled limiters may be designed without fear of instability. It is true that the gain per stage of an RC-coupled amplifier will be less than that of a tuned and matched IF amplifier. However, the cost of an additional stage may be more than offset by the other savings that are realized. RC-coupled stages are very much cheaper to build than those with tuned impedance-matching networks, from the point of view both of component cost and of alignment expense.

A transistor is not a unilateral device, and hence alignment of a series of cascaded tuned stages is both expensive and tedious. It is true that the cost of the filter must be considered. However, owing to the fact that impedance levels change with signal strength, causing selectivity variations, in a high-quality receiver some kind of lumped selectivity would be necessary in any case. Placing all the selectivity at the input to the discriminator may result in the limiter being blocked by very strong unwanted signals. It is preferable to place the filter ahead of the limiter, for example between the converter and the IF amplifier. It should have a very steep attenuation on either side of the pass band, with excellent skirt selectivity; otherwise the limiter will compensate for the filtering action and materially broaden the pass band.

Partial transistorizing of a receiver calls for matching from the high output resistance of a tube to the low input resistance of a transistor. The ratios required are on the order of 500:1, and efficient transformers would be quite expensive and impractical. A degenerative common-emitter stage giving little or no power gain may prove to be the simplest and most economical solution of the impedance transformation problem.

The gain available with transistors at frequencies suitable for FM IF amplifiers is smaller than that of electron tubes. The gain of the IF amplifier need only be sufficient to bring up the level of the weakest anticipated signal to the limiting level. The lower the limiting level can be made, the fewer stages of IF amplification that are required; hence the interest in low-level limiters such as those described in Chapter 12.

Point-contact diodes may be used in the discriminator, the design of which can be quite standard. Suitable impedance transformations should be made at the input and output, as the impedances on either side of the discriminator will be considerably lower than those encountered in an electron-tube receiver. A suitable arrangement of IF amplifier and discriminator is shown in Fig. 11.17.

Since mobile-communication-type receivers are usually operative even when no carrier is present, a circuit is frequently provided to prevent noise generated in the head end and elsewhere from reaching the speaker under zero-input signal conditions. This circuit, known as a squelch, renders the audio output stages insensitive unless a carrier of greater than a predetermined level is present at the antenna.

By placing a high-pass filter after the discriminator, the noise spectrum which is present may be utilized for squelch purposes. The noise components above the audio range of interest (usually 300 to 3000 cps)

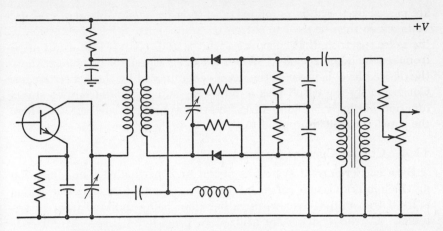

Fig. 11.17   Amplifier, discriminator, and audio output circuits

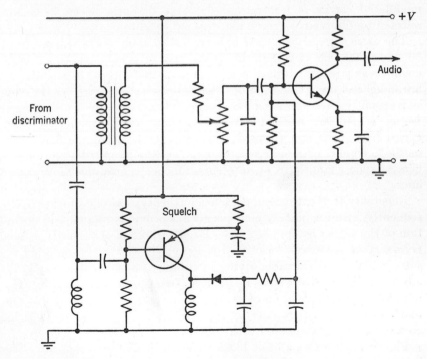

Fig. 11.18   Squelch circuit

are passed by the filter, amplified, and then rectified. The resultant d-c voltage can then be used to cut off the audio amplifier. The portion of the noise spectrum that coincides with the audio band is thus prevented from reaching the speaker. When a carrier equal to, or greater than, the desired level is present, the noise is eliminated by the limiter stages. Consequently the cutoff bias is removed, and the audio output stages function normally. Figure 11.18 shows a typical squelch circuit where the squelch output is applied to the base of the preamplifier stage.

11.4 Carrier-Current Systems

By a carrier-current system is meant any method of communication in which information is conveyed by means of a modulated carrier which is itself transmitted over wires rather than being radiated from an antenna. Carrier systems are utilized to provide both speech and code communication. A widely used example of the code type of equipment is that operated by power companies to convey information from a power plant to a control center. In such an application the code-modulated carrier is transmitted over the 60-cycle power lines and selected by filters at the receiving station.

The carrier frequencies used in a typical system lie in the band from 30 kc to 200 kc. It is desirable to be able to accommodate as many channels as possible within this spectrum. Several types of modulation are in general use. One type is a "keyed-carrier" system; i.e. the code is transmitted by switching the carrier on and off in a prearranged sequence. Another method is to change the carrier frequency by a few cycles backwards and forwards according to a definite code. Both methods employ extremely narrow bandwidths, permitting large numbers of such channels to operate simultaneously over the same power lines.

Reliability is of extreme importance in this type of equipment. Consequently, standby battery power is always provided to maintain operation of the carrier equipment. As a large number of channels is usually necessary at any given locality, a reduction in power consumption results in a very considerable saving in standby battery cost. Similarly, any reduction in size results in reduced floor space and expense. The relatively early application of transistors to carrier equipment was due to the advantages they offer in these respects as well as to their increased reliability compared with tubes.

Figure 11.19 shows a basic block diagram of a carrier channel. The line traps are provided in order to confine the carrier signal to the desired portion of the 60-cycle power line. The capacitors marked C prevent the 60-cycle current from getting into the carrier equipment

since they present a high reactance at that low frequency. The inductances L have a high reactance at carrier frequencies. The variable inductances are adjusted to resonate with the line at the carrier frequency.

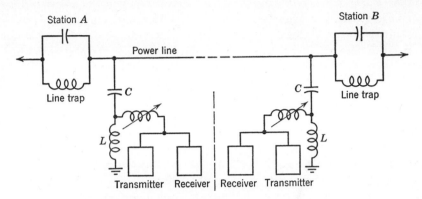

Fig. 11.19   Block diagram of carrier-current system

Figure 11.20 is a block diagram of the transmitter and receiver. Transistors may be utilized in all stages, both in the transmitter and receiver.
The transmitter is modulated in one of two ways. Either the oscillator
is keyed on and off, for the keyed-carrier system, or the oscillator frequency is changed between two discrete values in the case of "frequency-

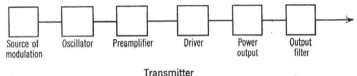

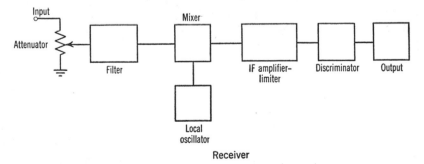

Fig. 11.20   Block diagram of transmitter and receiver

shift" keying. The first method is straightforward; the second is more difficult and may be approached in one of two ways.

One method is to have two crystal-controlled oscillators; the frequency of each can be lowered by a few cycles by keying-in an additional capacitor. If, for example, a nominal center frequency of 200 kc is required, one oscillator might have a 2-mc crystal and the other a 2.2-mc crystal. The resultant frequency produced in a mixer stage will be 200

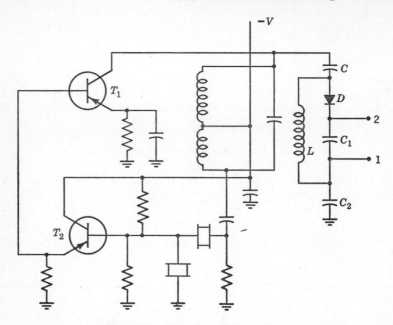

Fig. 11.21   Frequency-shift oscillator

kc. This beat frequency is raised a few cycles by lowering the frequency of the 2-mc oscillator slightly. This is accomplished by keying-in the additional capacitor. Similarly the frequency may be reduced by a few cycles by lowering the frequency of the 2.2-mc oscillator.

The alternative method is to use one oscillator with two crystals. By keying-in an additional reactive element the natural frequency of the oscillator is shifted from close to the resonant frequency of one crystal to approximately the resonant frequency of the other. The control of the oscillator is thus switched from one crystal to the other.

Both these methods of modulation lend themselves to transistorizing. Figure 11.21 shows a frequency-shift type of oscillator. Transistor T_1 is used as a crystal-controlled Hartley oscillator. The conventional Hartley circuit has been modified here by the addition of a crystal network in the feedback path as well as an extra transistor T_2. The crystals act as "stops" to limit the shift in frequency to points corresponding to the positive and negative peaks of the associated receiver discriminator. The oscillator frequency may be shifted from a frequency approximately 0.04% above the channel center frequency to one approximately 0.04% below it by a shunt capacitance C across the oscillator tank. Transistor T_2 is connected in the common-collector configuration, thereby acting as a high-impedance buffer stage. In this way the low input impedance of T_1 does not load down the frequency-determining components. Capacitor C is keyed in and out of the circuit by changing the bias on diode D. Making terminal 1 positive with respect to 2 causes the diode to conduct, thus connecting capacitor C in shunt with the top portion of the tank circuit, shifting the frequency downward. C_1 and C_2 bypass the carrier to ground while L isolates the carrier-frequency circuits from the control circuit.

As shown in Fig. 11.20 the output of the modulated oscillator is passed through a series of amplifiers in order to obtain the necessary output level. The preamplifier might consist of two low-power transistors in push-pull, connected in the common-emitter configuration. The driver, fed from the preamplifier via a tuned impedance-matching network, would perhaps consist of two more transistors in push-pull, connected in the common-base configuration. The common-base arrangement is often used since, with this configuration, high-frequency high-power operation may be obtained. The output stage might require two power transistors in the common-base push-pull connection, resulting in a final output of 5 watts or more. The output transformer should be tuned in order to remove any undesirable modulation products.

The receiver, for either type of modulation, must meet rigorous gain and limiting requirements. The high gain is necessary, not only because of the attenuation due to the power lines but also because of the input filter attenuation, which is severe. The very narrow bandwidths—approximately 0.08% of the center frequency—require multiple-tuned circuits, which should be placed ahead of the first transistor in order to prevent cross modulation. The maximum gain of the amplifier–limiter in the receiver is usually on the order of 100 db. The need for limiting arises because power companies often have occasion to temporarily re-route the links between various power stations, control centers, etc. Thus a carrier channel between two stations may be 100 miles long over one route and 200 miles over an alternative line. These changes in line length and resulting changes in incoming signal level must not result in failure of any carrier channels. For variations of input level of 80 db it is usually required that the receiver output not vary by more than 1 db.

One approach to the problem of receiver design is to use a broadly-tuned (Fig. 9.37) or untuned amplifier–limiter. A gain of over 20 db per stage can be realized with such an amplifier at the high end of the band. This apparently low figure is due to the severe limiting characteristic required, which necessitates the use of low-Q circuits in the interests of stability. (See Sec. 6.5.3.) Silicon junction diodes are provided for limiting,[15] silicon being used in preference to germanium because its limiting level is relatively unaffected by temperature. Interstage coupling transformers are usually wound on toroidal coil forms. This is done to prevent instability arising from the interaction of transformer fields. The transformers can be made on a plug-in basis so that the standard amplifier may be used for any channel in the band from 30 to 200 kc. To equalize the performance of the receiver, the interstage-coupling transformers for use at the lower end of the band, where the transistor gain is highest, may be wound with a smaller step-down ratio, thus introducing a loss due to mismatch.

If the amplifier is untuned, the gain per stage falls slightly. The circuitry becomes extremely simple, limiting being done by careful choice of operating point and load resistor. The junction diodes are no longer required and the tuned interstage-coupling transformers are replaced by simple RC circuits. The gain may be made roughly the same at either end of the band by using small bypass and coupling capacitors which will introduce degeneration and attenuation at the lower frequencies. It is not important to have a very flat gain over the whole range since excessive gain will always be eliminated by limiting action.

Another approach to receiver design is to use a superheterodyne system which takes advantage of the increase of transistor gain at lower frequencies by converting all incoming signals to a low frequency, for example 10 kc. Considerable selectivity is still necessary ahead of the mixer to prevent cross modulation. Some selectivity is also required after the mixer to reduce the severity of the mixer noise by reducing the bandwidth.

The circuitry of the discriminator is usually quite standard. Since the frequency shift is very small, accurate tuning of the discriminator is essential. For this reason, a crystal is generally employed.

11.5   Applications of Transistors to Television

The incentive to include transistors in the design of television equipment has not until recently attained the same level as that which accompanied the transistorizing of other systems, notably AM receivers. This was due not only to economic factors but also to limitations of the early transistors. In addition, the particular points in which transistors excel, namely portability and high electrical efficiency, are not of prime importance in home television receivers. Many of the electrical limitations of the early devices have since been reduced or eliminated. This, coupled with a decline of the economic disadvantages, has made the application of transistors to various television functions appear attractive.

It is the purpose of this section to describe some parts of the television system where transistors may be advantageously utilized. The following section deals with transistor circuitry suitable for television receiver applications. Many of the receiver circuit concepts, however, can *with suitable refinements* be adapted for studio equipment use. Thus, the principles underlying the circuitry developed for the receiver video amplifier and deflection system, for example, can be applied to the corresponding parts of a television camera.

An important part of the television system is the synchronizing pulse generator. It is in this function that the use of transistors is particularly attractive. The high electrical efficiency and small size of the transistor result in a considerable economy of space and reduction in heat generation over that of corresponding electron-tube equipment. The last portion of the television discussion is devoted to the description of a transistor synchronizing generator.

11.5.1 Television Receivers

The development of a transistorized television receiver is complicated by the fact that many of the individual parts of the system place severe electrical requirements on the transistors. Nevertheless, the technical feasibility of a completely transistorized television receiver has been demonstrated.[16] The problem of the economic feasibility of such a receiver will gradually be resolved as improved transistors become available.

A completely different problem presents itself if a tube-transistor receiver is considered. The inclusion of transistors in certain parts of a tube receiver offers definite and immediate advantages of both a technical and economic nature. For example, transistor synchronizing and deflection circuitry results in simplifications over that of corresponding electron-tube designs.

11.5.1.1 Television-Receiver Block Diagram

The block diagram of a transistor television receiver is shown in Fig. 11.22. Although the diagram is similar to that of an electron-tube receiver, the detailed circuitry need not necessarily follow conventional procedure. The special electrical properties of transistors allow a fresh approach to the design of the circuitry for individual subsections of the system.   For example, the low-impedance levels associated with the transistor make it possible to drive the speaker voice coil and the vertical and horizontal deflection yoke windings without the customary output transformers.   The reader who is familiar with electron-tube art

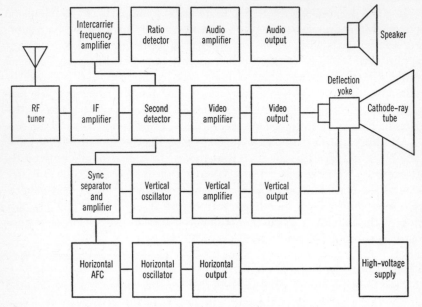

Fig. 11.22   Transistor television receiver block diagram

will note that in the following discussion a number of functions are performed by transistors that have no analogue in tube circuitry.

The design of individual sections of the signal channel, namely the intermediate-frequency amplifier, second detector, video amplifier, and audio amplifier, have been discussed in detail elsewhere in this book. It is desirable, however, to indicate their relationship to each other in this system.   The synchronizing and deflection channels have not been treated, and some detail will be given to the problems involved in this part of the receiver.

Just as the second detector is the center of an AM radio, so the second detector is the heart of a television receiver.   Once the type of detector has been established, the gain of the video and IF amplifiers can be determined, if the picture-tube signal requirements and the level of the weakest signal to be received are known.

11.5.1.2   RF Tuners

Transistors are being developed which may ultimately provide wide-band RF gain over the VHF television band. Transistors are commercially available, however, that will oscillate at these frequencies. It is

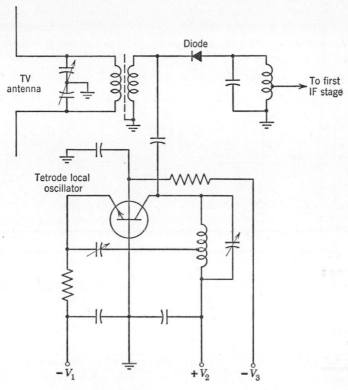

Fig. 11.23   RF tuner employing diode mixer

possible, therefore, to construct a diode mixer and thereby derive the IF signal.

Figure 11.23 shows a tuner composed of a transistor oscillator and a diode mixer. The television signal from the antenna is mixed with the local-oscillator output in the crystal diode and the resulting difference frequency appears at the output transformer. The use of such a tuner, however, is beset with a number of problems. Since no RF stage is used, the problem of oscillator radiation is present. In addition, the lack of an RF amplifier results in an overall loss in signal power so that increased gain must be included in the IF amplifier for a given receiver

sensitivity.   Until VHF transistors become commercially available the
use of electron tubes for RF amplification and mixing is indicated.

11.5.1.3   IF Amplifier

The problem of obtaining wide-band gain with transistors at intermediate frequencies is much less difficult than in the case of the RF
tuner.   Figure 11.24 shows two stages of a multistage transistor television IF amplifier.   Maximum power gain per stage is obtained by

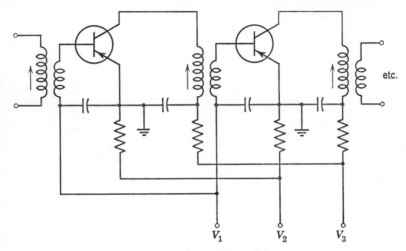

Fig. 11.24   Transistor IF amplifier stages

matching the input and output impedances of each stage with a coupling
transformer according to the principles outlined in Chapter 6.   The desired band-pass characteristic for the amplifier can be obtained by stag-
gered tuning, i.e. by tuning one or more of the stages off the center frequency, and by the addition of appropriate resonant traps.   The number of stages used depends on the power gain realizable from each transistor at the intermediate frequency selected, the desired sensitivity of
the receiver, the output level of the RF tuner, and the power required
by the second detector.

The selection of the intermediate frequency is a compromise based
on a number of factors.   From the system viewpoint it is desirable
that a high frequency be chosen so that image frequency interference
problems are minimized.   On the other hand, a frequency at which
the power gain of the transistor is low must not be selected or an excessive number of stages would be required.   In order to limit the
number of transistors in the amplifier to a reasonable number, it is

desirable to select an operating frequency such that a power gain of at least 15 db per transistor is obtained.

Figure 11.25 shows the circuit of a tetrode IF amplifier. In order to utilize the maximum bandwidth obtainable from each stage, the tank circuit of each transistor consists of a variable inductance only. This inductance resonates with the output capacitance of the transistor and the stray circuit capacitance. The coupling transformers are designed to match the input and output impedances approximately at the center

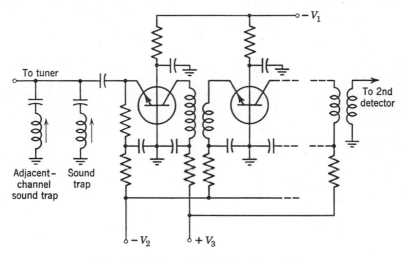

Fig. 11.25   Tetrode television IF amplifier

frequency for all stages. Bias point and the interbase bias voltage are adjusted to give optimum performance. The desired band-pass characteristic is obtained by tuning the individual stages away from the center frequency. Two series-resonant traps, one tuned to reject the adjacent-channel sound signal, and the other tuned to the sound-carrier frequency, are inserted in the input circuit.

Without neutralization, the reflected impedance from one stage to the other complicates the alignment procedure considerably. This difficulty can be minimized by adopting the procedures outlined in Chapter 6.

11.5.1.4   Second Detectors

Among the semiconductor devices that are suitable for performing the second-detector function are diodes and high-frequency transistors. Diode detection can be used provided a sufficiently high impedance level can be maintained at the video-amplifier input. Rectification efficiency is adversely affected if the level is low. A transistor, on the other hand, can function as the second detector into a relatively low-impedance video amplifier. The IF voltage required for operation of the two second-detector types is on the order of 0.5 volt for the diode and 100 mv for the transistor.

Figure 11.26 shows two second-detector circuits, one incorporating a diode, the other a transistor as the rectifying device. A low-pass filter, composed of an inductance L and capacitors C_1 and C_2, is designed to pass video frequencies and block IF signals at the detector output. The use of the filter is not necessary if the cutoff frequency of the transistors in the video amplifier is much below the intermediate frequency.

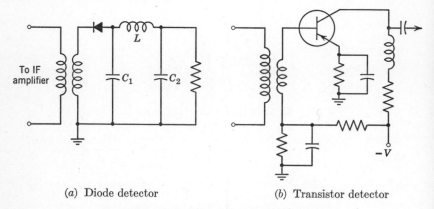

(a) Diode detector   (b) Transistor detector

Fig. 11.26   Television second-detector circuits

In addition to performing the second-detector function, the transistor detector can be looked upon as the first stage of the video amplifier. Rectification occurs at the emitter-base diode of the transistor and the diode output, amplified by transistor action, appears at the collector.

11.5.1.5   Video Amplifiers

The design objectives of a video amplifier suitable for a television receiver are: (1) voltage amplification, 50 to 100, (2) frequency response, 3 db down at 30 cps and 3.5 mc, (3) output voltage at least 40 volts peak-to-peak at the grid of a typical picture tube.

Figure 11.27 shows the circuit of a three-stage transistor video amplifier which meets these requirements. The design procedures of the amplifier follow those discussed in Chapter 7 and therefore are not repeated here. Stages 1 and 2 are designed for a voltage amplification of approximately 3 each, whereas the output stage, with its higher load impedance, provides a voltage amplification of about 10. High-frequency compensation is provided by the peaking inductances in the collector circuits

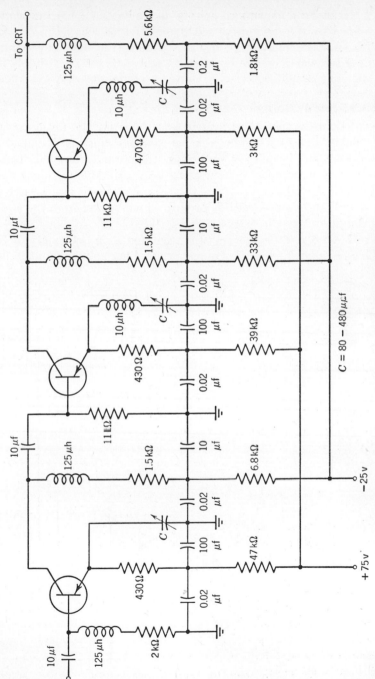

Fig. 11.27   Transistor video amplifier

and by the emitter bypass capacitors and inductors. Decoupling is accomplished by the resistor-capacitor combination located in the collector bias-supply circuit of each stage. Transistors with a common-base cutoff frequency on the order of 15 mc or better are suitable for use in the video amplifier.

11.5.1.6 Sound Circuitry

The intercarrier-type sound system is suitable for the transistor receiver. Sound signals at the intercarrier frequency may be obtained at the second-detector output. A multistage transistor IF amplifier tuned to this frequency amplifies the signal to a level suitable for demodulation by a ratio detector or discriminator. Standard audio-amplifier techniques may then be employed for driving a loudspeaker from the audio output obtained from the detector.

Figure 11.28 illustrates a transistor television sound channel. It includes a multistage intercarrier-frequency amplifier and an audio ampli-

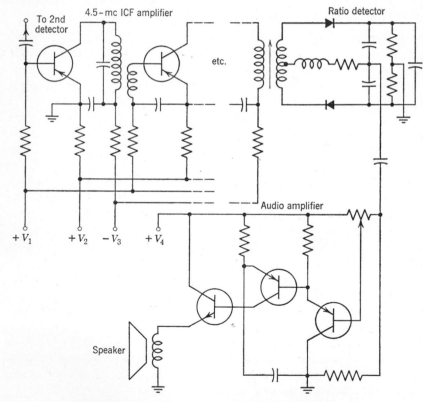

Fig. 11.28   Transistor television sound system

fier. The stages of intercarrier amplification are designed according to the principles set forth in Chapter 6. Unlike the IF amplifier which is stagger-tuned, the stages are tuned to a single frequency. The last stage drives a ratio transformer which is connected into a conventional ratio detector circuit. Two semiconductor diodes perform the rectification. The audio signal appears at the ratio detector output.

A three-stage direct-coupled audio amplifier connected to the detector output drives a suitable loudspeaker. A common-collector input stage serves to raise the impedance level of the amplifier input and hence reduces the ratio detector load. The second stage is connected in the common-emitter configuration and furnishes driving power for the common-collector output stage.

The bias circuitry is arranged so that the d-c operating point of the power output stage varies in accordance with the volume-control setting. Since most of the time the receiver operates at reduced volume levels, a substantial saving in battery power is effected.

11.5.1.7 Synchronizing Circuitry

The timing pulses which are necessary for synchronizing the receiver horizontal and vertical deflection circuits are derived from the video signal at the second-detector output or from the video amplifier. Two functions must be performed in this part of the receiver: (a) the synchronizing pulses must be removed from the video signal, and (b) the resulting combined horizontal and vertical pulse information must be separated into horizontal and vertical pulse outputs. In addition, amplification is usually included to maintain the pulse magnitudes at usable levels.

Figure 11.29 shows the synchronizing-pulse circuitry of a transistor television receiver. Video signals from the second-detector output are amplified by an n-p-n common-emitter stage which in turn is direct-coupled to a p-n-p sync clipper. The polarity of the video signal is arranged so that the synchronizing pulses are in the negative sense at the base of the sync clipper transistor, and the transistor accordingly conducts and charges capacitor C. This sets the operating conditions such that the transistor is biased beyond cut-off and hence passes only the most negative portions of the video signal, i.e. the synchronizing pulses. The only signals to be found at the collector of the sync clipper transistor, therefore, are horizontal and vertical synchronizing pulses. A second sync amplifier, coupled to the sync clipper output, increases the level of the pulses. The horizontal synchronizing pulses are available at the collector of the sync amplifier transistor. The vertical pulses, on the other hand, are obtained by integration of the serrated vertical

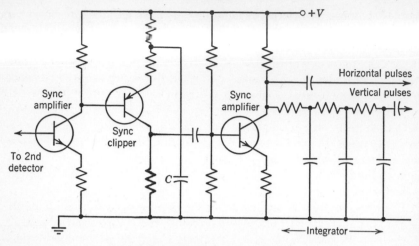

Fig. 11.29   Synchronizing pulse circuitry

pulses present at the sync amplifier output.   An RC network, of the
form used in tube receivers, performs the integrating function.

11.5.1.8   Horizontal Deflection Circuits

The horizontal deflection system consists of a phase detector and amplifier, a relaxation oscillator, and an output switching transistor which
drives the horizontal windings of the deflection yoke.   This provides
the horizontal deflection of the electron
beam in the picture tube.

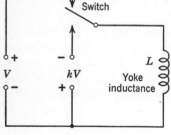

Fig. 11.30   Linear bidirectional
current circuit

The operation of the system depends
on the ability of transistors to act as
fast switches.   All that is necessary to
produce the desired linear bidirectional
change of current with time in the deflection yoke inductance is periodically
to connect the yoke alternately to each
of two sources of constant voltage in
the manner shown in Fig. 11.30.   Linear
bidirectional currents will flow in the
inductance if the switch is periodically
operated from one contact to the other.   For television purposes, the
switching operation should be performed at the horizontal repetition
rate, and k should be equal to the fraction of the cycle allotted for retrace
purposes.   In order that the current shall swing by equal amounts in
each direction, the switch must remain in contact with battery V for

k times the time of a period of operation and at the other position for the remainder of the cycle.

A simplified form of this circuit [16] is shown in Fig. 11.31. The switch in this circuit is closed for $1/k$ times the time for one cycle and open for the remainder of the period. A high-frequency resonant circuit formed by the LC combination allows the yoke current to reverse direc-

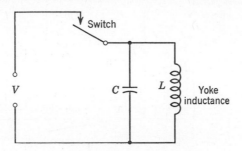

Fig. 11.31   Variation of Fig. 11.30

tion rapidly during the open time, after which the switch is closed and the stored energy of the resonant circuit is returned to the battery.

The transistor in the circuit shown in Fig. 11.32 duplicates the switching action of the latter circuit. In this arrangement, the following transistor properties are utilized: The transistor becomes a low impedance path if (a) the collector-base diode should become biased in the forward

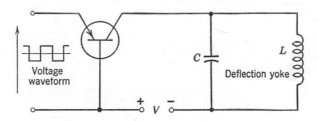

Fig. 11.32   Transistor deflection circuit

direction, or (b) if a forward bias is applied to the emitter circuit when the collector is biased for normal transistor operation. On the other hand, the transistor presents a high impedance if the emitter is reverse-biased when the collector is biased in the normal manner. These properties closely approach those of the ideal switch in Fig. 11.31.

Circuit operation is as follows: An operating cycle may be considered to begin when the input signal causes the emitter to be biased in the forward direction so that the transistor becomes a low-impedance path.

This effectively connects the yoke inductance across a constant voltage, current increasing in the yoke linearly with time. At the time the input signal reverses polarity, the transistor becomes nonconducting and current flows through capacitor C at a frequency determined by the LC combination. At the end of one-half cycle of this oscillation, the yoke

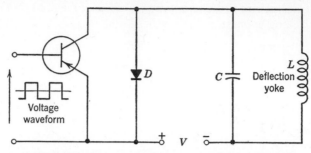

Fig. 11.33 Common-emitter television sweep circuit

current is reversed, and the voltage across the yoke is such as to cause the collector-base diode of the transistor to conduct, hence reconnecting the yoke to the supply voltage. The yoke current during the diode conduction time, therefore, will decrease linearly. Completion of the cycle occurs when the yoke current has returned to zero and the transistor begins its conduction period again.

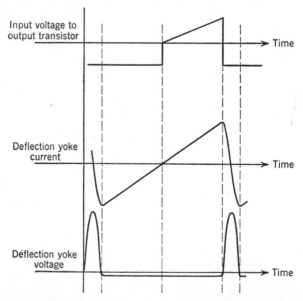

Fig. 11.34 Voltage and current waveforms of horizontal deflection circuit

It is possible to use other transistor configurations in the television sweep application. Figure 11.33 illustrates a common-emitter deflection circuit. An external diode D is shunted across the transistor to serve in the damping function. Figure 11.34 shows the voltage and current waveforms of this circuit.

Figure 11.35 shows a possible version of the deflection system. The output switching transistor T_4 is periodically turned "on" and "off" by

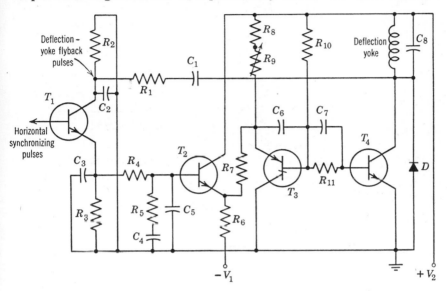

Fig. 11.35   Horizontal deflection system

the p-n-p-n relaxation oscillator T_3 (Sec. 8.3.1.1), the frequency of which is controlled at the horizontal repetition rate by a direct current supplied by transistor T_2. A phase-detector transistor T_1 completes the deflection system.

Horizontal synchronization is accomplished by comparing the frequency and phase of the "flyback" pulses which are generated at the horizontal coils of the deflection yoke with the transmitted horizontal synchronizing pulses. The result of this frequency or phase comparison is a direct current whose amplitude and polarity will depend on the phase and frequency relationship of the incoming synchronizing pulses with the flyback pulses generated by the deflection system.

The n-p-n phase-detector transistor T_1 has sawtooth and synchronizing pulse voltages applied to its electrodes. A sawtooth voltage formed by integration of the horizontal deflection coil voltage is applied to the transistor collector. Resistors R_1 and R_2 and capacitor C_2 comprise the

integrating network. Horizontal synchronizing pulses are applied to the
base of the transistor. The resulting effects of these connections are as
follows: If the horizontal relaxation oscillator is properly timed, the collector voltage of T_1 passes through zero on the retrace cycle at the
instant that the synchronizing pulse arrives at the base of T_1, and no
change will occur in the d-c emitter current. Hence no phase correction
is applied to the oscillator. On the other hand, if the synchronizing

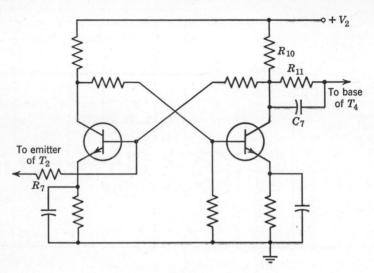

Fig. 11.36   Multivibrator oscillator

pulse arrives ahead of or behind the center of the sawtooth retrace slope,
positive or negative currents are developed in the emitter of the phase-
detector transistor. These currents increase or decrease the oscillator
frequency and hence correct the oscillator timing.

The horizontal oscillator is a relaxation type which depends for its
operation on the N-type negative-resistance characteristic exhibited by
the p-n-p-n transistor biased in the conjugate-emitter or hook-collector
mode (see Chapter 8). Oscillation occurs by virtue of the capacitor
C_6, which shunts the negative input resistance of the transistor. Circuit
operation is such that during a cycle the collector-base circuit of the
p-n-p-n transistor alternately provides a low- and a high-impedance
path. This switching action is utilized to drive the output transistor
T_4 with a voltage waveform similar to that indicated in Fig. 11.34.
Forward bias for the base-emitter diode of the output transistor of sufficient value to saturate its collector is derived from the supply voltage
through resistors R_{10} and R_{11}. The output transistor is, therefore,

biased in the "on" condition during this period. When the p-n-p-n transistor conducts, the junction of R_{10} and R_{11} is virtually returned to ground, and the potential present on the capacitor C_7 reverse-biases the emitter-base diode, thereby turning the output transistor "off." Thus the output transistor conducts when the p-n-p-n unit is nonconducting, and is nonconducting when the p-n-p-n conducts. Operating frequency and the percentage of the cycle devoted to conduction are set by R_8, R_9, C_6, and the potential across R_{10}. Frequency control of the oscillator is effected by varying the p-n-p-n emitter bias with the d-c control current derived from the phase detector. The d-c control current is introduced by means of resistor R_7.

A conventional transistor multivibrator such as that shown in Fig. 11.36 can be used in place of the p-n-p-n relaxation oscillator. In this application, unsymmetrical operation is used to obtain the desired driving waveform (Fig. 11.34) for the horizontal output transistor. Automatic frequency control is achieved by varying the base potential of a multivibrator transistor with the control current obtained from resistor R_7. The design details of suitable transistor multivibrators are discussed in Chapter 8.

11.5.1.9 Vertical Deflection Circuits

The vertical sweep system is composed of a relaxation oscillator and amplifier which drives the vertical windings of the deflection yoke. This provides the vertical deflection of the electron beam in the picture tube.

Figure 11.37 shows the vertical deflection system. A p-n-p-n transistor relaxation oscillator T_2 of the type used in the horizontal sweep section is utilized to generate a sawtooth-voltage waveform. The sawtooth voltage is formed by alternately charging capacitor C_2 at an approximately linear rate through resistor R_4 and rapidly discharging it through the p-n-p-n oscillator collector circuit each time the p-n-p-n unit conducts. Amplification of the capacitor-voltage waveform is accomplished by transistor T_3 which, in turn, controls the current flow in the power transistor T_4. Since the deflection-yoke vertical-winding impedance is primarily resistive, the amplified sawtooth voltage produces a linear deflection current in the yoke. The amplitude of this current can be adjusted by the vertical size control, R_6. This resistor introduces degeneration in the amplifier transistor T_3, with consequent alteration of the stage gain. Vertical centering of the picture-tube electron beam is accomplished by allowing direct current to flow into the deflection yoke windings, by means of the variable resistor R_1 and the inductance L_1. The p-n-p-n relaxation oscillator is synchronized at the vertical scanning rate by the synchronizing pulses obtained from the integrator of Fig.

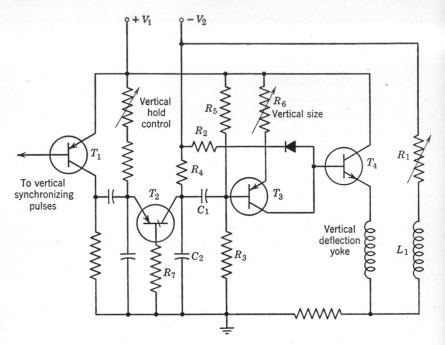

Fig. 11.37   Vertical deflection system

11.29.   A stage of amplification is necessary to increase the pulse level of the integrator output to a value suitable for synchronizing the oscillator. Transistor T_1 performs this function. A conventional transistor multivibrator can be used in place of the p-n-p-n relaxation oscillator in the manner indicated in Sec. 11.5.1.8.

11.5.1.10   Picture-Tube High-Voltage Supply

The picture-tube accelerating potential can be obtained either by high-voltage recovery from the horizontal sweep system or by an independent transistor supply. The former method, which is in widespread use in electron-tube receivers, requires the use of an output transformer which would be connected into the collector circuit of the horizontal output switching transistor T_4 of Fig. 11.35. High-voltage d-c is obtained by rectification of the horizontal "flyback" pulse which appears at the transformer secondary winding.

Alternatively, a conventional Hartley oscillator can be utilized to generate the accelerating potential. In this method a high-voltage winding coupled to the oscillator tank circuit provides an a-c voltage which can be rectified and filtered by standard methods for the required d-c potential. The oscillator frequency should be synchronized at the horizontal repetition rate in order to reduce undesirable picture defects which may result from unavoidable oscillator interference.

11.5.1.11   Automatic Gain Control

The automatic control of the gain of a transistor television receiver can be effected by altering the power gain of the IF amplifier in opposition to the changes in the strength of the received signal. Since transistor power gain is sensitive to bias conditions, a d-c control signal can be used for gain-control purposes. All that is necessary is to derive a d-c signal with a magnitude proportional to the RF signal strength and apply it to appropriate electrodes of the transistors in the IF stages.

Several practical difficulties arise when gain control by d-c bias change is employed. The most important effects are the shift in amplifier frequency response and change in effective circuit Q's with a change in a transistor electrode bias. For example, in the tetrode IF amplifier of Fig. 11.25 a decrease of the collector voltage alone will increase the transistor output capacitance and hence will result in a downward shift of the resonant frequency. A decrease of the emitter current, on the other hand, will decrease the output capacitance and produce an upward shift of the resonant frequency. Decreasing emitter current also causes increasing transistor impedances, and thereby reduced bandwidth. A decrease of interbase bias voltage increases the output capacitance with attendant shift in the resonant frequency. Therefore, in order to prevent a shift of the IF center frequency by the automatic gain control, simultaneous changes of two or more of the transistor d-c bias values must be employed. These d-c control currents and voltages should be applied in such proportions that the upward and downward shifts of frequency cancel.

Figure 11.38 illustrates an AGC circuit which employs simultaneous control of emitter current and interbase bias voltage. Three tetrode IF stages are controlled. A p-n-p triode is used to amplify the AGC signal which may be derived from the receiver second detector. R_1 and R_2 are used to bias the triode so that, in the absence of a control signal, the d-c resistance between collector and emitter of the p-n-p is not excessive. The AGC signal should be applied to the triode across the base and emitter leads in such a polarity that this control signal decreases the forward bias applied to the emitter of the triode. The control-signal polarity is then negative at the base of the p-n-p unit. When the control signal increases, the forward bias current of the triode decreases, thereby presenting a high-resistance d-c path between emitter and collector. The voltage drop V_2, therefore, increases. This increase of V_2

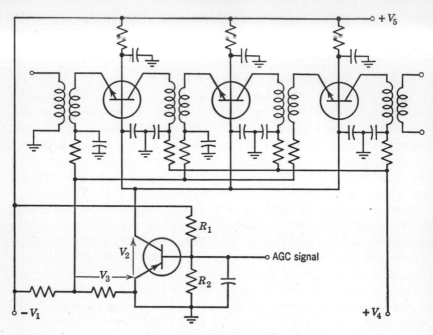

Fig. 11.38 Transistor AGC circuit

decreases the interbase bias voltage and at the same time decreases the difference between V_3 and V_2, which is the tetrode emitter bias voltage. Consequently, both the tetrode emitter bias current and interbase bias voltage are decreased by the control signal. A reduction in IF gain thus results without significant shift in the IF response characteristic.

11.5.2 Television Synchronizing Generator

Synchronizing-generator equipment is used at the television transmitter to produce timing pulses. These are transmitted along with the video information on the RF carrier and serve to synchronize the receiver deflection circuits with the studio camera scanning rate. The electrical and physical properties of transistors make them ideally suited to perform many of the functions found in this type of synchronizing generator.

11.5.2.1 Synchronizing-Generator Block Diagram

Figure 11.39 shows the block diagram of a synchronizing generator suitable for *industrial* television applications. An industrial television generator need not supply serrated vertical pulses or equalizing pulses such as those required in standard television since the horizontal and vertical pulses are not combined. The system is composed of a stable

31.5-kc oscillator, two frequency dividers, and an automatic frequency control.   One divider is arranged for division by 2 in order to obtain the horizontal pulses at a 15.75-kc repetition rate, whereas the second divider performs the division by 525 to obtain the vertical pulses at a 60-cps rate.   The output of the 525 divider is compared with the 60-cps power line frequency at the automatic frequency control.   Any difference in phase results in a correction being applied to the 31.5-kc oscillator in a manner such as to remove the difference.   This locks the phase of the

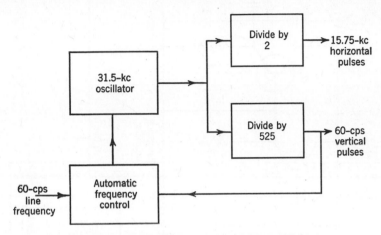

Fig. 11.39   Synchronizing generator block diagram

oscillator to the power line frequency, and reduces the possibility of picture defects of the moving-bar type which might otherwise occur if 60-cps power-line interference is present in the system.

11.5.2.2   Transistor Television Synchronizing Generator

Figure 11.40 shows the circuit of a transistor industrial television synchronizing generator.   The 31.5-kc oscillator, composed of transistor T_4, resistor R_8, capacitors C_7 and C_8, and inductance L, is a conventional Colpitts of the type discussed in Chapter 8.   A moderate degree of frequency stability is achieved through the use of a large value of emitter resistance R_8.   A reactance transistor T_3, which is shunted across the tuned circuit of the oscillator, shifts the operating frequency of the oscillator when a d-c control signal appears at its input.   The output of the oscillator is of sufficient magnitude to overdrive the transistor amplifier T_5.   This produces a square wave of voltage which is utilized by the divider circuits.

The d-c control signal which drives the reactance transistor is derived from a phase detector composed of two diodes D_1 and D_2, a potentiom-

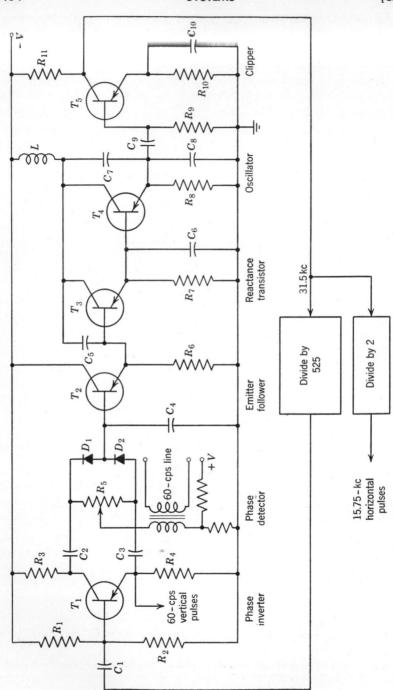

Fig. 11.40 Industrial television synchronizing generator

eter R_5, two coupling capacitors C_2 and C_3, and a phase inverter stage T_1. Positive pulses from the 525 divider are amplified by the phase inverter T_1 and applied to two of the arms of a bridge formed by the diodes D_1 and D_2 and the potentiometer R_5. Negative pulses are applied at one arm, positive pulses at the other. A 60-cps voltage derived from the power line is introduced at the potentiometer midpoint. The terminal common to both diodes assumes the average value of the 60-cps sine wave during the period when keying pulses are present. This average value is zero if the zero instantaneous value of the sine wave occurs at the time the center of the pulse from the phase inverter is present. If, on the other hand, this situation does not hold, in other words, if a phase difference exists, then the average value of the sine wave is no longer zero, and the common terminal of the diodes assumes a positive or negative potential according to the phase difference. This voltage varies the base potential of transistor T_2, which in turn applies a d-c corrective current to the reactance transistor. Hence, the oscillator frequency is changed, and the phase difference which existed between the 60-cps pulses and the 60-cps power line is eliminated.

The dividers are of the cascaded binary scaler variety discussed in Chapter 10. Feedback is employed to provide the desired dividing ratios. Division by 2, to provide the horizontal pulses, is obtained from a single binary scaler. The vertical pulse output is obtained from the 525 divider. The latter division is accomplished in steps. Factors of 15, 7, and 5 are convenient for this purpose.

Bibliography

1. A. P. Stern and J. A. A. Raper, "Transistor AM Broadcast Receivers," *IRE Convention Record*, *2*, pt. 7 (Broadcasting and Television), 8–14 (1954).

2. L. E. Barton, "An Experimental Transistor Personal Broadcast Receiver," *Proc. IRE*, *42*, 1062–1066 (1954).

3. A. P. Stern and J. A. A. Raper, "Transistor Broadcast Receivers," *Elec. Engg.*, *73*, 1107–1112 (1954).

4. D. D. Holmes, T. O. Stanley, and L. A. Freedman, "A Developmental Pocket-Size Broadcast Receiver Employing Transistors," *Proc. IRE*, *43*, 662–670 (1955).

5. L. A. Freedman, T. O. Stanley, and D. D. Holmes, "An Experimental Automobile Receiver Employing Transistors," *Proc. IRE*, *43*, 671–678 (1955).

6. J. W. Englund, "Application of Transistors to Battery-Powered Portable Receivers," *IRE Convention Record*, *4*, pt. 3, 68 (1956).

7. D. D. Holmes and T. O. Stanley, "Stability Considerations in Transistor IF Amplifiers," *Transistors I*, 403–421, RCA Laboratories, Princeton (1956).

8. C. C. Cheng, "Neutralization and Unilateralization," *IRE Trans.*, *CT-2*, no. 2, 138–145 (1955).

9. A. P. Stern, C. A. Aldridge, and W. F. Chow, "Internal Feedback and Neutralization of Transistor Amplifiers," *Proc. IRE*, *43*, 838–847 (1955).

10. G. Y. Chu, "Unilateralization of Junction-Transistor Amplifiers at High Frequencies," *Proc. IRE, 43,* 1001–1006 (1955).

11. W. F. Chow and A. P. Stern, "Automatic Gain Control of Transistor Amplifiers," *Proc. IRE, 43,* 1119–1127 (1955).

12. J. A. Worcester, "A Discussion of the Design Problems Encountered in the Development of a Transistorized Radio Receiver," *I.R.E. Trans., BTR-2,* 6–9 (1956).

13. C. R. Hurtig, "Constant-Resistance AGC Attenuator for Transistor Amplifiers," *IRE Trans., CT-2,* no. 2, 191–196 (1955).

14. G. A. Allard, "Partial Transistorization of an FM Communication Receiver," Paper presented at AIEE Winter General Meeting, New York, February 1956.

15. J. A. A. Raper, "A Transistorized Tuned Amplifier–Limiter," *IRE Trans., CT-3,* no. 1, 67 (1956).

16. G. C. Sziklai, R. D. Lohman, and G. B. Herzog, "A Study of Transistor Circuits for Television," *Proc. IRE, 41,* 708–717 (1953).

Chapter 12

Special Circuits

12.0 Introduction

In each of the preceding chapters, a major phase of the application of transistors has been discussed in detail. There are, however, certain special circuits which do not fit conveniently into any of the other chapters, and yet are too important to be omitted. Some of these circuits, in fact, are near-ideal applications, for they make particular use of those characteristics of semiconductor devices that are not found in electron tubes or other circuit elements.

Some of these special circuits will be discussed here.

12.1 Low-Level Limiters

Low-level limiting is often very desirable, particulary since the advent of transistors. Since, in a transistorized FM system, the gain available per transistor in stages following the discriminator is considerably higher

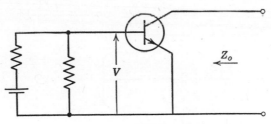

Fig. 12.1 Transistor stage

than in those preceding it, the lower the level at which satisfactory limiting and discrimination can be achieved, the more efficiently are the transistors used. This necessitates the use of a limiter capable of operating at very low levels (in the region of millivolts).

Consider the circuit of Fig. 12.1. If V is changed, the output impedance changes in the manner shown in Fig. 12.2. This circuit forms the basis for a low-level limiter, as follows: Figure 12.3 shows a push-pull version of Fig. 12.1. With this arrangement, the diode effects of the two unbiased junctions cancel each other and do not appear in the out-

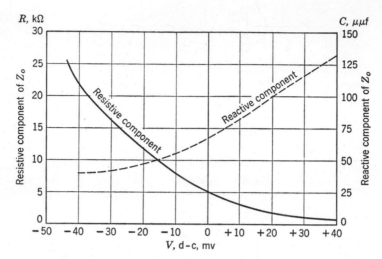

Fig. 12.2   Output impedance versus emitter-to-base voltage

put impedance. This output impedance is now used as a controlled element in the potentiometer circuit of Fig. 12.4.

The operation of the circuit is as follows. The output signal is derived from the potentiometer whose shunt arms are two controlled impedances.

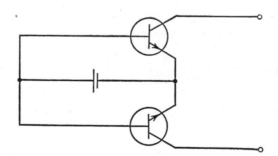

Fig. 12.3   Push-pull transistor stage

The input signal is fed to the potentiometer, as well as to the controlled impedances A and B. V_1 and V_2 are 180° out of phase, so that A is operative for one half of the input wave and B for the other half. The final circuit is that of Fig. 12.5. Resistance r may be added to improve

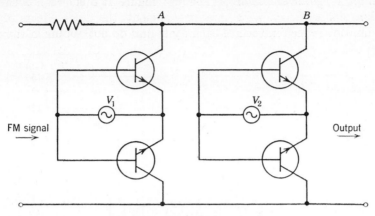

Fig. 12.4   Basic limiter circuit

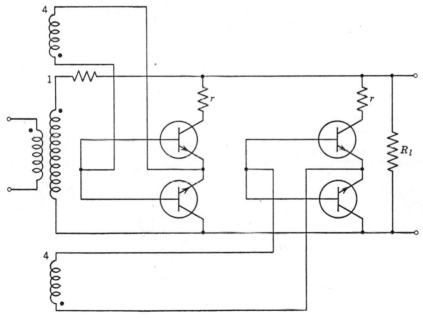

Fig. 12.5   Practical low-level limiter

the limiting action somewhat. The perfomance of this circuit is shown in Fig. 12.6.

It limiting is permissible at a slightly higher level (fractions of a volt),

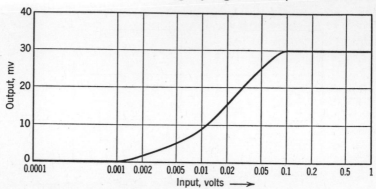

Fig. 12.6   Limiting characteristic of circuit of Fig. 12.5

an extremely flat limiting characteristic can be obtained using a single junction diode as a limiter, as shown in Fig. 12.7. Symmetrical limiting is obtained, owing to hole storage effects. When a constant voltage is

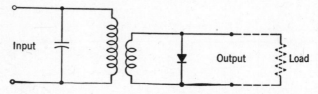

Fig. 12.7   Symmetrical limiter using a junction diode

applied across the junction in the forward direction, it will be assumed, for the sake of simplicity, that all the carriers crossing the junction are holes. The resultant hole distribution is shown in Fig. 12.8. If the polarity of

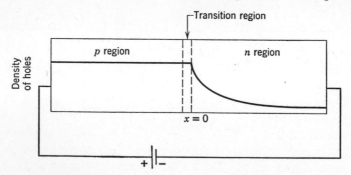

Fig. 12.8   Diode biased in the conducting direction

the applied voltage is suddenly reversed, the transition region is swept clear of carriers almost immediately, practically all the reverse voltage drop being across a very thin barrier region. The situation is represented by Fig. 12.9. At the instant of switching t_0, the gradient at $x = 0$ is practically infinite. Since the hole current is proportional to the hole concentration gradient at the barrier, initially a large hole current will flow back into the p region. This flow of holes, which diminishes as the

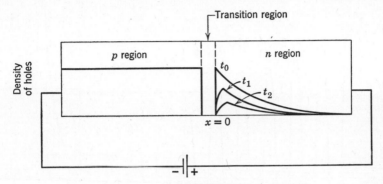

Fig. 12.9   Diode biased in the reverse direction

gradient is reduced, constitutes a current in the reverse direction through the diode.

If an alternating voltage is connected across the diode, the resultant current through the diode will be frequency-dependent. Figure 12.10 shows how the wave shape will change with increasing frequency. In each case the negative area represents the stored charge. It will be seen

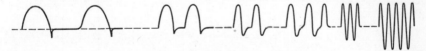

Fig. 12.10   Diode current as a function of time for increasing frequency of applied signal

that, if the frequency is sufficiently high, a complete negative half-wave will be passed before the supply of stored holes is used up.

The action of the limiter can be seen by reference to Fig. 12.11. The dashed curve A represents the virtual back characteristic at the instant of switching polarity. This curve is time-dependent and would, if allowed sufficient time, move all the way around in the direction of the arrow until it took up position B, the normal back characteristic of the diode.

It is seen from the above discussion that this limiter will only function at those frequencies at which the detection efficiency is low. Using suitable varieties of both silicon and germanium junction diodes, the output of the limiter is essentially sinusoidal down to about 60 to 70 kc and effective limiting is possible to about 30 kc.

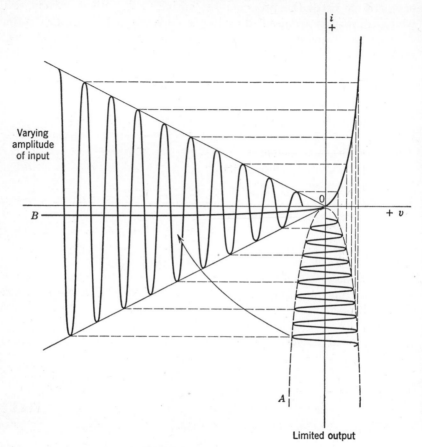

Fig. 12.11   Graphical representation of limiter action

The amplitude at which limiting starts is controllable by means of a small bias, in either the forward or the backward direction. A back bias of 0.4 volt, for example, shifts the limiting curve of a germanium junction diode until it resembles that of a silicon junction diode.

This circuit may be used in transistorized equipment where extremely flat limiting is required. Variations of over 80 db in level at the input of a four-stage amplifier–limiter result in output changes of less than 1 db.

For a zero-biased germanium diode, effective limiting commences at signal levels of about 0.1 volt rms.

12.2   Transistor Active Filters

Active filters may be of two basic types: (a) filters in which transistors are used to affect the properties of a single component, (b) filters in which transistors are used to affect the circuit performance as a whole.

Since the transistor is inherently more temperature-sensitive than the resistances and reactances of which passive filters are built, the inclusion of an active element is only justifiable when its presence will (a) permit the design of a smaller, lighter, or less expensive filter than is obtained by passive filter design techniques, (b) permit the design of a filter that is physically unrealizable with passive elements.

In the majority of cases, it is the first of these reasons that leads to the utilization of active elements.

In filter design, large inductances with high Q are perhaps the heaviest, bulkiest, and most expensive components. Such components find considerable use in low-frequency filters. It is in this frequency region that the filter designer is most attracted to active circuit techniques, in the hope of either reducing the weight, size, and cost of inductances or of eliminating them entirely.

12.2.1   Inductance and Q Multipliers

L and Q multiplications are perhaps the most common functions that active elements are called upon to perform.

A simple circuit may be designed as follows: Consider an inductance, of value L, with associated series resistance r. The Q of this coil is $\omega L/r$. If such a coil is placed in series with a negative resistance of the open-circuit-stable type (N-type characteristic) discussed in Sec. 8.3.1, of value $-R$, the effective Q is raised to $\omega L/(r - R)$.

If this improved coil is now placed in the emitter circuit of a transistor in the common-emitter configuration, then

$$Z_i = (h_{11b} + r - R + j\omega L)/(1 + h_{21b}) \qquad (12.1)$$

The reactive component has thus been multiplied by $1/(1 + h_{21b})$, and the overall Q raised to $\omega L/(h_{11b} + r - R)$.

Theoretically, any value of Q may be obtained in this manner. However, the higher Q is made, the closer the circuit comes to instability. A practical L and Q multiplier is shown in Fig. 12.12. This circuit is, however, sensitive to temperature changes.

Q multiplication without L multiplication may be effected in a number of ways. In general, any circuit potentially capable of oscillation will multiply the Q of its tank coil if it is damped to a point of stability. In practical filter design, the Q multiplier is more often used than the Q and L multiplier described above. The reason for this may be seen in the design procedure of constant k- and m-type filters. For such filters, the values of inductances are accurately computed, and these, in conjunction with the capacitances, fix the pole-zero locations of the appropriate net-

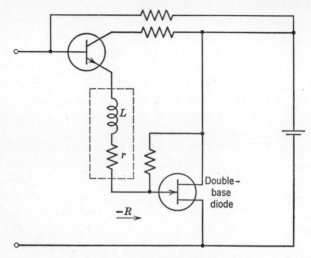

Fig. 12.12 L- and Q-multiplier circuit

work functions. The Q of these inductances is tacitly assumed to be infinity—any departure from this value results in a less-than-ideal filter. Thus, any improvement in Q is an improvement in the filter performance, as long as the circuit remains stable. Furthermore, in filters of this type, a high Q is really needed over a narrow frequency band (e.g., in m-derived sections, at the points of infinite attenuation). Thus, narrow-band negative resistances may be used.

The design of an active filter using Q multipliers proceeds as follows: (a) design a passive filter using RLC elements; (b) use a Q multiplier with some or all of the inductances involved.

Q multipliers may also use a negative resistance of the short-circuit-stable type (S-type characteristic) in shunt with the inductance. This is sometimes more convenient.

12.2.2   Feedback Filters

Feedback filters [1] are one form of filter in which active elements affect the performance of the filter as a whole. In such filters, a transistor is used in a feedback amplifier configuration. One such circuit is shown in Fig. 12.13. In this circuit, the transistor is placed in the feedback loop, and the network in the forward path. We may show that the

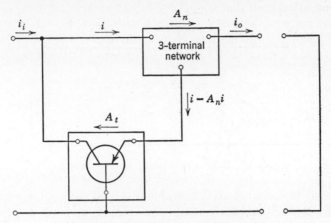

Fig. 12.13　Feedback filter configuration

short-circuit current-transfer ratio of the overall system is

$$A_i = i_o/i_i \cong A_n/(1 - A_t + A_n A_t) \qquad (12.2)$$

whence
$$A_n \cong A_i(1 - A_t)/(1 - A_i A_t) \qquad (12.3)$$

where A_n = short-circuit current-transfer ratio of the 3-terminal network in the direction indicated,

A_t = short circuit current-transfer ratio of the transistor in the
direction indicated.

The above expression is reasonably accurate provided that

$$|y_{11n}| \gg |y_{22b}| \qquad (12.4)$$

$$|y_{22n}| \ll |1/h_{11b}| \qquad (12.5)$$

where the subscript n refers to the three-terminal network in question, and the subscript b refers to the transistor parameters in the common-base configuration. This forms the basis of the design technique. An example will illustrate this technique.

Design a high-pass filter having a short-circuit current-transfer ratio as follows: (a) flat in the pass band, (b) 3 db down at 200 cps, (c) 12 db per octave slope in the rejection band.

The transfer function of such a filter about a normalized frequency of one radian per second is given by [2]

$$A_i = s^2/(s^2 + 1.414s + 1) \qquad (12.6)$$

where s is the operational function d/dt.

Since A_t is the short-circuit current-transfer ratio of the transistor and its associated circuitry in the common-base connection, its value may be adjusted such that $0 \leq A_t \leq 1$. Once a value of A_t is chosen,

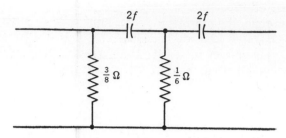

Fig. 12.14   Passive network in the feedback loop

eq. 12.3 may be solved to give the value of A_n. The designer must select a value for A_t such that the resulting function A_n is capable of synthesis as a passive network comprising only resistive and capacitive elements.[3,4]

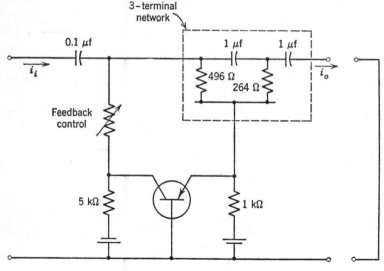

Fig. 12.15   Feedback filter

For example, one possible choice of A_t is 3/7. For this value of A_t,

$$A_n = s^2/(s + 0.828)(s + 4.828) \qquad (12.7)$$

Figure 12.14 shows the network having this characteristic.

Since this network is designed around a cutoff frequency of one radian per second, and the final circuit is to have a cutoff frequency of 200 cps, the capacitance values of Fig. 12.14 must be divided by $2\pi \times 200$. Since, furthermore, the network is designed at unit impedance level, this level may be raised by a factor K by (a) multiplying all resistances by K, (b) dividing all capacitances by K.

For this example, the impedance level must be raised sufficiently that inequalities 12.4 and 12.5 are satisfied. An impedance level of $10^6/(200\pi)$ ohms was chosen to result in conveniently available capacitor values. The overall circuit is shown in Fig. 12.15.

12.2.3 Filters Using Negative-Impedance Converters

This is perhaps the most highly developed form of active filter. With this type of filter it is possible to realize any transfer function Z_{21} that is ordinarily realizable with RLC elements, using only RC elements.

The negative-impedance converter has been described in considerable detail by Merrill [5] in its electron-tube version, and Linvill [6,7] in its transistor version. Such a converter has the property that its input impedance is the negative of its output termination. Thus, if the load is Z_l, the input impedance is $-Z_l$. Its circuit properties are directly dependent on the value of h_{21b}, and are relatively independent of frequency. The device is ordinarily quite stable with temperature; additional circuitry involving a pair of extra transistors results in extreme stability and impedance conversion accuracy.

The filter design is based on the following principle: the a matrix of the converter may be written as

$$\begin{bmatrix} 1, & 0 \\ 0, & -1 \end{bmatrix}$$

If such a network is cascaded with two four-terminal networks A and B

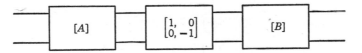

Fig. 12.16   Cascaded networks

as shown in Fig. 12.16, the overall Z_{21} is given by

$$Z_{21} = Z_{21A}Z_{21B}/(Z_{22A} - Z_{11B}) \tag{12.8}$$

The design of a filter with a prescribed Z_{21} may best be illustrated with the aid of an example.

Design a low-pass filter with a transfer characteristic

$$Z_{21} = 1/(s^2 + s + 1) \tag{12.9}$$

We begin the synthesis procedure by dividing both numerator and denominator of eq. 12.9 by the polynomial $(s + a)(s + b)$. As in most synthesis procedures, a certain amount of initial selection is necessary on the part of the designer. For this example, a and b must be arbitrarily-chosen positive numbers. Whereas this choice may be shown to be arbitrary insofar as the theoretical realizability of the networks are concerned, only experience will indicate a choice that will result in reasonably practical values of R and C. Selecting a and b at 0.5 and 1.0, respectively, we may write

$$Z_{21} = (Z_{21A}Z_{21B})/(Z_{22A} - Z_{11B})$$

$$= [1/(s + 0.5)(s + 1.0)]/[(s^2 + s + 1)/(s + 0.5)(s + 1.0)] \quad (12.10)$$

It is now necessary to synthesize

$$Z_{22A} - Z_{11B} = (s^2 + s + 1)/(s + 0.5)(s + 1.0) \quad (12.11)$$

and $\qquad Z_{21A}Z_{21B} = 1/(s + 0.5)(s + 1.0) \qquad (12.12)$

The synthesis of $Z_{22A} - Z_{11B}$ may be carried out as follows:

$$Z_{22A} - Z_{11B} = (s^2 + s + 1)/(s + 0.5)(s + 1.0)$$

$$= 1 + 1.5/(s + 0.5) - 2/(s + 1.0) \quad (12.13)$$

We now let

$$Z_{22A} = 1 + 1.5/(s + 0.5) \quad (12.14)$$

whence $\qquad Z_{11B} = 2/(s + 1.0) \qquad (12.15)$

Both these functions may be synthesized in networks containing only R and C elements. If Z_{22A} and Z_{11B} are synthesized in ladder form, with no *series* capacitors, it can be shown that [8]

$$Z_{21A} = 1/(s + 0.5) \quad (12.16)$$

$$Z_{21B} = 1/(s + 1.0) \quad (12.17)$$

whence $\qquad Z_{21A}Z_{21B} = 1/(s + 0.5)(s + 1.0) \qquad (12.18)$

The overall network is shown in Fig. 12.17. This may be redrawn as in

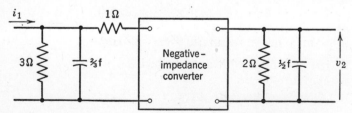

Fig. 12.17 Negative impedance filter (low-pass)

Fig. 12.18. The design may now be scaled to any desired value of frequency and impedance level as was done previously in Sec. 12.2.2.

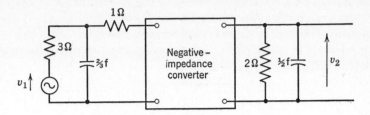

Fig. 12.18   Modified version of Fig. 12.17

As a second example, let

$$Z_{21} = s^2/(s^2 + s + 1) \qquad (12.19)$$

This filter is identical with the last, except that it is a high-pass structure. Using the same values as before,

$$Z_{21A}Z_{21B} = s^2/(s + 0.5)(s + 1.0) \qquad (12.20)$$

$$Z_{22A} - Z_{11B} = (s^2 + s + 1)/(s + 0.5)(s + 1.0)$$

$$= 1 + 1.5/(s + 0.5) - 2/(s + 1.0) \qquad (12.21)$$

whence $\qquad Z_{22A} = 1 + 1.5/(s + 0.5) \qquad (12.22)$

$$Z_{11B} = 2/(s + 1.0) \qquad (12.23)$$

If Z_{22A} and Z_{11B} could be synthesized in ladder form with no *shunt* capacitors [4] the following relationship would hold:

$$Z_{21A}Z_{21B} = s^2/(s + 0.5)(s + 1.0)$$

Unfortunately, Z_{11B} may only be synthesized in RC form with a shunt capacitance. Furthermore, a synthesis of Z_{22A} in this form leads to a generator source impedance that is purely capacitive. We get around these difficulties by an artifice as follows:

Let $\qquad Z_{22A} = 1 + 1.5/(s + 0.5) + 1 \qquad (12.24)$

Then $\qquad Z_{11B} = 2/(s + 1.0) + 1 \qquad (12.25)$

An extra degree of freedom is achieved in this manner and allows the networks to be synthesized in the form shown in Fig. 12.19. Once the design is completed, it may be scaled to the desired value of frequency and impedance level. The synthesis of Z_{22A} and Z_{11B} is usually carried out in ladder form. This is not necessary, however, and often these functions may be realized in lattice structures,[8] or their unbalanced

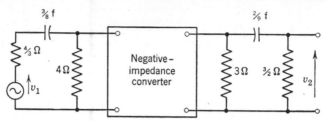

Fig. 12.19 Negative impedance filter (high-pass)

equivalents. This usually results in more complex terms in the numerator of the expression for Z_{21}, resulting in different filter performance characteristics.

12.3 Positive Temperature Coefficient Elements

Very often temperature compensation of transistor circuits requires the application of temperature-sensitive elements with a relatively large

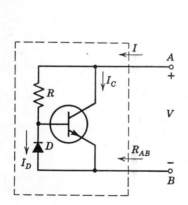

Fig. 12.20 Positive temperature-coefficient transistor circuit

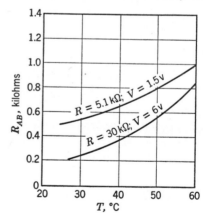

Fig. 12.21 Output resistance versus temperature

temperature coefficient. As a rule, most of the commercially available temperature-sensitive elements (such as thermistors) have a negative temperature coefficient. The few commercially available elements with a positive coefficient usually require considerable power or else their coefficient is very small.

Figure 12.20 shows a circuit arrangement, consisting of a transistor and a diode with associated resistors, which has a large positive coefficient and which is capable of very low power operation. The operation of this circuit may be understood with reference to the temperature-

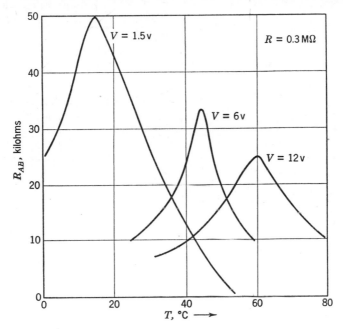

Fig. 12.22   Output resistance versus temperature

stabilized circuit of Fig. 3.14 in Chapter 3. For that circuit it was shown that the emitter current may be made independent of temperature by selecting a diode with a reverse current equal to the I_{CBO} of the transistor. Now, if the diode is selected with a reverse current greater than I_{CBO}, overcompensation will result, and the emitter current of the transistor will decrease with increasing temperature. By suitable choice of elements, it is possible to make the total current I (see Fig. 12.20) decrease with increasing temperature, corresponding to an effective increase in the d-c resistance R_{AB}. Figure 12.21 shows the resistance-versus-temperature curve, obtained experimentally under the above conditions.

One of the features of this circuit is that, for large values of R, pronounced peaks result in the characteristics, as shown in Fig. 12.22. The location of these peaks can be controlled by the applied voltage. This type of characteristic suggests the possibility of using this circuit as a sensitive temperature-controlled device, as well as a sensitive voltage-controlled device.

12.4 Transistor D-C Converters

A common problem encountered in the design of many electronic systems is to obtain medium- and high-voltage direct current from a low-voltage d-c source. Most methods for producing the desired voltage conversion employ mechanical elements such as rotating machinery or mechanical vibrators. For low-power applications, converters of the motor-generator type are ordinarily characterized by limited efficiency and are subject to brush and commutator problems. The mechanical-vibrator system, on the other hand, employs a vibrating reed, a transformer and a rectifier to perform the conversion. Despite the merits of simplicity and high operating efficiency, a number of objections arise concerning the use of such a system in certain critical applications. The objections can usually be traced to shortcomings of the mechanical vibrator. Among these are limited life, transient voltage generation produced by arcing as the contacts wear, and low operating frequency. The last condition is especially significant in airborne applications, for low operating frequency requires the use of relatively large and heavy transformers and filter components. Because transistors are capable of operating as fast switches, their use as an electrical substitute for the mechanical vibrator is extremely attractive. Among the advantages that can be realized with such a substitution are high operating efficiency, long life, and the ability to operate at relatively high frequencies with consequent reduction in transformer and filter size.

12.4.1 Converter Principles

The operation of the transistor d-c converter is based on the generation of alternating current from the low-voltage d-c source. Standard a-c techniques are then used for voltage step-up, and rectification supplies the desired high-voltage direct current. Most designs [9-11] utilize a form of the RL-type symmetrical multivibrator oscillator, which was discussed in Sec. 8.3.2.2, for the generation of an alternating current. A more general form of this oscillator, namely the unsymmetrical version, [12,13] is used in the converter discussion which follows.

The basic configuration of the transistor converter is shown in Fig. 12.23. A p-n-p high-power transistor T_1 (an n-p-n unit can be used with slight circuit modification) in conjunction with a low-power p-n-p transistor T_2 and a transformer operate as an unsymmetrical multivibrator-type oscillator. The circuit is arranged so that the collector of the power transistor is connected to one battery terminal, thereby eliminating the necessity of electrically insulating the collector from a grounded heat sink.

Alternating current is created in the transformer windings when the transistors alternately switch the supply voltage V_S across the windings W_1 and W_2. Switching occurs at the time that the transformer core becomes saturated. The transistors are actuated by suitable base

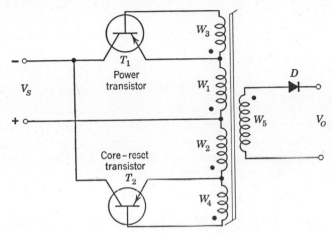

Fig. 12.23   Transistor d-c-d-c converter

currents supplied by the feedback windings W_3 and W_4, while winding W_5 furnishes the output current at the desired voltage. A half-wave rectifier and a filter connected to the output winding complete the transistor converter. Winding and rectifier polarities are arranged so that power is delivered to the filter only during the time that the power transistor T_1 is conducting. The symmetrical case is obtained when two power transistors are used, W_1 and W_2 have equal number of turns, and a full-wave rectifier is connected across W_5.

An estimate of the converter operating frequency can be obtained by considering the time that is required for the circuit to traverse the transformer-core hysteresis characteristics. Following the discussion of Sec. 8.3.2.2, the transistor T_1 conduction time, t_1, (which amounts to the time required for the core flux density to change from saturation in one direction to saturation in the opposite direction) is given by

$$t_1 = 2N_1 A B_m / V_S \tag{12.26}$$

where N_1 is the number of turns in winding W_1, V_S is the converter supply voltage, A is the area of the core in square meters, and B_m is the saturation flux density in webers per square meter.

The same considerations apply when T_2 is conducting so that its conduction time t_2 is given by

$$t_2 = 2N_2AB_m/V_S \tag{12.27}$$

where N_2 is the number of turns in winding W_2. If the switching time is neglected, the period T is given by

$$T = t_1 + t_2 \tag{12.28}$$

$$= 2AB_m(N_1 + N_2)/V_S \tag{12.29}$$

The converter operating frequency is given by

$$f = 1/T = V_S/2AB_m(N_1 + N_2) \tag{12.30}$$

A review of the circuit operation indicates that transistor T_2 serves to reverse the magnetization of the transformer core after each conduction cycle of the power transistor T_1. Since no power is delivered to the load at the transformer output during the core-reset period, transistor T_2 need only supply the small amount of power that is ordinarily required for the magnetizing function. A low-power transistor (50 to 150 mw) is suitable for this purpose in most applications.

The time periods t_1 and t_2 can be arranged so that the power-handling capabilities of the power transistor are advantageously utilized. If I is the maximum continuous collector-current rating of the power transistor, the power delivered to the transformer winding W_1 by this transistor (neglecting transistor losses) is

$$P = V_SIt_1/T \tag{12.31}$$

The inverse voltage present across the power-transistor collector-emitter terminals during the reset period t_2 is given by

$$V = V_ST/t_2 \tag{12.32}$$

$$= V_ST/(T - t_1) \tag{12.33}$$

If t_1/T is eliminated from eq. 12.31, we obtain

$$P = V_SI(1 - V_S/V) \tag{12.34}$$

Maximum power is obtained when V is large compared with V_S. The value of V, however, must not exceed the permissible inverse-voltage rating of the power transistor; hence, the maximum power for a given V_S is

$$P = V_SI(1 - V_S/V_P) \tag{12.35}$$

where V_P is the permissible inverse-voltage rating of the power transistor.

The turns ratio of winding 1 to winding 2 corresponding to the maximum power condition stated in eq. 12.35 is

$$N_1/N_2 = (V_P/V_S) - 1 \qquad (12.36)$$

so that the fraction of the time that the power transistor conducts is

$$t_1/T = 1 - V_S/V_P \qquad (12.37)$$

A comparison of the power-handling abilities of the single-power-transistor circuit with that of the two-power-transistor symmetrical version is now in order. For the former the expression for the power, eq. 12.35, is

$$P_1 = V_S I(1 - V_S/V_P) \qquad (12.38)$$

The corresponding expression for the two-transistor circuit is

$$P_2 = V_S I \qquad (12.39)$$

It is seen that, for a low supply voltage V_S, coupled with high permissible inverse-voltage transistors, the power P_1 of the single-transistor case approaches that of the two-transistor converter. Since the ratio V_S/V_P is ordinarily small in many applications, only a small decrease in power output results from the use of the single-power-transistor converter compared with the two-transistor counterpart.

12.4.2 Design Considerations

The following is a collection of design equations for the single-power-transistor converter arranged in an order suitable for the calculation of an initial design. The equations are approximate in that a number of secondary effects are neglected. For example, the voltage impressed on a transformer winding when a transistor conducts is assumed to be equal to the supply voltage; the transistor voltage drop is neglected.

If I_2 is the maximum current capacity of the low-power transistor, H_c the coercive force of the transformer core in ampere-turns per meter and L the mean magnetic path length in meters, the number of turns in winding 2 is

$$N_2 = H_c L/I_2 \qquad (12.40)$$

assuming a square-loop toroidal core. The number of turns in winding 1 can be determined from eq. 12.36, namely

$$N_1 = N_2[(V_P/V_S) - 1] \qquad (12.41)$$

where the symbols are as defined previously. From eq. 12.30 the operating frequency is

$$f \quad V_S/2AB_m(N_1 + N_2) \tag{12.42}$$

The number of turns required in the feedback winding W_3 is

$$N_3 = N_1V_1/V_S \tag{12.43}$$

where V_1 is the feedback base-emitter voltage required to saturate the power transistor T_1 for the maximum collector current which will be expected to flow under full loading of the converter. Similarly, the number of turns required for the feedback winding W_4 is

$$N_4 = N_2V_2/V_S \tag{12.44}$$

where V_2 is the feedback base-emitter voltage required to saturate the low-power transistor T_2 at the collector current I_2 in eq. 12.40. The number of turns required in the output winding W_5 is given by

$$N_5 = N_1V_O/V_S \tag{12.45}$$

where V_O is the desired output voltage of the converter including an allowance for the voltage drop in the rectifier and filter.

The inverse voltages experienced by the transistors and rectifier are as follows:

For the power transistor T_1:

Collector-emitter $\qquad V_{CE} = V_S(1 + N_1/N_2) \tag{12.46}$

Base-emitter $\qquad V_{BE} = V_S(N_3/N_2) \tag{12.47}$

Similarly for transistor T_2:

$$V_{CE} = V_S(1 + N_2/N_1) \tag{12.48}$$

$$V_{BE} = V_S(N_4/N_1) \tag{12.49}$$

For the rectifier D:

$$V_{RECT} = V_SN_5(1/N_1 + 1/N_2) \tag{12.50}$$

The selection of the transformer core is complicated by a number of interrelated factors. Thus the magnetic path length (see eq. 12.40) and the core area, coupled with such factors as available winding space, power level, frequency, must all be considered in the light of the important converter requirement, namely that the overall converter efficiency be as high as possible. In addition, consideration must also be given to the transistor capabilities. For example, the operating frequency resulting from the core choice should not be so high that the transistor switching times are an appreciable part of the cycle.

A very desirable core from the standpoint of efficient converter operation is the toroidal, tape-wound variety. It can be obtained in a variety of magnetic materials. Those materials that exhibit a relatively square hysteresis loop, high saturation flux density, and low coercive force should be selected.

The converter as described is not ordinarily self-starting. One method of initiating the oscillation is to apply momentarily a small forward bias in the base circuit of the power transistor. Although this condition may be disadvantageous for certain applications, it does give the circuit the property of overload protection. The feedback current in the base circuit of the power transistor can be adjusted for optimum operation at the specified converter load. When this load value is exceeded by a certain amount, oscillation ceases and the input power to the converter drops to zero.

It should be noted that, during the operation of the circuit, the transistors are in one or the other of two states of conduction: either full conduction, wherein the collector circuit is saturated and only a small voltage appears across the transistor, or minimum conduction, wherein little collector current flows with the full inverse voltage present at the transistor terminals. In either case the power dissipation within the transistor is small. Thus transistors that are rated for low-power linear amplifier applications can be used to deliver relatively high power in the converter application.

12.4.3 Special Cases of the Converter

An important special case, the symmetrical converter, results when T_1 and T_2 are power transistors, N_1 equals N_2, N_3 equals N_4, and a full-wave rectifier is connected to W_5. The equations stated in the previous section hold for this converter provided the above substitutions are made. Maximum power capability results if the supply voltage is one-half the peak inverse-voltage rating of the transistors.

Another useful case occurs when transistors T_1 and T_2 are interchanged in the circuit of Fig. 12.23 and the polarity of the rectifying diode is reversed. This type of operation results in a short duty cycle for the power transistor and a small transformer turns-per-volt ratio. It is possible, therefore, to generate large output voltages with only a few secondary turns.

12.5 Transistor Inverters for Motor Applications

Certain applications require that a-c motors be operated from d-c supply sources. When these situations arise, inverters are required to convert the d-c energy to the required alternating current. Mechanical inverters, such as motor-generator sets, or electronic inverters, such as thyratron circuits, are usually used in these applications. However, as high power transistors are developed, the use of transistorized inverters may be anticipated. Such transistor circuits for motor applications offer distinct advantages over conventional techniques. For example, in high-altitude aircraft or missiles where many small motors are used in control systems, it is desirable to eliminate brushes in motor-generator

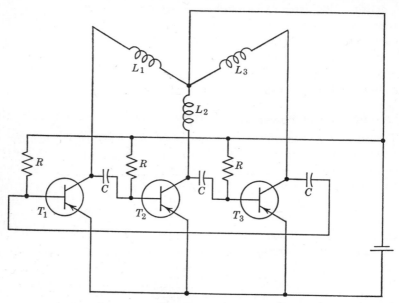

Fig. 12.24   Transistor d-c to three-phase a-c inverter

equipment because of the rapid rate of deterioration of such parts. Furthermore, owing to the rugged requirements of aircraft applications, vacuum and gas-tube electronic components are also undesirable. The use of transistor inverters overcomes both objections since it allows induction motors to be operated from d-c supplies while at the same time offering the inherent ruggedness and reliability of semiconductor components. In addition, the electronic inverter can be frequency-controlled, making the overall system more versatile than an a-c motor operated from a fixed-frequency supply.

A transistor d-c to three-phase a-c inverter circuit is illustrated in Fig. 12.24. The inductances L_1, L_2, and L_3 represent the Y-connected stator of a three-phase motor. The transistors are connected as a three-stage phase-shift oscillator with feedback from the collector of T_3 to the base of T_1. By varying the a-c coupling between transistors, i.e.

by varying the magnitude of the three coupling capacitors C, the oscillation frequency of the circuit may be varied. Each of the three transistors conducts approximately 120° out of phase with each other, the time constant being controlled by the coupling networks comprising L, C, and R. The transistors are primarily used as switches which are phase-locked in a free-running circuit. Thus, as L_1 is energized owing to T_1 becoming conducting, a positive step is transmitted to the base of T_2, causing the latter to become nonconducting. The interruption of current in L_2 causes the collector of T_2 to swing negative, and this negative step is transmitted to the base of T_3. T_3 then switches on, energizing L_3, and the feedback path from T_3 to T_1 provides a path for regenerative feedback. The frequency of the power supplied to the motor can be varied over a wide range by control of the coupling capacitors.

12.6 Regulated Power Supplies

Transistor regulators offer the advantages of compactness, less weight, and greater reliability over their electron-tube counterparts, and, in addition, have a performance equal to or better than that of the tube versions. Breakdown diodes may be used as voltage reference sources, and thus, complete solid-state regulator circuits are possible.

An elementary power-supply circuit for low-level applications [14] is illustrated in Fig. 12.25a. The breakdown diode B is used for voltage stabilization and the excess voltage, i.e. $v_I - v_O$, appears across the series resistor R_S. This simple diode regulator circuit has limited application owing to the low power-dissipation capabilities of the breakdown diode (e.g. 15 mw at 25° C) and owing to the relatively high impedance of the diode in the breakdown region (e.g. 100 ohms for silicon diodes). The regulation characteristics of the circuit of Fig. 12.25a, expressed in terms of the ratio of the fractional change in output voltage to the fractional change in input voltage, K_V, and the ratio of the fractional change in output voltage to the fractional change in load resistance, K_R, are given by

$$K_V \cong 1/(1 + R_S V_R / R_B v_I) \tag{12.51}$$

$$K_R \cong 1/[1 + R_S R_L / (R_B{}^2 + R_S R_B)] \tag{12.52}$$

where

$$K_V = (dv_O/v_O)/(dv_I/v_I)$$

$$K_R = (dv_O/v_O)/(dR_L/R_L)$$

In eqs. 12.51 and 12.52, R_B is the equivalent a-c resistance of the breakdown diode and V_R represents the equivalent voltage source.

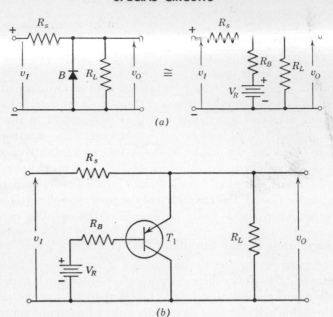

Fig. 12.25 (a) Breakdown-diode voltage regulator. (b) Shunt-type voltage regulator.

The *shunt-type transistor regulator* of Fig. 12.25b is an improved modification of the simple diode regulator. The reference source is shown as a battery V_R in series with a resistance R_B. In practice, this may be a breakdown diode or any other suitable voltage reference. If the output voltage v_O tends to increase, the excess voltage appears between emitter and base of transistor T_1. This causes the collector current to increase and hence increases the voltage drop across R_S, thereby preventing the load voltage from increasing. The regulation characteristics for the circuit of Fig. 12.25b are [15]

$$K_V \cong 1/(1 + \alpha_e V_R R_S/v_I R_B) \qquad (12.53)$$

$$K_R \cong 1/(1 + R_L/R_S + \alpha_e R_L/R_B) \qquad (12.54)$$

Comparison of eqs. 12.51 and 12.52 with 12.53 and 12.54, respectively, shows that the regulation characteristics have been improved roughly by a factor of α_e as the result of using a transistor in the shunt connection. In addition, the circuit of Fig. 12.25b can handle approximately α_e times the current handled by the circuit of Fig. 12.25a since the reference source is in series with the base of T_1 rather than directly across the load. It is apparent that the higher α_e, the better is the performance of the regulator circuit. Thus, additional circuit improvement may be obtained by using two transistors in a compound connection (see Sec. 4.6.2) in place of the single transistor T_1.

A disadvantage of the shunt-type regulator is its low efficiency due to power dissipation in the series resistor R_S. Higher efficiency may usually be obtained with a *series-type regulator*, such as that illustrated in Fig. 12.26. In the series-type circuit the excess voltage, $v_I - v_O$, is taken up across the collector junction of T_1. Increasing output voltage causes a compensating increase in collector-to-emitter voltage across T_1 due to the reduction in collector current of T_2. The regulation characteristics of this circuit are

$$K_V \cong 1/(1 + \alpha_{e2}V_R/v_I R_B h_{22e2}) \tag{12.55}$$

$$K_R \cong 1/(1 + \alpha_{e1}\alpha_{e2}R_L/R_B) \tag{12.56}$$

Equation 12.55 also expresses the per cent ripple reduction between v_O and v_I. Note that, in the series-type circuit, the transistor T_1 carries

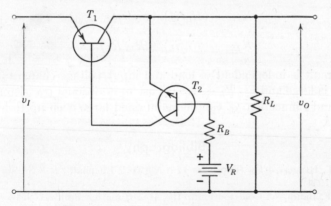

Fig. 12.26   Series-type voltage regulator

the full load current and that T_2 acts essentially as a feedback amplifier which regulates the current flow through T_1. In most cases, therefore, T_1 is a power transistor while T_2 may be a low-power device.

Another basic regulator circuit utilizes the constant-current properties exhibited by a triode transistor with fixed base-bias current. A current regulator based on this property is shown in Fig. 12.27. The battery V_R in series with the resistor R_B provides a constant base current, and, hence, a nearly constant current flows in the collector-emitter circuit of

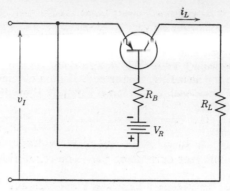

Fig. 12.27 Current regulator

the transistor. The regulation characteristics are given by [15]

$$K_{IV} \cong 1/(1 + \alpha_e V_R/v_I R_B h_{22e})$$ (12.57)

$$K_{IR} \cong -h_{22e}R_L/(1 + h_{22e}R_L)$$ (12.58)

where

$$K_{IV} = (di_L/i_L)/(dv_I/v_I)$$

$$K_{IR} = (di_L/i_L)/(dR_L/R_L)$$

This circuit is independent of load and input voltage changes provided that α_e is large and $h_{22e}R_L \ll 1$. By use of additional transistors in the compound connection, α_e can be maintained large even up to high load currents.

Bibliography

1. J. T. Bangert, "The Transistor as a Network Element," *Bell System Tech. J.*, *33*, 329 (1954).

2. R. F. Baum, "A Contribution to the Approximation Problem," *Proc. IRE, 36*, 863 (1948).

3. A. Fialkow and I. Gerst, "Two Terminal Pair Networks Containing Two Kinds of Elements Only," *BPI Symposium on Network Synthesis*, 50, April 1952.

4. A. Fialkow and I. Gerst, "The Transfer Function of General Two Terminal Pair RC Networks," *Quart. Appl. Math.*, 10, 113 (July 1952).

5. J. L. Merrill, "Theory of the Negative Impedance Converter," *Bell System Tech. J., 30*, 88 (1951).

6. J. G. Linvill, "Transistor Negative Impedance Converters," *Proc. IRE, 41*, 725 (1953).

7. J. G. Linvill, "RC Active Filters," *Proc. IRE, 42*, 555 (1954).

8. F. Bower, J. Fleck, and P. Ordung, "The Synthesis of RC Networks," Yale University Report, August 1948.

9. R. R. Smyth, "Transistors as Power Conversion Devices," Paper presented at IRE–AIEE Transistor Circuit Conference, University of Pennsylvania, February 18, 1955.

10. George C. Uchrin and W. O. Taylor, "A New Self-Excited Square-Wave Transistor Power Oscillator," *Proc. IRE, 43*, 99 (1955).

11. G. H. Royer, "A Switching Transistor D-C to A-C Converter Having an Output Frequency Proportional to D-C Input Voltage," *Trans. AIEE, Commun. & Electronics, 74*, 322 (1955).

12. D. A. Paynter, "An Unsymmetrical Square-Wave Power Oscillator," *IRE Trans., CT-3*, 64 (1956).

13. D. A. Paynter, "A Single Power Transistor D-C–D-C Converter," Paper presented at IRE–AIEE Transistor Circuit Conference, University of Pennsylvania, February 17, 1956.

14. H. R. Lowry, "Transistorized Regulated Power Supplies," *Electronic Design, 38* (February 15, 1956) and *32* (March 1, 1956).

15. S. Sherr and P. M. Levy, "Design Considerations for Semiconductor Regulated Power Supplies," *Electronic Design, 22* (July 15, 1956).

Matrix Algebra
of Two-Port Devices

The system of linear equations

$$y_1 = a_{11}x_1 + a_{12}x_2 + \cdots + a_{1n}x_n$$

$$y_2 = a_{21}x_1 + a_{22}x_2 + \cdots + a_{2n}x_n$$

.

.

.

$$y_n = a_{n1}x_1 + a_{n2}x_2 + \cdots + a_{nn}x_n$$

may be written symbolically in the form

$$
\begin{bmatrix} y_1 \\ y_2 \\ y_3 \\ \cdot \\ \cdot \\ \cdot \\ y_n \end{bmatrix}
=
\begin{bmatrix} a_{11}, a_{12}, \cdots, a_{1n} \\ a_{21}, a_{22}, \cdots, a_{2n} \\ \cdot \\ \cdot \\ \cdot \\ a_{n1}, a_{n2}, \cdots, a_{nn} \end{bmatrix}
\begin{bmatrix} x_1 \\ x_2 \\ \cdot \\ \cdot \\ \cdot \\ x_n \end{bmatrix}
$$

An abbreviated form of this equation is

$$[y] = [a][x]$$

The rectangular array $[a]$ is known as the *matrix of the transformation*.

The number of rows and columns that a matrix has may be dissimilar. Thus, a matrix may have m rows and n columns, and is referred to as an (m, n) matrix. When $m = n = p$, the matrix is a pth-order matrix. In the above illustration, $[y]$ is an $(n, 1)$ matrix, $[a]$ is an nth-order matrix, and $[x]$ is an $(n, 1)$ matrix.

The methods for representation of a two-port device have been discussed in Chapter 2. We have seen that this involves the relationship of two voltages and two currents. For example, one such relationship is the following matrix representation·

$$\begin{bmatrix} v_1 \\ v_2 \end{bmatrix} = \begin{bmatrix} z_{11} & z_{12} \\ z_{21} & z_{22} \end{bmatrix} \begin{bmatrix} i_1 \\ i_2 \end{bmatrix}$$

Tables of matrix interrelations are included at the end of this appendix.

The rules of matrix algebra will be briefly outlined, with specific reference to two-port devices. These rules may be easily verified by reverting to the original algebraic form.

Rule 1. Two matrices are equal only when there is a one-to-one correspondence of their terms. Thus, if

$$[z] = [Z]$$

then

$$z_{11} = Z_{11}; \qquad z_{12} = Z_{12}$$

$$z_{21} = Z_{21}; \qquad z_{22} = Z_{22}$$

Rule 2. The sum or difference of two matrices is a matrix that is term-for-term equivalent to the sum or difference of the terms of the two matrices. Thus, if

$$[y] \pm [y'] = [y'']$$

then $y_{11} \pm y_{11}' = y_{11}''$,   and so on.

Rule 3. When a matrix is multiplied by a factor, each element of the matrix is multiplied by the factor. Thus, if

$$k[h] = [h']$$

then $k\, h_{21} = h_{21}'$,   and so on.

The array may now be written as $[k\, h]$, or in expanded form as

$$\begin{bmatrix} k\, h_{11} & k\, h_{12} \\ k\, h_{21} & k\, h_{22} \end{bmatrix}$$

If we define Δ as the determinant of the terms comprising the matrix, i.e. if

$$\Delta^h = \text{determinant of } \begin{bmatrix} h_{11} & h_{12} \\ h_{21} & h_{22} \end{bmatrix}$$

then $k^2 \Delta^h = \text{determinant of } k \begin{bmatrix} h_{11} & h_{12} \\ h_{21} & h_{22} \end{bmatrix}$

Rule 4. Multiplication of matrices.

$$[c] = [a][b] \quad \text{when} \quad c_{ij} = \sum_{k=1}^{k=n} a_{ik}b_{kj}$$

This restricts the multiplication of matrices to only those where the number of columns of $[a]$ is equal to the number of rows of $[b]$. If a matrix of order (l, m) is multiplied by a matrix of order (m, n), the result is a matrix of order (l, n). By way of example,

$$\begin{bmatrix} h_{11} & h_{12} \\ h_{21} & h_{22} \end{bmatrix} \begin{bmatrix} i_1 \\ v_2 \end{bmatrix} = \begin{bmatrix} h_{11}i_1 + h_{12}v_2 \\ h_{21}i_1 + h_{22}v_2 \end{bmatrix}$$

A problem often encountered in the manipulation of two-port devices is

$$\begin{bmatrix} a_{11} & a_{12} \\ a_{21} & a_{22} \end{bmatrix} \begin{bmatrix} b_{11} & b_{12} \\ b_{21} & b_{22} \end{bmatrix} = \begin{bmatrix} a_{11}b_{11} + a_{12}b_{21}, & a_{11}b_{12} + a_{12}b_{22} \\ a_{21}b_{11} + a_{22}b_{21}, & a_{21}b_{12} + a_{22}b_{22} \end{bmatrix}$$

Rule 5. The distributive and associative laws hold in the multiplication of matrices; i.e.

$$([a] + [b]) \times [c] = [a] \times [c] + [b] \times [c]$$

$$[a] \times [b] \times [c] = ([a] \times [b]) \times [c] = [a] \times ([b] \times [c])$$

Rule 6. In multiplying matrices, the commutative law does not generally hold; i.e.

$$[a] \times [b] \neq [b] \times [a]$$

The terms *premultiplication* and *postmultiplication* are commonly used to differentiate between the two ways in which one matrix may be multiplied by another.

Rule 7. Inversion of matrices.

$$[a]^{-1} = [b] \quad \text{if} \quad b_{ij} = \Delta_{ji}^a/\Delta^a$$

where Δ_{ji}^a is the cofactor for the jth row, ith column. For example:

$$\begin{bmatrix} y_{11} & y_{12} \\ y_{21} & y_{22} \end{bmatrix}^{-1} = \frac{1}{\Delta^y} \begin{bmatrix} y_{22} & -y_{12} \\ -y_{21} & y_{11} \end{bmatrix}$$

Rule 8.

$$[a] \times [a]^{-1} = [a]^{-1} \times [a] = [1] = \begin{bmatrix} 1 & 0 \\ 0 & 1 \end{bmatrix}$$

$[1]$ is defined as the *unit* matrix.

Any matrix may be premultiplied or postmultiplied by the **unit** matrix and remain unchanged.

Rule 9. Division by a matrix is not permissible, but multiplication by the inverse matrix may be used to this end. Thus, if

$$[v] = [z][i]$$

$$[z]^{-1}[v] = [z]^{-1}[z][i]$$

$$= [1][i] = [i]$$

Therefore, $$[i] = [z]^{-1}[v]$$

The above is a brief summary of the rules of matrix algebra that are of particular value in the analysis of two-port devices.

The different forms of matrix representation for two-port devices have been given in eqs. 2.1 to 2.6. The interrelations of these sets is given in the table at the end of this appendix, together with relationships of the various determinants. Tables are also given for the interrelations of the transistor parameters in the various configurations of interest.

An important application of matrix algebra is in the analysis of interconnected networks. Thus, it may be shown that, under certain conditions:[1,2]

(*a*) If the matrices of two networks are $[z']$ and $[z'']$, then $[z' + z'']$ is the matrix of the network formed by their series connection (see Fig. 1).

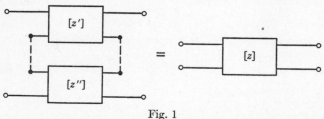

Fig. 1

(*b*) If $[y']$ and $[y'']$ refer to the networks, $[y' + y'']$ refers to the network formed by their parallel connection (see Fig. 2).

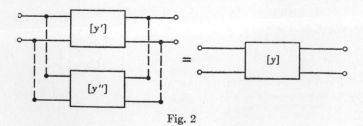

Fig. 2

(c) $[h' + h'']$ refers to the network formed by the connection of $[h']$ and $[h'']$ in series on their input side and in parallel on their output side (see Fig. 3).

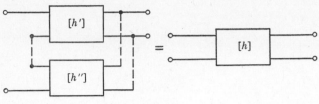

Fig. 3

(d) $[g' + g'']$ refers to the network formed by the connection of $[g']$ and $[g'']$ in parallel on their input side and in series on their output side (see Fig. 4).

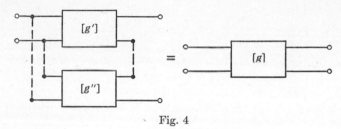

Fig. 4

(e) $[a'] \times [a'']$ refers to the network formed by the connection of $[a']$ and $[a'']$ in cascade, in the order indicated (see Fig. 5).

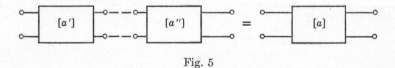

Fig. 5

Once the matrix of a network is known, it is possible to determine its behavior completely with respect to its terminations. The properties of the terminated two-port device are given in Table 3 at the end of this appendix.

Bibliography

1. E. A. Guillemin, *Communication Networks*, Vol. II, Wiley, New York, 1935.

2. R. F. Shea et al., *Principles of Transistor Circuits*, Wiley, New York, 1953.

3. L. A. Pipes, "The Matrix Theory of Four-Terminal Networks," *Phil. Mag.*, *30*, 370 (1940).

Table 1

Matrix Interrelations

	In Terms of					
	z	y	h	g	a	b
$[z]$	—	$\dfrac{y_{22}}{\Delta^y}\ \dfrac{-y_{12}}{\Delta^y}$ $\dfrac{-y_{21}}{\Delta^y}\ \dfrac{y_{11}}{\Delta^y}$	$\dfrac{\Delta^h}{h_{22}}\ \dfrac{h_{12}}{h_{22}}$ $\dfrac{-h_{21}}{h_{22}}\ \dfrac{1}{h_{22}}$	$\dfrac{1}{g_{11}}\ \dfrac{-g_{12}}{g_{11}}$ $\dfrac{g_{21}}{g_{11}}\ \dfrac{\Delta^g}{g_{11}}$	$\dfrac{a_{11}}{a_{21}}\ \dfrac{\Delta^a}{a_{21}}$ $\dfrac{1}{a_{21}}\ \dfrac{a_{22}}{a_{21}}$	$\dfrac{b_{22}}{b_{21}}\ \dfrac{1}{b_{21}}$ $\dfrac{\Delta^b}{b_{21}}\ \dfrac{b_{11}}{b_{21}}$
$[y]$	$\dfrac{z_{22}}{\Delta^z}\ \dfrac{-z_{12}}{\Delta^z}$ $\dfrac{-z_{21}}{\Delta^z}\ \dfrac{z_{11}}{\Delta^z}$	—	$\dfrac{1}{h_{11}}\ \dfrac{-h_{12}}{h_{11}}$ $\dfrac{h_{21}}{h_{11}}\ \dfrac{\Delta^h}{h_{11}}$	$\dfrac{\Delta^g}{g_{22}}\ \dfrac{g_{12}}{g_{22}}$ $\dfrac{-g_{21}}{g_{22}}\ \dfrac{1}{g_{22}}$	$\dfrac{a_{22}}{a_{12}}\ \dfrac{-\Delta^a}{a_{12}}$ $\dfrac{-1}{a_{12}}\ \dfrac{a_{11}}{a_{12}}$	$\dfrac{b_{11}}{b_{12}}\ \dfrac{-1}{b_{12}}$ $\dfrac{-\Delta^b}{b_{12}}\ \dfrac{b_{22}}{b_{12}}$
$[h]$	$\dfrac{\Delta^z}{z_{22}}\ \dfrac{z_{12}}{z_{22}}$ $\dfrac{-z_{21}}{z_{22}}\ \dfrac{1}{z_{22}}$	$\dfrac{1}{y_{11}}\ \dfrac{-y_{12}}{y_{11}}$ $\dfrac{y_{21}}{y_{11}}\ \dfrac{\Delta^y}{y_{11}}$	—	$\dfrac{g_{22}}{\Delta^g}\ \dfrac{-g_{12}}{\Delta^g}$ $\dfrac{-g_{21}}{\Delta^g}\ \dfrac{g_{11}}{\Delta^g}$	$\dfrac{a_{12}}{a_{22}}\ \dfrac{\Delta^a}{a_{22}}$ $\dfrac{-1}{a_{22}}\ \dfrac{a_{21}}{a_{22}}$	$\dfrac{b_{12}}{b_{11}}\ \dfrac{1}{b_{11}}$ $\dfrac{-\Delta^b}{b_{11}}\ \dfrac{b_{21}}{b_{11}}$
$[g]$	$\dfrac{1}{z_{11}}\ \dfrac{-z_{12}}{z_{11}}$ $\dfrac{z_{21}}{z_{11}}\ \dfrac{\Delta^z}{z_{11}}$	$\dfrac{\Delta^y}{y_{22}}\ \dfrac{y_{12}}{y_{22}}$ $\dfrac{-y_{21}}{y_{22}}\ \dfrac{1}{y_{22}}$	$\dfrac{h_{22}}{\Delta^h}\ \dfrac{-h_{12}}{\Delta^h}$ $\dfrac{-h_{21}}{\Delta^h}\ \dfrac{h_{11}}{\Delta^h}$	—	$\dfrac{a_{21}}{a_{11}}\ \dfrac{-\Delta^a}{a_{11}}$ $\dfrac{1}{a_{11}}\ \dfrac{a_{12}}{a_{11}}$	$\dfrac{b_{21}}{b_{22}}\ \dfrac{-1}{b_{22}}$ $\dfrac{\Delta^b}{b_{22}}\ \dfrac{b_{12}}{b_{22}}$
$[a]$	$\dfrac{z_{11}}{z_{21}}\ \dfrac{\Delta^z}{z_{21}}$ $\dfrac{1}{z_{21}}\ \dfrac{z_{22}}{z_{21}}$	$\dfrac{-y_{22}}{y_{21}}\ \dfrac{-1}{y_{21}}$ $\dfrac{-\Delta^y}{y_{21}}\ \dfrac{-y_{11}}{y_{21}}$	$\dfrac{-\Delta^h}{h_{21}}\ \dfrac{-h_{11}}{h_{21}}$ $\dfrac{-h_{22}}{h_{21}}\ \dfrac{-1}{h_{21}}$	$\dfrac{1}{g_{21}}\ \dfrac{g_{22}}{g_{21}}$ $\dfrac{g_{11}}{g_{21}}\ \dfrac{\Delta^g}{g_{21}}$	—	$\dfrac{b_{22}}{\Delta^b}\ \dfrac{b_{12}}{\Delta^b}$ $\dfrac{b_{21}}{\Delta^b}\ \dfrac{b_{11}}{\Delta^b}$
$[b]$	$\dfrac{z_{22}}{z_{12}}\ \dfrac{\Delta^z}{z_{12}}$ $\dfrac{1}{z_{12}}\ \dfrac{z_{11}}{z_{12}}$	$\dfrac{-y_{11}}{y_{12}}\ \dfrac{-1}{y_{12}}$ $\dfrac{-\Delta^y}{y_{12}}\ \dfrac{-y_{22}}{y_{12}}$	$\dfrac{1}{h_{12}}\ \dfrac{h_{11}}{h_{12}}$ $\dfrac{h_{22}}{h_{12}}\ \dfrac{\Delta^h}{h_{12}}$	$\dfrac{-\Delta^g}{g_{12}}\ \dfrac{-g_{22}}{g_{12}}$ $\dfrac{-g_{11}}{g_{12}}\ \dfrac{-1}{g_{12}}$	$\dfrac{a_{22}}{\Delta^a}\ \dfrac{a_{12}}{\Delta^a}$ $\dfrac{a_{21}}{\Delta^a}\ \dfrac{a_{11}}{\Delta^a}$	—

Table 2
Determinant Interrelations

| | In Terms of | | | | | |
	z	y	h	g	a	b
Δ^z	—	$\dfrac{1}{\Delta^y}$	$\dfrac{h_{11}}{h_{22}}$	$\dfrac{g_{22}}{g_{11}}$	$\dfrac{a_{12}}{a_{21}}$	$\dfrac{b_{12}}{b_{21}}$
Δ^y	$\dfrac{1}{\Delta^z}$	—	$\dfrac{h_{22}}{h_{11}}$	$\dfrac{g_{11}}{g_{22}}$	$\dfrac{a_{21}}{a_{12}}$	$\dfrac{b_{21}}{b_{12}}$
Δ^h	$\dfrac{z_{11}}{z_{22}}$	$\dfrac{y_{22}}{y_{11}}$	—	$\dfrac{1}{\Delta^g}$	$\dfrac{a_{11}}{a_{22}}$	$\dfrac{b_{22}}{b_{11}}$
Δ^g	$\dfrac{z_{22}}{z_{11}}$	$\dfrac{y_{11}}{y_{22}}$	$\dfrac{1}{\Delta^h}$	—	$\dfrac{a_{22}}{a_{11}}$	$\dfrac{b_{11}}{b_{22}}$
Δ^a	$\dfrac{z_{12}}{z_{21}}$	$\dfrac{y_{12}}{y_{21}}$	$-\dfrac{h_{12}}{h_{21}}$	$\dfrac{g_{12}}{g_{21}}$	—	$\dfrac{1}{\Delta^b}$
Δ^b	$\dfrac{z_{21}}{a_{12}}$	$\dfrac{y_{21}}{y_{12}}$	$-\dfrac{h_{21}}{h_{12}}$	$-\dfrac{g_{21}}{g_{12}}$	$\dfrac{1}{\Delta^a}$	—

Table 3
Properties of the Terminated Two-Port Device

| | In Terms of | | | | | |
	z	y	h	g	a	b
Z_i	$\dfrac{\Delta^z + z_{11}Z_l}{z_{22} + Z_l}$	$\dfrac{1 + y_{22}Z_l}{y_{11} + \Delta^y Z_l}$	$\dfrac{h_{11} + \Delta^h Z_l}{1 + h_{22}Z_l}$	$\dfrac{g_{22} + Z_l}{\Delta^g + g_{11}Z_l}$	$\dfrac{a_{12} + a_{11}Z_l}{a_{22} + a_{21}Z_l}$	$\dfrac{b_{12} + b_{22}Z_l}{b_{11} + b_{21}Z_l}$
Z_o	$\dfrac{\Delta^z + z_{22}Z_g}{z_{11} + Z_g}$	$\dfrac{1 + y_{11}Z_g}{y_{22} + \Delta^y Z_g}$	$\dfrac{h_{11} + Z_g}{\Delta^h + h_{22}Z_g}$	$\dfrac{g_{22} + \Delta^g Z_g}{1 + g_{11}Z_g}$	$\dfrac{a_{12} + a_{22}Z_g}{a_{11} + a_{21}Z_g}$	$\dfrac{b_{12} + b_{11}Z_g}{b_{22} + b_{21}Z_g}$
$\dfrac{v_2}{v_1}$	$\dfrac{z_{21}Z_l}{\Delta^z + z_{11}Z_l}$	$\dfrac{-y_{21}Z_l}{1 + y_{22}Z_l}$	$\dfrac{-h_{21}Z_l}{h_{11} + \Delta^h Z_l}$	$\dfrac{g_{21}Z_l}{g_{22} + Z_l}$	$\dfrac{Z_l}{a_{12} + a_{11}Z_l}$	$\dfrac{\Delta^b Z_l}{b_{12} + b_{22}Z_l}$
$\dfrac{i_2}{i_1}$	$\dfrac{-z_{21}}{z_{22} + Z_l}$	$\dfrac{y_{21}}{y_{11} + \Delta^y Z_l}$	$\dfrac{h_{21}}{1 + h_{22}Z_l}$	$\dfrac{-g_{21}}{\Delta^g + g_{11}Z_l}$	$\dfrac{-1}{a_{22} + a_{21}Z_l}$	$\dfrac{-\Delta^b}{b_{11} + b_{12}Z_l}$

Table 4

Matrix Interrelations of the Transistor h Parameters

	In Terms of		
	Common-base Parameters	Common-emitter Parameters	Common-collector Parameters
$[h_b]$	—	$\dfrac{1}{1+h_{21e}+\Delta^h_e-h_{12e}}\begin{bmatrix} h_{11e} & ; & (\Delta^h_e-h_{12e}) \\ -(\Delta^h_e+h_{21e}) & ; & h_{22e} \end{bmatrix}$ $\Delta^h_b = \Delta^h_e/(1+h_{21e}+\Delta^h_e-h_{12e})$	$\dfrac{1}{\Delta^h_c}\begin{bmatrix} h_{11c} & ; & (\Delta^h_c+h_{21c}) \\ -\Delta^h_c-h_{12c} & ; & h_{22c} \end{bmatrix}$ $\Delta^h_b = (1+h_{21c}+\Delta^h_c-h_{12c})/\Delta^h_c$
$[h_e]$	$\dfrac{1}{1+h_{21b}+\Delta^h_b-h_{12b}}\begin{bmatrix} h_{11b} & ; & (\Delta^h_b-h_{12b}) \\ -(h_{21b}+\Delta^h_b) & ; & h_{22b} \end{bmatrix}$ $\Delta^h_e = \Delta^h_b/(1+h_{21b}+\Delta^h_b-h_{12b})$	—	$\begin{bmatrix} h_{11c} & ; & (1-h_{12c}) \\ -(1+h_{21c}) & ; & h_{22c} \end{bmatrix}$ $\Delta^h_e = 1+h_{21c}+\Delta^h_c-h_{12c}$
$[h_c]$	$\dfrac{1}{1+h_{21b}+\Delta^h_b-h_{12b}}\begin{bmatrix} h_{11b} & ; & (1+h_{21b}) \\ -(1-h_{12b}) & ; & h_{22b} \end{bmatrix}$ $\Delta^h_c = 1/(1+h_{21b}+\Delta^h_b-h_{12b})$	$\begin{bmatrix} h_{11e} & ; & (1-h_{12e}) \\ -(1+h_{21e}) & ; & h_{22e} \end{bmatrix}$ $\Delta^h_c = 1+h_{21e}+\Delta^h_e-h_{12e}$	—

In some cases these tables result in the difference of large numbers and care must be taken to insure sufficient accuracy in the final result.

442

Table 5

Matrix Interrelations of Transistor h Parameters (Approximate)

	In Terms of		
	Common-base Parameters	Common-emitter Parameters	Common-collector Parameters
$[h_b]$	—	$\dfrac{1}{1+h_{21e}}\begin{bmatrix} h_{11e} & ; & (\Delta^h_e - h_{12e}) \\ -h_{21e} & ; & h_{22e} \end{bmatrix}$ $\Delta^h_b \cong \Delta^h_e/(1+h_{21e})$	$-\dfrac{1}{h_{21c}}\begin{bmatrix} h_{11c} & ; & (\Delta^h_c + h_{21c}) \\ h_{12c} & h_{21c}; & h_{22c} \end{bmatrix}$ $\Delta^h_b \cong -(h_{21c} + \Delta^h_c)/h_{21c}$
$[h_e]$	$\dfrac{1}{1+h_{21b}}\begin{bmatrix} h_{11b} & ; & (\Delta^h_b - h_{12b}) \\ -h_{21b} & ; & h_{22b} \end{bmatrix}$ $\Delta^h_e \cong \Delta^h_b/(1+h_{21b})$	—	$\begin{bmatrix} h_{11c} & ; & (1 - h_{12c}) \\ -h_{21c} & ; & h_{22c} \end{bmatrix}$ $\Delta^h_e \cong h_{21c} + \Delta^h_c$
$[h_c]$	$\dfrac{1}{1+h_{21b}}\begin{bmatrix} h_{11b} & ; & (1 + h_{21b}) \\ -1 & ; & h_{22b} \end{bmatrix}$ $\Delta^h_c \cong 1/(1+h_{21b})$	$\begin{bmatrix} h_{11e} & ; & 1 \\ -(1 + h_{21e}) & ; & h_{22e} \end{bmatrix}$ $\Delta^h_c \cong 1 + h_{21e}$	—

In some cases these tables result in the difference of large numbers and care must be taken to insure sufficient accuracy in the final result.

Table 6

Interrelations of r and h Parameters

	In Terms of		
	Common-base	Common-emitter	Common-collector
r_e	$\dfrac{\Delta^h{}_b - h_{12b}}{h_{22b}}$	$\dfrac{h_{12e}}{h_{22e}}$	$\dfrac{1 - h_{12c}}{h_{22c}}$
r_b	$\dfrac{h_{12b}}{h_{22b}}$	$\dfrac{\Delta^h{}_e - h_{12e}}{h_{22e}}$	$\dfrac{\Delta^h{}_c + h_{21c}}{h_{22c}}$
r_c	$\dfrac{1 - h_{12b}}{h_{22b}}$	$\dfrac{1 + h_{21e}}{h_{22e}}$	$-\dfrac{h_{12c}}{h_{22c}}$
a	$\dfrac{h_{12b} + h_{21b}}{h_{12b} - 1}$	$\dfrac{h_{12e} + h_{21e}}{1 + h_{21e}}$	$\dfrac{h_{12c} + h_{21c}}{h_{21c}}$

Bibliography

In the interest of brevity the following bibliography is restricted to items published from 1951 on. The reader who desires to consult papers of a prior date is referred to the bibliography on pages 519–526 of *Principles of Transistor Circuits*, Wiley, New York, 1953.

1951

Bardeen, J., "Theory of Relation between Hole Concentration and Characteristics of Germanium Point Contacts," *Bell System Tech. J.*, *29*, 469–495 (October).

Bowers, W. B., "Transistor Frequency Multiplying Circuit," *Electronics*, *24*, 140 (March).

Fink, D. G., and R. K. Jurgen (Editors), "The Junction Transistor," *Electronics*, *24*, 82–85 (November).

Hunter, L. P., "The Inverse Voltage Characteristic of a Point Contact on *n*-Type Germanium," *Phys. Rev.*, *79*, 151–152 (January).

Hunter, L. P., "Graphical Analysis of Transistor Characteristics," *Proc., IRE 38*, 1387–1391 (December).

Koros, L. L., and R. F. Schwartz, "Transistor Frequency Modulator Circuit," *Electronics*, *24*, 130–132 (July).

Longini, R. L., "Electric Forming of *n*-Germanium Transistors Using Donor-Alloy Contacts," *Phys. Rev.*, *84*, 1254 (December).

Muller, R. H., "The Junction Transistor," *Anal. Chem.*, *23*, Sup. 19A (December).

Pfann, W. G., "Significance of Composition of Contact Point in Rectifying Junctions on Germanium," *Phys. Rev.*, *81*, 882 (March).

Pietenpol, W. J., "*p-n* Junction Rectifier and Photocell," *Phys. Rev.*, *82*, 121–122 (April).

Prim, R. C., "Some Results Concerning the Partial Differential Equations Describing the Flow of Holes and Electrons in Semi-Conductors," *Bell System Tech. J.*, *30*, 1174 (October).

Raisbeck, G., "Transistor Circuit Design," *Electronics*, *24*, 128–132 (December).

Reich, H. J., et al., "Effect of Auxiliary Current on Transistor Operation," *J. Appl. Phys.*, *22*, 682–683 (May).

Ridenour, L. N., "Revolution in Electronics," *Sci. American*, *185*, 13–17 (August).

Saby, J. S., "Recent Developments in Transistors and Related Devices," *Tele-Tech*, *10*, 32–34 (December).

Scott, T. R., "Crystal Triodes," *Elec. Commun.*, *28*, 195–208 (September).

Scott, T. R., "Crystal Triodes," *Proc. IEE, 98*, pt. 3, 169–177 (May).
Schultheiss, P. M., and H. J. Zuleli, Transistor Trigger Circuits," *Proc. IRE, 39*, 627 (June).
Shockley, W., "Hot Electrons in Germanium and Ohm's Law," *Bell System Tech. J., 30*, 990 (October).
Shockley, W., "Transistor Electronics," *Science, 114*, 487 (November).
Shockley, W., M. Sparks, and G. K. Teal, "The *p-n* Junction Transistors," *Phys. Rev., 83*, 151–162 (July).
Slade, B. N., "High-Performance Transistor with Wide Spacing between Contacts," *RCA Rev., 12*, 517–526 (December).
Slade, B. N., "Method of Improving the Electrical and Mechanical Stability of Point-Contact Transistors," *RCA Rev., 12*, 651–659 (December).
Stelmark, J. P., "Electric Forming in *n*-Germanium Transistors Using Phosphorus Alloy Contacts," *Phys. Rev., 83*, 165 (July).
Wallace, R. L. Jr., "Duality, a New Approach to Transistor Circuit Design," *Proc. IRE, 39*, 702 (June).
Wallace, R. L. Jr., and W. J. Pietenpol, "*n-p-n* Transistors," *Bell System Tech. J., 30*, 530–563 (August).
Wallace, R. L. Jr., and W. J. Pietenpol, "Properties and Applications of *n-p-n* Transistors," *Proc. IRE, 39*, 753–767 (July); *Bell System Tech. J., 30*, 530–563 (July).
Wallace, R. L. Jr., and G. Raisbeck, "Duality as a Guide in Transistor Circuit Design," *Bell System Tech. J., 30*, 381–417 (April).
"Auxiliary Current Alters Transistor Characteristics," *Electronics, 24*, 192 (September).

1952

Aronson, M. H., "Instrument Electronics, Solid State Amplifiers," *Instruments, 25*, 608–609 (July).
Billig, E., "Effect of Minority Carriers on the Breakdown of Point Contact Rectifiers," *Phys. Rev., 87*, 1060 (September 15).
Carswell, H. J., "Transistor Electronic Aids to Communications," *Public Util., 50*, 135–142 (July 31).
Chaplin, G. B. B., "Display of Transistor Characteristics on Cathode Ray Oscilloscope," *J. Sci. Instr., 29*, 142–145 (May).
Debye, P. P., and E. M. Cromwell, "Mobility of Electrons in Germanium," *Phys. Rev., 87*, 1131 (September 15).
Epstein, G. S., et al., "Transistorizing Communication Equipment," *Electronics, 25*, 98–102 (May).
Fuller, C. S., and J. O. Struthers, "Copper as Acceptor Element in Germanium," *Phys. Rev., 87*, 526 (August).
Golay, M. J. E., "Equivalent Circuit of the Transistor," *Proc. IRE, 40*, 360 (March).
Hall, R. N., "Electron-Hole Recombination in Germanium," *Phys. Rev., 87*, 387 (July 15).
Howe, G. W. O., "Duality between Triode and Transistor," *Wireless Engr., 29*, 57–58 (March).
Kingsbury, E. F., and R. S. Ohl, "Photoelectric Properties of Ionically Bombarded Silicon," *Bell System Tech. J., 31*, 104–121 (January).
Montgomery, H. C., "Electrical Noise in Semi-Conductors," *Bell System Tech. J., 31*, 950–975 (September).

Morton, J. A., "New Transistor Gives Improved Performance," *Electronics, 25*, 100–103 (August).

Morton, J. A., "Present Status of Transistor Development," *Bell System Tech. J., 31*, 411–442 (May).

O'Connor, J. A., "Germanium's Electronic Upsurge," *Chem. Eng., 59*, 158–160 (April).

O'Connor, J. A., "What Can Transistors Do?," *Chem. Eng., 59*, 154–156 (May).

Oser, E. A., R. O. Endres, and R. P. Moore, Jr., "Transistor Oscillators," *RCA Rev., 13*, 369 (September).

Renne, H. S., "The Junction Transistor," *Radio & TV News, 47*, 38–39 (April).

Scott, T. R., "Crystal Triodes," *Proc. IEE*, pt. 3, 168–177 (May).

Shea, R. F., "Transistor Power Amplifiers," *Electronics, 25*, 106–108 (September).

Sittner, W. R., "Current Multiplication in the Type A Transistor," *Proc. IRE, 40*, 448–454 (April).

Sparks, M., "The Junction Transistor," *Sci. American, 187*, 28–32 (July).

Teal, G. K., M. Sparks, and E. Buehler, "Single Crystal Germanium," *Proc. IRE, 40*, 906–908 (August).

Trent, R. L., "Binary Counter Uses Two Transistors," *Electronics, 25*, 100–101 (July).

Valdes, L. B., "Transistor Forming Effects in *n*-Type Germanium," *Proc. IRE, 40*, 445–448 (April).

The following articles appeared in *Proc. IRE, 40* (November 1952):

Coblenz, A., and H. L. Owens, "Variation of Transistor Parameters with Temperature," 1472–1476.

Alexanderson, E. F. W., "Control Applications of the Transistor," 1508–1512.

Anderson, A. E., "Transistor Reversible Binary Counter," 1541–1559.

Armstrong, L. D., "*p-n* Junctions by Impurity Introduction through an Intermediate Metal Layer," 1341–1342.

Bryan, G. W., "Application of Transistors to High-Voltage Low-Current Supplies," 1521–1524.

Conwell, E. M., "Properties of Silicon and Germanium," 1314–1327.

Danko, S. F., and R. A. Gerhold, "Printed Circuitry for Transistors," 1524–1529.

Early, J. M., "Effects of Space-Charge Layer Widening in Junction Transistors," 1401–1407.

Ebers, J. J., "Four-Terminal *p-n-p-n* Transistors," 1361–1365.

Farley, B. G., "Dynamics of Transistor Negative-Resistance Circuits," 1497–1508.

Felker, J. H., "Regenerative Amplifier for Digital Computer Applications," 1584–1597.

Follingstad, H. G., J. N. Shive, and R. E. Yaeger, "An Optical Position Encoder and Digit Register," 1573–1584.

Giacoletto, L. J., "Junction Transistor Equivalent Circuits and Vacuum Tube Analogy," 1490–1493.

Golden, N., and R. Nielsen, "Oscilloscopic Display of Transistor Static Electrical Characteristics," 1437–1440.

Hall, R. N., "Power Rectifiers and Transistors," 1512–1519.

Harris, J. R., "A Transistor Shift Register and Serial Adder," 1597–1603.

Hunter, L. P., and H. Fleisher, "Graphical Analysis of Some Transistor Switching Circuits," 1559–1562.

Keonjian, E., and J. S. Schaffner, "An Experimental Investigation of Transistor Noise," 1458–1461.

Lehovec, K., "New Photoelectric Devices Utilizing Carrier Injection," 1407–1410.

Lindberg, O., "Hall Effect," 1414–1420.

Lo, A. W., "Transistor Trigger Circuits," 1531 1541.

McDume, G. E. Jr., "Pulse Duration and Repetition Rate of a Transistor Multivibrator," 1487–1490.

Montgomery, H. C., "Transistor Noise in Circuit Applications," 1461–1472.

Morton, J. A., "Present Status of Transistor Development," 1314–1327.

Navon, D., R. Bray, and H. Y. Fan, "Lifetime of Injected Carriers in Germanium," 1342–1348.

Pearson, G. L., and B. Sawyer, "Silicon p-n Junction Alloy Diodes," 1348–1352.

Petritz, R. L., "On the Theory of Noise in p-n Junctions and Related Devices," 1440–1456.

Pritchard, R. L., "Frequency Variations of Current-Amplification Factor for Junction Transistors," 1476–1481.

Roth, L., and W. E. Taylor, "Preparation of Germanium Single Crystals," 1338–1341.

Rouault, C. L., and G. N. Hall, "High-Voltage, Medium-Power Rectifier," 1519–1521.

Saby, J. S., "Fused Impurity p-n-p Junction Transistors," 1358–1361.

Shea, R. F., "Transistor Operation: Stabilization of Operating Points," 1435–1437.

Shekel, J., "Matrix Representation of Transistor Circuits," 1493–1497.

Shive, J. N., "Properties of M-1740 p-n Junction Photocell," 1410–1414.

Shockley, W., "A Unipolar 'Field Effect' Transistor," 1365–1377.

Shockley, W., "Transistor Electronics: Imperfections, Unipolar and Analog Transistors," 1289–1314.

Slade, B. N., "The Control of Frequency Response and Stability of Point-Contact Transistors," 1382–1385.

Steele, E. L., "Theory of Alpha for p-n-p Diffused Junction Transistors," 1424–1429.

Stuetzer, O. M., "Junction Fieldistors," 1377–1382.

Stuetzer, O. M., "Transistors in Airborne Equipment," 1529–1531.

Thomas, D. E., "Low-Drain Transistor Audio Oscillator," 1385–1395.

Thomas, D. E., "Transistor Amplifier-Cutoff Frequency," 1481–1483.

Trent, R. L., "A Transistor Reversible Binary Counter," 1562–1573.

Valdes, L. B., "Effect of Electrode Spacing on the Equivalent Base Resistance of Point-Contact Transistors," 1429–1435.

Valdes, L. B., "Measurement of Minority Carrier Lifetime in Germanium," 1420–1424.

Wallace, R. L. Jr., L. G. Schimpf, and E. Dickten, "A Junction Transistor Tetrode for High-Frequency Use," 1395–1401.

Waltz, M. C., "On Some Transients in the Pulse Response of Point-Contact Germanium Diodes," 1483–1487.

1953

Armstrong, L. D., and D. A. Jenny, "Behavior of Germanium Junction Transistors at Elevated Temperatures and Power Transistor Design," IRE Convention Records, 1, pt. 6 (Electron Devices), 22–27.

Baker, H. R., et al., "Phase-Bistable Transistor Circuits," Proc. IRE, 41, 1119–1124 (September).

Ballard, R. C., "Portable Transistor FM Receiver," Tele-Tech, 12, 79 (August).

Bashkow, T. R., "Stability Analysis of a Basic Transistor Switching Circuit," Proc. Natl. Electronics Conf., 9, 748–755.

Blecher, F. H., "Automatic Gain Control of Junction Transistor Amplifiers," *Proc. Natl. Electronics Conf.*, *9*, 731–737.

Blount, F. E., "Transistor Oscillator for Use in Multi-frequency Pulsing Current Supply," *Bell System Tech. J.*, *32*, 1313–1331 (November).

Bradley, W. E., et al., "Surface-Barrier Transistor," *Proc. IRE*, *41*, 1702–1734 (December).

Chow, W. F., and J. J. Suran, "Transient Analysis of Transistor Amplifiers," *Electronics*, *26*, 189–191 (November).

Chow, W. F., and J. J. Suran, "Transient Analysis of Junction Transistor Amplifiers," *Proc. IRE*, *41*, 1125–1129 (September).

Early, J. M., "Design Theory of Junction Transistors," *Bell System Tech. J.*, *32*, 1271–1312 (November).

Enenstein, N. H., "A Transient Equivalent Circuit for Junction Transistors," *IRE Trans.*, *ED-4*, 37–55 (December).

Enenstein, N. H., and M. E. McMahon, "Pulse Response of Junction Transistors," *IRE Trans.*, *ED-3*, 5–9 (June).

Fahnestock, J. D., "Transistorized Hearing Aids," *Electronics*, *26*, 154–155 (April).

Fleming, L., "Transistor Oscillator Circuit," *Electronics*, *26*, 196 (June).

Garner, L. E. Jr., "Transistor Sine-Wave Clipper," *Radio & TV News*, *49*, 50–51 (May).

Ghandhi, S. K., "Transistor Feedback Amplifiers," *Proc. Natl. Electronics Conf.*, *9*, 738–747.

Giacoletto, L. J., "Terminology and Equations for Linear Active Four-Terminal Networks including Transistors," *RCA Rev.*, *14*, 28–46 (March).

Hellmers, A. H., "Transistor Cathode Follower," *Radio & TV News*, *50*, 169 (October).

Hollman, H. E., "Transistor Oscillators," *Tele-Tech*, *12*, 82–83 (October).

Keonjian, E., "D-C Amplifier Employing Junction-Type Transistors," *Elec. Eng.*, *72*, 961–964 (November).

Keonjian, E., and J. S. Schaffner, "Noise in Transistor Amplifiers," *Electronics*, *26*, 104–107 (February).

Kramer, S. I., "Transistor Relaxation Oscillators," *IRE Convention Record, 1*, pt. 5 (Circuit Theory), 125–129.

Kretzmer, E. R., "An Amplitude-Stabilized Transistor Oscillator," *Proc. Natl. Electronics Conf.*, *9*, 756–766.

Lesk, I. A., and V. P. Mathis, "The Double-Base Diode: A New Semiconducting Device," *IRE Convention Record, 1*, pt. 6 (Electron Devices), 2–9.

Linvill, J. G., "Transistor Negative Impedance Converters," *Proc. IRE*, *41*, 725–729 (June).

Linvill, J. G., "A New RC Filter Employing Active Elements," *Proc. Natl. Electronics Conf.*, *9*, 342–352.

Lohman, R. D., "Complementary Symmetry Transistor Circuits," *Electronics*, *26*, 140–143 (September).

Mason, S. J., "Power Gain in Feedback Amplifiers," *MIT Tech. Rept. 257*, RLE (August 5).

Nelson, J. R., "Transistor IF Amplifiers," *Tele-Tech*, *12*, 68–69 (December).

Pittman, G. F. Jr., "Application of Transistors to the Control of Magnetic Amplifiers," *Proc. Natl. Electronics Conf.*, *9*, 64–71.

Prim, R. C., and W. Shockley, "Joining Solutions at the Pinch-off Point in 'Field Effect' Transistor," *IRE Trans.*, *ED-4*, 1–15 (December).

Quisenberry, M. E., "Transistor Receiver," *Radio & TV News*, *50*, 122 (July).

Ryder, R. M., and W. R. Sittner, "Transistor Reliability Studies," *IRE Convention Record, 1, pt. 6* (Electron Devices), 9–19.

Schaffner, J. S., and J. J. Suran, "Transient Response of the Grounded-Base Transistor Amplifier with Small Load Impedance," *J. Appl. Phys., 24,* 1355–1357 (November).

Schooley, A. H., "Transistor Amplifiers Applied to Delay Lines," *Proc. Natl. Electronics Conf., 9,* 726–730.

Spencer, R. H., "Transistor-Controlled Magnetic Amplifier," *Electronics, 26,* 136–140 (August).

Stansel, F. R., "Common-Collector Transistor Amplifier at Carrier Frequencies," *Proc. IRE, 41,* 1096–1102 (September).

Starke, H. F., "Transistor D-C Amplifier," *Radio & TV News, 50,* 82–83 (December).

Sulzer, P. G., "Transistor Broadcast Regenerator," *Electronics, 26,* 200 (June).

Sulzer, P. G., "Junction Transistor Circuit Applications," *Electronics, 26,* 170–173 (August).

Sulzer, P. G., "Low Distortion Transistor Audio Oscillator," *Electronics, 26,* 171–173 (September).

Suran, J. J., and W. F. Chow, "Transistor Transient Response," *Tele-Tech, 12,* 67–69 (November).

Sziklai, G. C., et al., "Study of Transistor Circuits for Television," *Proc. IRE, 41,* 708–717 (June).

Valdes, L. B., "Characteristics of the M-1768 Transistor," *IRE Convention Record, 1,* pt. 6 (Electron Devices), 15–21.

Vogelsong, J. H., "Transistor Pulse Amplifier Using External Regeneration," *Proc. IRE, 41,* 1444–1450 (October).

Walter, S., "Transistors in Trigger Circuits," *Proc. IRE, 41,* 1190 (September).

Williams, F. C., and G. B. Chaplin, "Method of Designing Transistor Trigger Circuits," *Proc. IEE, 100,* pt. 3, 228–244 (July).

Zadeh, L. A., "Analysis of Vacuum Tube and Transistor Circuits," *Proc. IRE, 41,* 989–992 (August).

Zeidler, H. M., "Transistor Characteristics," *IRE Trans., ED-2,* 2–11 (January).

1954

Aldrich, R. W., and I. A. Lesk, "The Double-Base Diode: a Semiconductor Thyratron Analog," *IRE Trans., ED-1,* 24–27 (February).

Alexander, F. C. Jr., "Transistors Use Emitter-Coupled Feedback," *Electronics, 27,* 188 (December).

Alexander, F. C. Jr., "Self-Keyed Transistor Oscillator," *Electronics, 27,* 214 (July).

Alsberg, D. A., "Transistor Metrology," *IRE Trans., ED-1,* 12–17 (August).

Baker, R. H., et al., "Transistor Shift Registers," *Proc. IRE, 42,* 1152–1159 (July).

Bangert, J. T., "Transistor as a Network Element," *Bell System Tech. J., 33,* 329–352 (March).

Barron, F. E., "Simple Circuit Stabilizes Transistor," *Electronics, 27,* 182 (November).

Barton, L. E., "Experimental Transistor Personal Broadcast Receiver," *Proc. IRE, 42,* 1062–1066 (July).

Bier, D., and S. Rosen, "Selective A-F Transistor Amplifier," *Electronics, 27,* 208 (December).

Blecher, F. H., "Automatic Gain Control of Junction Transistor Amplifier," *Electronics*, *27*, 224 (January).

Brock, R. L., "Transistor Flip-Flop Uses Two Frequencies," *Electronics*, *27*, 175–177 (June).

Burnett, J. R., "A Synthesis Procedure for Linear Transistor Circuits," *IRE Convention Record*, *2*, pt. 2 (Circuit Theory), 125–129.

Caldwell, W. H., "Transistor Phase Inverter," *Radio & TV News*, *52*, 71 (September).

Chow, W. F., "High Frequency Transistor Amplifiers," *Electronics*, *27*, 142–145 (April).

Cohen, R. M., "Application Considerations for RCA Commercial Transistors," *IRE Trans.*, *ED-1*, 32–48 (February).

Davis, L. Jr., L. G. Rubin, and W. D. Straub, "Rapid Determination of Some Electrical Properties of Semiconductors," *IRE Trans.*, *ED-1*, 34–42 (April).

Early, J. M., "*P-N-I-P* and *N-P-I-N* Junction Transistor Triodes," *Bell System Tech. J.*, *33*, 517–533 (May).

Ebers, J. J., and J. L. Moll, "Large-Signal Behavior of Junction Transistors," *Proc. IRE*, *42*, 1761–1772 (December).

Foley, J. S., "Unilateral Four-Terminal Sets," *Electronics*, *27*, 186–187 (February).

Follingstad, H. G., "An Analytical Study of *z*, *y*, and *h* Parameter Accuracies in Transistor Sweep Measurements," *IRE Convention Record*, *2*, pt. 3 (Electron Devices and Component Parts), 104–116.

Fournier, R. V., and H. Terkanian, "Designing a Transistor Sonar Preamplifier," *Tele-Tech and Elec. Ind.*, *13*, 78–80 (November).

Gade, D. W., "Feedback in Junction Transistors," *Electronics*, *27*, 174–176 (July).

Giacoletto, L. J., "The Study and Design of Alloyed-Junction Transistors," *IRE Convention Record*, *2*, pt. 3 (Electron Devices and Component Parts), 99–103.

Ghandhi, S. K., "Design of Transistor Power Amplifiers," *Electronics*, *27*, 146–149 (March).

Ghandhi, S. K., "Design Criteria for Transistor Feedback Amplifiers," *Tele-Tech and Elec. Ind.*, *13*, 94–95 (March).

Giacoletto, L. J., "Power Transistors for Audio Output Circuits," *Electronics*, *27*, 144 (January).

Guillemin, E. A., et al., "Design Considerations of Junction Transistors at High Frequencies Based upon an Accurate Equivalent Circuit," *Proc. Natl. Electronics Conf.*, *10*, 636–654.

Harris, B., and A. Macovaki, "Symmetrical-Transistor Phase Detector for Horizontal Synchronization," *RCA Rev.*, *15*, 18–26 (March).

Hollman, H. E., "Self-Oscillating U-H-F Transistors," *Tele-Tech and Elec. Ind.*, *13*, 75–77 (April).

Huang, C., E. Slobodzinski, and B. White, "Transistor Shift Registers," *IRE Convention Record*, *2*, pt. 4 (Electronic Computers), 140–144.

Hughes, J. M., "Superregenerative Transistor Receiver," *Radio & TV News*, *51*, 72–73 (March).

Keonjian, E., "Temperature-Compensated D-C Transistor Amplifier," *Proc. IRE*, *42*, 661–671 (April).

Keonjian, E., and J. S. Schaffner, "Shaping of the Characteristics of Temperature-Sensitive Resistors," *Elec. Eng.*, *73*, 933–936 (October).

Kingston, R. H., "Switching Time in Junction Diodes and Junction Transistors," *Proc. IRE*, *42*, 829–834 (May).

Kramer, S. I., "Designing Transistor Relaxation Oscillators," *Tele-Tech and Elec. Ind., 13, 78–79* (May).

Krause, C. A., "Gain-Stabilized Transistor Amplifier," *Electronics, 27*, 183–185 (February).

Kretzmer, E. R., "Amplitude Stabilized Transistor Oscillator," *Proc. IRE, 42*, 391–402 (February).

Lebow, I. L., and R. H. Baker, "Transient Response of Transistor Switching Circuits," *Proc. IRE, 42*, 938–943 (June).

Linvill, J. G., "*RC* Active Filters in Which the Negative-Impedance Converter Uses Transistors," *Proc. IRE, 42*, 555–564 (March).

Lohman, R. D., "A Transistor Analog" (abstract), *IRE Convention Record, 2*, pt. 2 (Circuit Theory), 118.

Madsen, J. F., "Transistorized Oscillator," *Electronics, 27*, 171 (September).

Markarian, H., "Network Partitioning Techniques Applied to the Synthesis of Transistor Amplifiers," *IRE Convention Record, 2*, pt. 2 (Circuit Theory), 130–134.

Moll, J. L., "Large-Signal Transient Response of Junction Transistors," *Proc. IRE, 42*, 1773–1784 (December).

Oakes, J. B., "Analysis of Junction Transistor Audio Oscillator Circuits," *Proc. IRE, 42*, 1235–1238 (August).

Oakes, J. B., "Junction Transistor Pulse Forming Circuits," *Electronics, 27*, 165–167 (September).

Pritchard, R. L., "Frequency Variations of Junction Transistor Parameters," *Proc. IRE, 42*, 786–799 (May).

Pritchard, R. L., and W. N. Coffey, "Small-Signal Parameters of Grown-Junction Transistors at High Frequencies," *IRE Convention Record. 2*, pt. 3 (Electron Devices and Component Parts), 89–98.

Prugh, T. A., and J. W. Keller, "Transistor Pulse Supply," *Electronics, 27*, 188 (July).

Prugh, T. A., and J. W. Keller, "Thyratron-Type Transistor Circuit," *Electronics, 27*, 190 (August).

Riddle, R. C., "Practical Two-Stage Transistor Amplifiers," *Electronics, 27*, 169–171 (April).

Rowe, W. D., "A Single Junction Transistor Bistable Flip-Flop Circuit," *Proc. Natl. Electronics Conf., 10*, 626–635.

Saby, J. S., "Transistors for High Power Applications," *IRE Convention Record, 2*, pt. 3 (Electron Devices and Component Parts), 80–83.

Schaffner, J. S., "Transistor Applications," *GE Rev., 57*, 50–54 (March).

Schenkerman, S., "Feedback Simplifies Transistor Amplifiers," *Electronics, 27*, 129–131 (November).

Shea, R. F., "Transistor Application Fundamentals," *Elec. Eng., 73*, 360–365 (April).

Shekel, J., "Reciprocity Relations in Active Three-Terminal Elements," *Proc. IRE, 42*, 1268–1270 (August).

Shockley, W., "Negative Resistance Arising from Transit Time in Semiconductor Diodes," *Bell System Tech. J., 33*, 799–826 (July).

Shockley, W., and W. P. Mason, "Dissected Amplifiers Using Negative Resistance," *J. Appl. Phys., 25*, 677 (May).

Statz, H., et al., "Design Considerations of Junction Transistors at Higher Frequencies," *Proc. IRE, 42*, 1620–1628 (November).

Stern, A. P., and J. A. Raper, "Transistor Broadcast Receivers," *Elec. Eng., 73*, 1107–1112 (December).

Stern, A. P., and J. A. Raper, "Transistor AM Broadcast Receivers," *IRE Convention Record, 2*, pt. 7 (Broadcasting and Television), 8–14.

Tate, H. J., "Temperature-Stabilized Transistor Amplifiers, with Nomograph," *Electronics, 27*, 144–147 (June).

Thomas, D. E., "A Point-Contact Transistor VHF FM Transmitter," *IRE Trans., ED-1*, no. 2, 43–52 (April).

Thornton, C. G., and L. D. Hanley, "A New High Temperature Silicon Diode," *IRE Convention Record, 2*, pt. 3 (Electron Devices and Component Parts), 84–88.

Webster, W. M., "Variation of Junction Transistor Current-Amplification Factor with Emitter Current," *Proc. IRE, 42*, 914–920 (June).

Zawels, J., "Transistor as a Mixer," *Proc. IRE, 42*, 542–548 (May).

Zierdt, Conrad H. Jr., "A Hermetically Sealed *PNP* Fused Junction Transistor for Medium Power Applications," *IRE Trans., ED-1*, 47–54.

Zucchino, M. B., "Transistor Preamplifier Drives Magnetic Servo," *Electronics, 27*, 168–171 (March).

1955

Bell, N. W., "Small-Signal Analysis of Floating-Junction Transistor Switch Circuits," *IRE Trans., ED-2*, 10–13 (October).

Beter, R. H., et al., "Directly Coupled Transistor Circuits," *Electronics, 28*, 132–136 (June).

Blecher, F. H., "A Junction-Transistor Integrator," *Proc. Natl. Electronics Conf., 55*, 415.

Bright, R. L., "Junction Transistors Used as Switches," *Trans. AIEE, Commun. & Electronics, 74*, 111–120 (March).

Bright, R. L., and A. P. Kruper, "Transistor Choppers for Stable D-C Amplifiers," *Electronics, 28*, 135–137 (April).

Chaplin, G. B. B., et al., "Transistor Digital Fast Multiplier with Magnetostrictive Storage," *Proc. IEE, 102*, pt. B, 422–425 (July).

Cheng, C. C., "Simplified Design Procedures for Tuned Transistor Amplifiers," *RCA Rev., 16*, 339–359 (September).

Chow, W. F., and A. P. Stern, "Principles of Automatic Gain Control of Transistor Amplifiers," *IRE Trans., BTR-1*, 1–15 (April).

Chow, W. F., and A. P. Stern, "Automatic Gain Control of Transistor Amplifiers," *Proc. IRE, 43*, 1119–1127 (September).

Chu, G. Y., "Unilateralization of Junction-Transistor Amplifiers at High Frequencies," *Proc. IRE, 43*, 1001–1006 (August).

Dasher, B. J., D. L. Finn, and T. N. Lowry, "Theory of Low-Frequency Oscillators Employing Point-Contact Transistors," *IRE Convention Record, 3*, pt. 2 (Circuit Theory), 45–50.

Decker, R. O., "Transistor Demodulator for High-Performance Amplifiers," *Trans. AIEE, Commun. & Electronics, 74*, 121–123 (March).

Decker, R. O., "Transistor Demodulator for Magnetic Amplifiers in A-C Servo Applications," *Elec. Eng., 74*, 590–592 (July).

Drouilhet, P. R. Jr., "Predictions Based on Maximum Oscillator Frequency," *IRE Trans., CT-2*, 178–183 (June).

Eckess, W. S., et al., "Transistor Pulse Generators," *Electronics, 28*, 132–133 (November).

Ettinger, G. M., "Transistor Amplifiers for Analog Computers," *Electronics, 28*, 119–121 (July).

Flood, J. E., "Junction Transistor Trigger Circuits," *Wireless Engr., 32*, 122–130 (May).

Freedman, L. A., et al., "Experimental Automobile Receiver Employing Transistors," *Proc. IRE*, *43*, 671–678 (June).

Gallagher, E. F., and R. L. Crosby, "A Transistorized Crystal Valve Receiver," *Proc. Natl. Electronics Conf.*, *55*, 455.

Gudmundsen, R. A., W. P. Waters, and W. V. Wright, "Recent Development in Silicon Fusion Transistors," *IRE Trans.*, *ED-2* (January).

Henle, R. A., "Multistable Transistor Circuits," *Elec. Eng.*, *74*, 570–572 (July).

Hilbourne, R. A., and D. D. Jones, "Transistor Power Amplifiers," *Proc. IEE, 102*, pt. B, 763–774 (November).

Holmes, D. D., et al., "Developmental Pocket-Size Broadcast Receiver Employing Transistors," *Proc. IRE*, *43*, 662–670 (June).

Houser, W. G., "A Unilateral Transistor Amplifier," *Proc. Natl. Electronics Conf.*, *55*, 74.

Hurtig, C. R., "Constant-Resistance AGC Attenuator for Transistor Amplifiers," *IRE Trans.*, *CT-2*, 191–196 (June).

Keonjian, E., "Stable Transistor Oscillator," *Elec. Eng.*, *74*, 672–675 (August).

Keonjian, E., and J. J. Suran, "Transistors Generate Multiwaveforms," *Electronics*, *28*, 138–139 (July).

Krenitsky, P., "Decade Counter Employs Silicon Transistors," *Electronics*, *28*, 112–113 (August).

Kruper, A. P., "Switching Transistors Used as a Substitute for Mechanical Low-Level Choppers," *Trans. AIEE, Commun. & Electronics*, *74*, 141–144 (March).

Linvill, J. G., "Nonsaturating Pulse Circuits Using Two Junction Transistors," *Proc. IRE*, *43*, 826–834 (July).

Linvill, J. G., and R. H. Mattson, "Junction Transistor Blocking Oscillator," *Proc. IRE*, *43*, 1632–1639 (November).

Millar, B., "Transistor Circuit Analysis," *Wireless Engr.*, *32*, 196 (July).

Miller, L. E., and J. H. Forster, "Accelerated Power Aging with Lithium Doped Point Contact Transistors," *IRE Trans.*, *ED-2*, 4–6 (July).

Moody, W. F., "A Silicon Diode Modulator," *Proc. Natl. Electronics Conf.*, *55*, 441.

Mooers, H. T., "Recent Developments in Power Transistors," *IRE Trans.*, *ED-2* (January).

Nussbaum, A., "Electrical Characteristics of Power Transistors," *Proc. IRE*, *43*, 315–322 (March).

Oakes, J. B., and R. C. Rand, "Single and Double Tuned Transistor IF Amplifier," *Proc. Natl. Electronics Conf.*, *55*, 52.

Partridge, G. R., "A Transistorized Pulse Code Modulator," *IRE Trans.*, *EC-3* (December).

Pearlman, A. R., "Some Properties and Circuit Applications of Composite Junction Transistors," *IRE Trans.*, *ED-2* (January).

Pederson, D. O., "Regeneration Analysis of Junction Transistor Multivibrators," *IRE Trans.*, *CT-2*, 171–178 (June).

Pittman, G. F. Jr., "High-Accuracy Static Time-Delay Device Utilizing Transistors," *Elec. Eng.*, *74*, 498–550 (June).

Pritchard, R. L., "Frequency Response of Theoretical Models of Junction Transistors," *IRE Trans.*, *CT-2*, 183–191 (June).

Pritchard, R. L., "High-Frequency Power Gain of Junction Transistors," *Proc. IRE*, *43*, 1075–1085 (September).

Rand, R. C., and J. B. Oakes, "Single and Double Tuned Transistor IF Amplifiers," *Proc. Natl. Electronics Conf.*, *11*.

Riddle, R. L., "High Fidelity Transistor Power Amplifier," *Electronics*, *28*, no. 9, 174 (September).

Royer, G. H., "Switching Transistor D-C to A-C Converter," *Trans. AIEE, Commun. & Electronics*, *74*, 322–326 (July).

Schaffner, J. S., "Variation of Junction Transistor Parameters," *Tele-Tech and Elec. Ind.*, *14*, 64–65 (January).

Sheehan, W. H., and J. H. Ivers, "Design of Transistorized High Gain Portable," *Electronics*, *28*, 159–161 (March).

Sherr, S., and T. Kwap, "Stabilizing Transistors against Temperature Variations," *Tele-Tech and Elec. Ind.*, *14*, 74–76 (March).

Slaughter, D. W., "Feedback-Stabilized Transistor Amplifier," *Electronics*, *28*, 174–175 (May).

Smith, D. H., "Silicon Alloy Junction Diode as a Reference Standard," *Elec. Eng.*, *74*, 43 (January).

Stampfl, R. A., and R. A. Hanel, "Transistor Amplifier with Extremely High Input Impedance," *Proc. Natl. Electronics Conf.*, *11*, 67.

Stern, A. P., et al., "Internal Feedback and Neutralization of Transistor Amplifiers," *Proc. IRE*, *43*, 838–847 (July).

Suran, J. J., "Double-Base Expands Diode Applications," *Electronics*, *28*, 198–202 (March).

Suran, J. J., "Low-Frequency Circuit Theory of the Double-Base Diode," *IRE Trans.*, *ED-2*, 40–48 (April).

Suran, J. J., and E. Keonjian, "A Semiconductor Diode Multivibrator," *Proc. IRE*, *43* (July).

Uchrin, G. C., and W. S. Taylor, "New Self-excited Square Wave Transistor Power Oscillator," *Proc. IRE*, *43*, 99 (January).

Van der Ziel, A., "Theory of Shot Noise in Junction Diodes and Junction Transistors," *Proc. IRE*, *43*, 1639–1646 (November).

Vasseur, J. P., "Principes des circuits à transistors," pp. 99–163, *Ann. radioélec.*, *10*, no. 40 (April).

Volkers, W. K., and N. E. Pederson, "The Hushed Transistor Amplifier," *Proc. Natl. Electronics Conf.*, *55*, 83.

Wanlass, C. L., "Transistor Circuitry for Digital Computers," *IRE Trans.*, *EC-4*, no. 4 (March).

Webster, R. R., "How to Design IF Transistor Transformers," *Electronics*, *28*, 156–158 (August).

Williams, C. E., "Transistor Amplifier Performance," *Electronics*, *28*, 196 (February).

Wulfsberg, C. N., "Zener-Voltage Breakdown Uses in Silicon Diodes," *Electronics*, *28*, 182 (December).

Zawels, J., "Natural Equivalent Circuit of Junction Transistors," *RCA Rev.*, *16*, 360–378 (September).

1956

Almond, J., and A. R. Boothroyd, "Broadband Transistor Feedback Amplifiers," *Proc. IEE*, *103*, pt. B, 93–101 (January).

Armstrong, H., et al., "Design Theory for *P-N* Junction Diodes," *IRE Trans.*, *ED-3*, 86–92 (April).

Armstrong, L., et al., "*PNP* Transistors Using High-Emitter Efficiency Alloy Materials," *RCA Rev.*, *17*, 37–45 (March).

Bashkow, T. R., "D-C Graphical Analysis of Junction Transistor Flip-Flops," *Trans. AIEE, Commun. & Electronics, 75,* 1–6 (March).

Beck, K. H., "An N-Stage, Series Transistor Circuit," *IRE Trans., CT-3,* 44–51 (March).

Blecher, F. H., "Transistor Circuits for Analog and Digital Systems," *Bell System Tech. J., 35,* 295–333 (March).

Carroll, J. M., "Diffusion Transistors Raise Frequency Limits," *Electronics, 29,* 137–139 (February).

Cheng, C. C., "Frequency Stability of Point Contact Transistor Oscillators," *Proc. IRE, 44,* 219–223 (February).

Chow, W. F., "Transistor Superregenerative Detection," *IRE Trans., CT-3,* 58–60 (March).

Cocking, W. T., "Transistor Operating Conditions," *Wireless World, 62,* 109–111 (March).

Coffey, W. N., "Measuring R-F Parameters of Junction Transistors," *Electronics, 29,* 152–155 (February).

Cripps, L. G., and E. Wolfendale, "A Guide to the Design of Sinusoidal Oscillators Using Junction Transistors," *Philips Electronics Application Bull.* (Eindhoven, Netherlands), *16,* no. 2.

DeSautels, A. N., "A Comparison of Three Common-Emitter Servo Preamplifiers," *Trans. AIEE, Commun. & Electronics, 75,* 17–25 (March).

Deuitch, D. E., "Transistor Circuits for Digital Computers," *Electronics, 29,* 160–162 (May).

Eckess, W., et al., "Transistor Generator Simulates Radar Target," *Electronics, 29,* 179–182 (May).

Fink, D. G., "Transistors versus Vacuum Tubes," *Proc. IRE, 44,* 479–481 (April).

Ghandhi, S. K., "Analysis and Design of Transistor Bias Networks," *Proc. Natl. Electronics Conf., 12.*

Gossick, B. R., "A Note on the Small Amplitude Transient Response of P-N Junctions," *Proc. IRE, 44,* 259 (February).

Gott, E., "High Speed Counter Uses Surface Barrier Transistor," *Electronics, 29,* 174–178 (March).

Greenberg, L. S., et al., "A Method of Determining Diffusion Coefficients of Drift Transistors," *IRE Trans., ED-3,* 97–99 (April).

Grinich, V., "An Eighty-Volt-Output Transistor Video Amplifier," *IRE Trans., CT-3,* 61–63 (March).

Grinich, V., "Two Representations for a Junction Transistor in the Common-Collector Configuration," *IRE Trans., CT-3,* 63–64 (March).

Keonjian, E., "Micropower Audio Amplifier," *IRE Trans., CT-3,* 68 (March)

Keonjian, E., "Micropower Operation of Silicon Transistors," *Tele-Tech and Elec. Ind.,* 76–78, 138–142 (May).

Keonjian, E., "Stable Transistor Oscillator," *IRE Trans., CT-3,* 38–44 (March).

Kinkel, J. F., and M. C. Wilson, "Vibration Meter Uses Transistors," *Electronics, 29,* 127–129 (April).

Kleinman, D. A., "The Forward Characteristic of the *PIN* Diode," *Bell System Tech. J., 35,* 685–706.

Lacy, J. W., and P. D. Davies, Jr., "Servo Amplifier Uses Silicon Power Transistors," *Electronics, 29,* 136–137 (January).

Lee, C. A., "A High Frequency Diffused Base Germanium Transistor," *Bell System Tech. J., 35,* 23–34 (January).

Lehovec, K., et al., "Current-Voltage Characteristics of Point Contact Rectifiers in the Forward Direction," *IRE Trans.*, *ED-3*, 1–5.

Macdonald, J. R., "Solution of a Transistor Transient-Response Problem," *IRE Trans.*, *CT-3*, 54–58 (March).

Mason, S., "Docile Behavior of Feedback Amplifiers," *Proc. IRE*, *44*, 781–787 (June).

Middlebrook, R., and R. Scarlett, "An Approximation to Alpha of a Junction Transistor," *IRE Trans.* *ED-3*, no. 1, 25–29 (January).

Moody, N. F., "A Silicon Junction Diode Modulator," *Electronic Eng.*, *28*, 94–100 (March).

Mueller, C., and N. Ditrick, "Uniform Planar Alloy Junctions for Germanium Transistors," *RCA Rev.*, *17*, 46–56 (March).

O'Connell, J., and L. Giacoletto, "A Variable Capacitance Germanium Junction Diode for VHF," *RCA Rev.*, *17*, 68–85 (March).

Pankove, J. I., "Transistor Fabrication by the Melt Quench Process," *Proc. IRE*, *44*, 185–188 (February).

Paynter, D. A., "An Unsymmetrical Square Wave Power Oscillator," *IRE Trans.*, *CT-3*, 64–65 (March).

Penfield, P., "Power Transistors," *Radio & TV News*, *55*, 37–41 (February).

Prince, M. B., "Diffused *p-n* Junction Silicon Rectifiers," *Bell System Tech. J.*, *35*, 661–684.

Pritchard, R. L., "Electric Network Representation of Transistors—a Survey," *IRE Trans.*, *CT-3*, 5–21 (March).

Raper, J. A., "A Transistorized IF Amplifier-Limiter," *IRE Trans.*, *CT-3*, 67–68 (March).

Rappaport, P., et al., "The Electron-Voltaic Effect in Germanium and Silicon *P-N* Junctions," *RCA Rev.*, *17*, 100–128 (March).

Rittmann, A. D., and T. J. Miles, "High Frequency Silicon Alloy Transistor," *IRE Trans.*, *ED-3*, 78–82 (April).

Schenkel, H., and H. Statz, "Junction Transistors with Alpha Greater than Unity," *Proc. IRE*, *44*, 360–371 (March).

Schwartz, S., "Transistor Characteristics for Circuit Designers," *Electronics*, *29*, 161–174 (January).

Shockley, W., "Transistor Physics," *Proc. IEE*, *103*, pt. B, 23–41 (January).

Simkins, Q. W., and J. H. Vogelsong, "Transistor Amplifiers for Use in a Digital Computer," *Proc. IRE*, *44*, 43–54 (January).

Slaughter, D. W., "The Emitter-Coupled Differential Amplifier," *IRE Trans.*, *CT-3*, 51–84 (March).

Stafiev, V. I., V. M. Tuchkevich, and N. S. Jakobchuck, "Operation of the Transistor Amplifier under a Special Condition," *J. Tech. Phys. USSR*, *26*, 15–21 (January).

Stanton, J. W., "A Transistorized D-C Amplifier," *IRE Trans.*, *CT-3*, 65–67 (March).

Stern, A. P., "Considerations on the Stability of Active Elements and Applications to Transistors," *IRE Convention Record*, *4*, pt. 2 (Circuit Theory) 46–52.

Stern, A. P., "Power Transfer in Double-Tuned Coupling Networks," *Proc. IRE*, *44*, 1063–1064 (August).

Suran, J. J., and F. A. Reibert, "Two-Terminal Analysis and Synthesis of Junction Transistor Multivibrators," *IRE Trans.*, *CT-3*, 26–38 (March).

Sylvan, T. P., "Logarithmic Attenuators Using Silicon-Junction Diodes," *IRE Trans.*, *CT-3*, 69 (March).

Tannenbaum, M., and D. E. Thomas, "Diffused Emitter and Base Silicon Transistors," *Bell System Tech. J.* 35, 1-22 (January).

Thomas, D. E., and G. D. Dacey, "Application Aspects of the Germanium Diffused Base Transistor," *IRE Trans.*, CT-3, 22-26 (March).

Turner, R., "A Five Watt Transistor Audio Amplifier," *Radio & TV News*, 55, 53-55 (April).

Uchrin, G. C., "Transistor Power Converter Capable of 250 Watts D-C Output," *Proc. IRE*, 44, 261-262 (February).

Uhlir, A., "High Frequency Shot Noise in P-N Junctions," *Proc. IRE*, 44, 557 (April).

Upham, J. L., and A. I. Dranetz, "Transistor Modulator for Airborne Recording," *Electronics*, 29, 166-169 (June).

Van Able, H. H., and J. J. Rongen, "The Design of Transistor D-C Converters," *Philips Electronic Application Bull.* (Eindhoven, Netherlands), 16, no. 2.

Wahl, A. J., and J. J. Kleimack, "Factors Affecting the Reliability of Alloy Junction Transistors," *Proc. IRE*, 44, 494-502 (April).

Witt, S. N., "Transistorizing Meacham Bridge Oscillators," *Electronics*, 29, 193-195 (March).

Wulfsberg, P. G., "Transistors Up Reliability of Broadcast Remotes," *Electronics*, 29, 122-125 (January).

Books

Arguimbau, L. B., and R. B. Adler, *Vacuum Tube Circuits and Transistors*, Wiley, 1956.

Coblenz, A., and H. L. Owens, *Transistor Theory and Applications*, McGraw-Hill, 1955.

Hunter, L. P., et al., *Handbook of Semiconductor Electronics*, McGraw-Hill, 1956.

Kittel, C., *Introduction to Solid State Physics*, 2nd ed., Wiley, 1956.

Lo, A. W., et al., *Transistor Electronics*, Prentice-Hall, 1955.

Shea, R. F., ed., *Principles of Transistor Circuits*, Wiley, 1953.

Shea, R. F., *Transistor Audio Amplifiers*, Wiley, 1955.

Shockley, W., *Electrons and Holes in Semiconductors*, Van Nostrand, 1950.

Solid State Physics; Advances in Research and Applications, Academic Press, 1955.

Index